BEEKEEPING
AN ILLUSTRATED HANDBOOK

No. 1524
$15.95

BEEKEEPING
AN ILLUSTRATED HANDBOOK

BY DIANE G. STELLEY

FIRST EDITION

FIRST PRINTING

Printed in the United States of America

Library of Congress Cataloging in Publication Data

Stelley, Diane G.
Beekeeping—an illustrated handbook.

Bibliography: p.
Includes index.
1. Bee culture. I. Title.
SF523.S69 1983 638'.1 82-19360
ISBN 0-8306-0124-4
ISBN 0-8306-1524-5 (pbk.)

Cover illustration by Al Cozzi.

Contents

Introduction

Beekeeping is both a science and an art. It is a science because it requires an understanding of the nature of bees, of plant life, and of the effects weather has on both bees and plant life. It is an art because you must time certain procedures judiciously and decide when to let the bees do the work their way and when to intervene. At the same time, you must always, always look out for the bees health and welfare.

Bees are not domesticated animals like dogs, horses, and cows. Man has simply learned to provide them with a more comfortable home than they usually find in the wild. When that home becomes too crowded or the colony is subjected to harrassment from people or animals and insect pests, the bees leave, find a natural nesting place, and get along pretty well without man, as they have for thousands of years.

To start beekeeping, you must first find a good place to keep bees, a place where there is fresh water, and enough plants with nectar and pollen for food, and where the bees will not become a nuisance to people or livestock. You will need to obtain a few specialized tools, protective clothing, and a hive.

Before starting out you should also assess your reactions to bee stings. Everyone who works with bees gets stung at one time or another despite protective clothing and good management. *Most* beekeepers take the stings in stride and suffer no more than a little irritation and swelling. A few people are highly sensitive to bee venon and when stung they suffer a severe, life-threatening reaction. If you don't know what your response is, get a doctor to test you. More details on bee stings are given in Appendix F.

The bee is truly a remarkable animal. One reward of beekeeping, nearly as special as tasting your own fresh honey, is the opportunity to observe and study this amazing insect.

What a thrill it is the first time you see a beautiful new creamy comb drawn out in perfect hexagonal symmetry or spot the queen for the first time among the hundreds of workers around her. What a joy it is to watch a forager return with a load of pollen so heavy she nearly topples backwards before she hauls it up to the landing strip.

If you are able to keep your bees near or in your yard, you will find that your neighbors—and flowers, fruits, and vegetables will benefit immensely. Beekeeping is a perfect adjunct to organic gardening. You benefit the environment because a beekeeper must be careful with pesticides and strive to use natural controls for insect pests, weeds, and other gardening problems.

Success in beekeeping, as with other agricultural pursuits, depends a great deal on local climate and day-to-day weather. Late frosts, severe winters, or long periods of rain in the spring or drought in the summer can adversely affect the availability of nectar and pollen for your bees.

In a good year you may have to add a super of empty frames every week for a couple months to keep pace with the nectar flow. You may harvest 60 to 90 pounds and still have plenty for the bees. In a bad year, there may be hardly enough for the bees and none for the beekeeper. In fact, you may have to expend money and time to feed the bees to keep them alive.

Conscientious attention to your bees on a regular basis will give you the best chance of succeeding despite weather variations. Keeping bees is not just having bees "out there." Keeping bees requires regular visits and maintenance. You could call it *keeping up* with bees.

People from many walks of life find beekeeping a richly rewarding hobby: doctors, naturalists, carpenters, businessmen, farmers, engineers, housewives, teachers, and secretaries. Not just for the honey. One widow, a former teacher, says, "I couldn't have gone through the time after my husband died if it hadn't been for my bees." A gentleman contemplating retirement had checked off a number of goals in his life: forest ranger, Death Valley guide, gold miner, and engineer. He was looking forward to yet another accomplishment—being a beekeeper!

Beekeeping is a great partnership enterprise. Husbands and wives, sisters and brothers, grandfather with grandsons, and close friends or neighbors can enjoy beekeeping together.

As you start beekeeping and seek more help and information, you will be opening new doors to new activities with new friends. You will meet people just beginning in beekeeping like yourself who are asking many questions and you will become acquainted with the professionals who have been in the game for 20, 30, or even 50 years. From neophyte to commercial operator, most apiarians are friendly and eager to share their knowledge and skills.

Through your local, county, or state beekeeping association and regional or national organizations, you will have the opportunity to attend conferences and workshops. At these workshops you can hear about the latest research, check out newly designed equipment, watch demonstrations, and even enter your honey in competition if you wish. You will meet people from other states and other countries and bump elbows with the top researchers and scientists in the field.

Beekeeping goes back in time to the caveman and forward into tomorrow with spaceships and genetic engineering. You will surely find that being a part of it is an exciting adventure!

Every writer is indebted to all those who went before and reported their interpretations of what they saw, their studies, anecdotes, techniques, successes and shortcomings for others to build on. It is perhaps even more so with a book on beekeeping. I want to thank all the beekeepers, entomologists, apiarians, and hobbyists—whatever they call themselves—who have written either formal published works or who have shared with me, verbally or in writing, their knowledge or experience with bees.

I am especially grateful to the Orange County Beekeepers Association, particularly Virginia Truesdell for making her periodical library available, and to Bill Huston, the Club's consultant, for freely and graciously answering questions (many that he has answered over and over before, I'm sure), and to many of the members for their interest and enthusiasm for this project.

A special thanks goes to Ron Neese, my instructor in beekeeping, who has served beekeepers well in Orange County in several capacities and has taken an active role in the Western Apiculture Society. His photos and design concepts are vital contributions to this book.

Zandy Neese, his wife, was also particularly helpful.

Another special thanks to Willa Bowman, 67 years young, whose enthusiasm for beekeeping inspires all of us, for her ideas and encouragement.

Thanks also to all the individuals and the personnel of various agencies, particularly the cooperative Extension Services, and to suppliers for providing photographs that help to bring the text to life. They are noted in the captions.

Thank you, staff of the Business Skills Center of the Huntington Beach Adult School for your patience and for scheduling me for a word processor for as much time as possible, saving me hours in rewrite, editing, and final copy time.

An especially warm thanks to my Master Mind group: Jesse, Lucy, Marla, Polly, and Sue for always bringing me back to purpose when I felt overwhelmed with what I had undertaken.

And finally, I want to express my gratitude to my friends and to my family—my parents, my son and daughter, and particularly to my husband who served as model for photos and as editor, and who gave me a year off from the job market to pursue this project. And who, more importantly, sustained me with his love and emotional support to complete it.

Chapter 1

Historical Highlights

When the first caveman reached into a bee-filled hole in a hollow tree for whatever he could find and came up with a handful of something sweet, he had to be delighted. He was no doubt even happier when he discovered that smoke from a burning torch would quiet most of the bees long enough for him to take the honey. Primitive peoples were not bee-keepers but bee-hunters. As evolution allowed people to live a more settled life, tribes built up a store of bee trees, caves, and logs. Later they cut holes in trees, dead stumps, and logs to encourage swarms.

The log-type hive persisted for centuries, especially among people whose simple and thrifty life-styles did not include commercial woodworking facilities. American pioneers kept bees in blue gum logs, a type of tree of little use for firewood but plentiful among the woods they were clearing. Old timers living in the Blue Ridge Mountains of North Carolina still manage bees in the blue gum log hives as their parents did (Fig. 1-1).

AN ANCIENT ART

The first record of beekeeping is estimated to have been carved from 15,000 to 7,000 years B.C., in a cave in Spain. Artwork found in the Temple of the Sun in Egypt dated 2600 B.C. depicts Egyptians smoking bees, removing honeycombs, pouring out honey, and sealing the honeycombs.

The Egyptians used earthenware pipes as hives. One painting

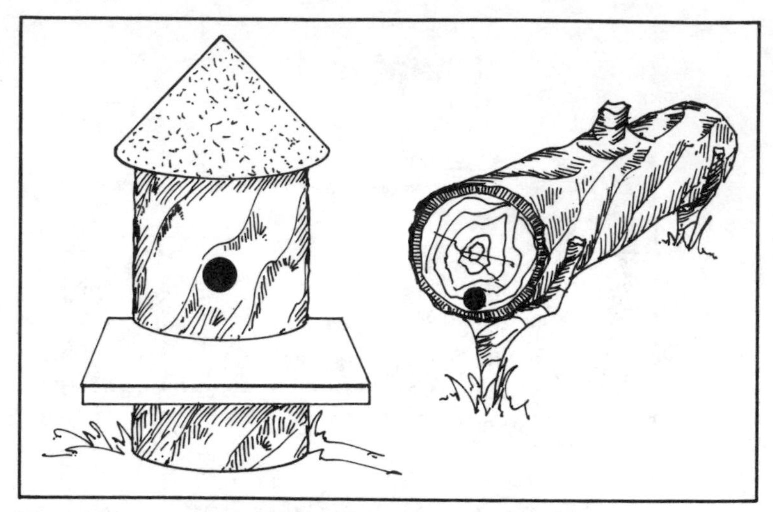

Fig. 1-1. Two versions of the log hive or "bee gum."

from a tomb at Thebes shows such a pipe with the midsection enlarged. Brood rearing took place near the entrance and honey was stored at the back. Beekeepers would cut the honey from the back, leaving the brood undisturbed. This kind of "depriving system" was used throughout the Mediterranean where bees were then regarded as semisacred.

The first written account of beekeeping appears in the ninth book of Aristotle's *Historia Animalum* (Natural History). Scholars think that this part was probably added later by a beekeeper in the early part of the third century B.C. It discusses the need to feed bees with something sweet, the fact that bees assume different tasks at different stages of adult life, and mentions foulbrood disease.

Two Roman writers, Varro and Vergil, who lived in the first century B.C. wrote about beekeeping but from different viewpoints. Vergil lived on a farm in Campainia. He was a poet who enjoyed the rural life of tending grapes, olives, and bees. His advice on beekeeping is presented in a long poem on agriculture that illustrates the practicality of placing the hive out of the wind and away from livestock and the importance of a water supply. (Along with the practical, he includes a notion popular in those days that bees were somehow propagated inside the carcass of a dead ox.)

Varro considered the commercial possibilities of beekeeping. He writes of the profit that Spanish brothers made from their beekeeping on a half acre, of a man who leased his hives for a fee, and the purchase of *propolis*, a reddish resinous cement collected by bees, by doctors as an important healing balsam. He mentions that the colony had a ruler but did not realize that it was female and the mother of all the bees.

In about A.D. 60 Columella, a retired Roman army officer, wrote another book on agriculture containing much of the information from Vergil. He included a description of Roman beekeeper tools. A Roman smoker was an earthen pot with a spout at each end, fueled with dry cow dung. The beekeeper blew through the larger spout. The *cluter oblonga*, a knife with wide sharp edges on both sides and a hooked scraper at the end for raking out dirt, was the forerunner of our hive tool.

In the fourth century Palladius, a Middle Eastern monk and chronicler, condensed Columella's work and arranged it in a month-by-month sequence as a practical textbook, leaving out all fables. His book, translated into English, was still being followed throughout the Dark Ages 1000 years later. Since the peasants or freemen who tended the land and beehives for the landed gentry could not read or write, no new information was available at that time. The principal scholars were monks who believed that the ancients like Aristotle were the absolute authority.

With the onset of the renaissance around the fourteenth century, more people were literate and the advent of printing allowed a greater distribution of books. However, new information on beekeeping was still sparse.

The clay-reinforced straw *skep* hive was used throughout Europe during the Dark Ages and brought to England by the Anglo Saxons. Its design had many disadvantages. It was difficult to inspect the bees or feed them, the space was fixed and could not be enlarged as the colony grew in warm weather nor contracted as they dwindled in winter, brood comb and honey were mixed together, and the straw often caught fire when the skeps were smoked. However the materials were cheap and any handy person could construct them in his cottage of evenings (Fig. 1-2).

Timber was not readily available to the common family and therefore any major changes in designs had to come from those with a somewhat better income and education. Innovaters were often men of the cloth.

In the mid 1600s Rev. William Mew of Gloucestshire, England, built an octagonal wooden hive with additional boxes above and passage holes with closable covers. This was the forerunner of the *super* with separate boxes for brood and honey. In 1675, King Charles II granted a patent to one John Gedde, a Scot, for his

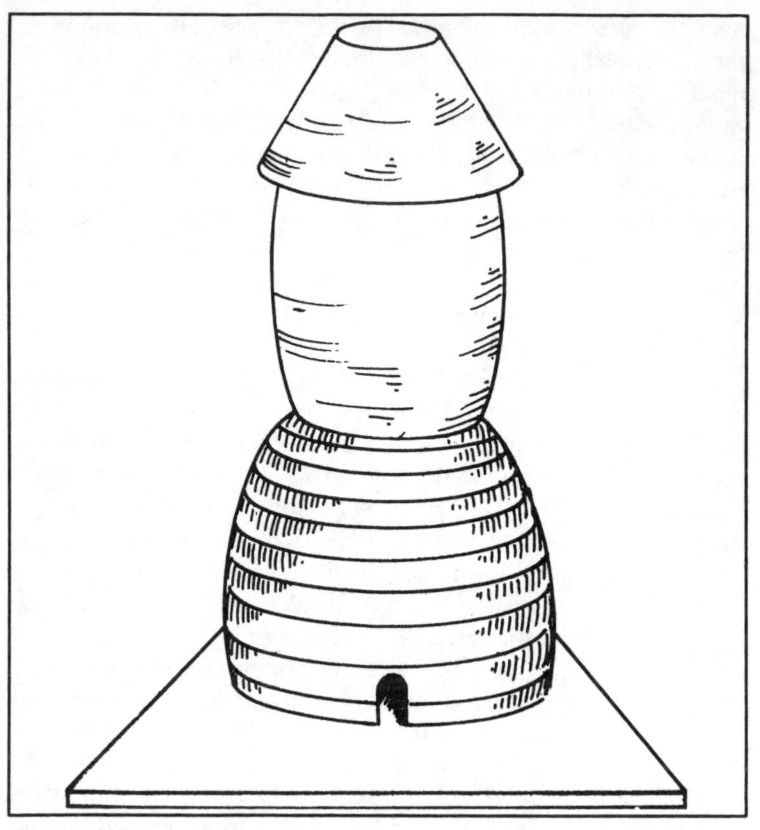

Fig. 1-2. Straw skep with bell jar.

wooden hive, which was much like Mew's except for a removable inside framework on which the bees were supposed to build combs. Gedde's hive was of thin wood and had to be kept out of the weather in a bee house.

Later in the seventeenth century various improvements in the straw skep were seen. A Greek design was tapered toward the bottom and plastered in and out with clay. Flat sticks were placed on top with small pieces hanging down to serve as guides for the bees. Since this arrangement was attached only at the top, it was possible to carefully cut out the bar and remove the comb of honey without harming the bees.

Also popular were flat-topped two story skeps. These consisted of one skep with a central hole and another skep below, or a bottom skep with a bell jar over the top covered with a protective cap. One two-part hive called the Renumerator and the Preserver was advocated by England's first beekeeper's association, the Western Apiarian Society of Exeter, established in 1798.

The desire to obtain maximum amounts of honey with the minimum destruction of bees was becoming more prevalent. The Association offered prizes to cottage beekeepers who could obtain good crops of honey without killing the bees. But because beekeeping continued to be practiced in much the same way as it had for centuries, the problem of preserving bees while gathering honey remained.

NINETEENTH CENTURY IMPROVEMENTS

Finally, in the nineteenth century, a number of better hive designs were developed. In 1819 Robert Kerr of Stewarton, built a better version of the Mew-Gedde hive. Hexagonal with supers, it had bars screwed in place for the comb and slides between to let the bees up into the next box (Fig. 1-3). A later version used frames

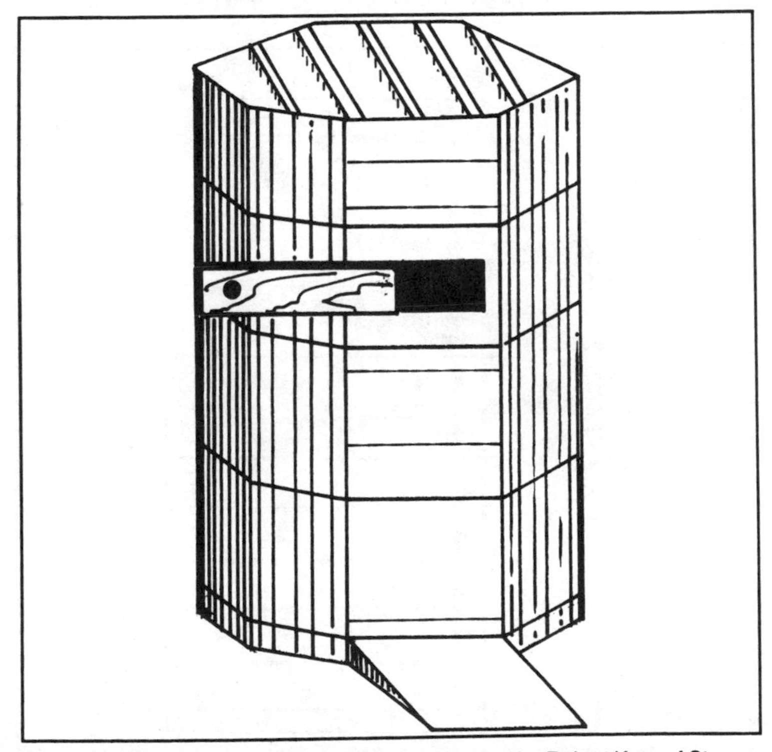

Fig. 1-3. Rendering of the hexagonal hive developed by Robert Kerr, of Stewarton, in 1819. It had supers and bars screwed in place and slides to let the bees up into the next box.

instead of bars. Both types were still subject to the old problem of the bees gluing the frames to the sides of the hives with propolis. Between 1830 and 1880, the United States patent office received numerous requests with drawings of modified skep and wooden hives that were supposed to solve this problem.

Thomas Nutt developed the *Collateral hive* around 1832. Three boxes were placed side by side—the central one was for the brood and the others were opened to the bees when the first box became full, for storing honey. Additional bell jars, boxes, skeps and feeding drawers were included. By and large the collateral was too elaborate for the average beekeeper. Those models in existence today in museums represent some of the most beautiful examples of cabinetmaking of the period.

Huber, a Swiss naturalist, designed a *Leaf Hive* consisting of separate frames hinged together on one side, which could be opened like the pages of a book to allow the beekeeper to examine both sides (Fig. 1-4). An Abbé in Paris wrote a book describing a hive

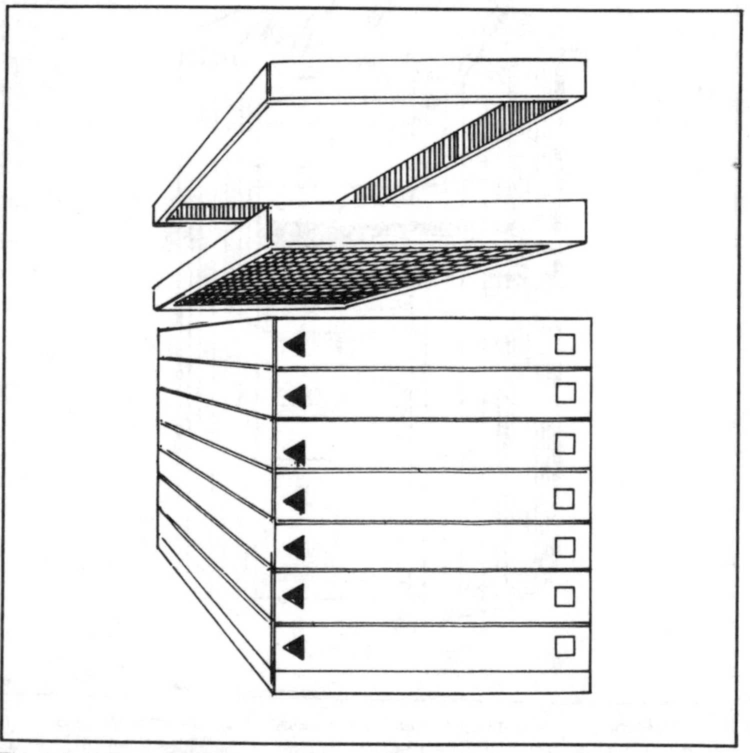

Fig. 1-4. Huber's leaf hive.

Fig. 1-5. The Reverend Lorenzo Lorraine Langstroth, father of modern beekeeping (courtesy, Dadant & Sons, Inc., Hamilton, IL 62341).

with self-spacing bars. Other inventions used frames that slid in from the side. None of these experiments solved the central problem: the bees eventually propolised the bars or frames together, to the sides or to the insides of the bottom and top of the hive.

In 1851, the Rev. Lorenzo Lorraine Langstroth hit upon the idea of removable hanging frames based on his concept of *bee space* (Fig. 1-5). Others before him had failed to realize that the honeybee will fill up any space over ⅜ inch (9mm) with either wax or propolis. Langstroth allowed for bee space between, above, and below his frames. Researchers have since determined that bee space varies from ¼ inch (6mm) to ⅜ inch (9mm) with the average at 5/16 inch (7mm).

Langstroth conceived of his revolutionary hive while traveling home in Philadelphia on an October evening. He recorded it in his journal because cool weather had already set in and he was unable to try it until the following summer. Convinced of its success, he applied for a patent that was granted the next fall. Rev. Langstroth returned to Massachusetts, where he had served as pastor of the Second Congregational Church in Greenfield. He was better known for his beekeeping than his preaching and chose Greenfield as the location of his hive. There he also began his book on beekeeping, *Langstroth and the Honey Bee.*

Because beekeeping did not become a substantial industry until after his death, Langstroth realized very little financial reward for his invention, but his movable frame revolutionized beekeeping and allowed hobbyists and commercial operators to expand as never before. It was at last possible to manage bees without killing them to get out the honey. Langstroth is known throughout the world as the father of modern beekeeping (Fig. 1-6).

OTHER IMPROVED EQUIPMENT

With the advent of a practical hive, other tools were needed to keep pace. In 1874 a briar pipe fitted with a rubber bulb so the

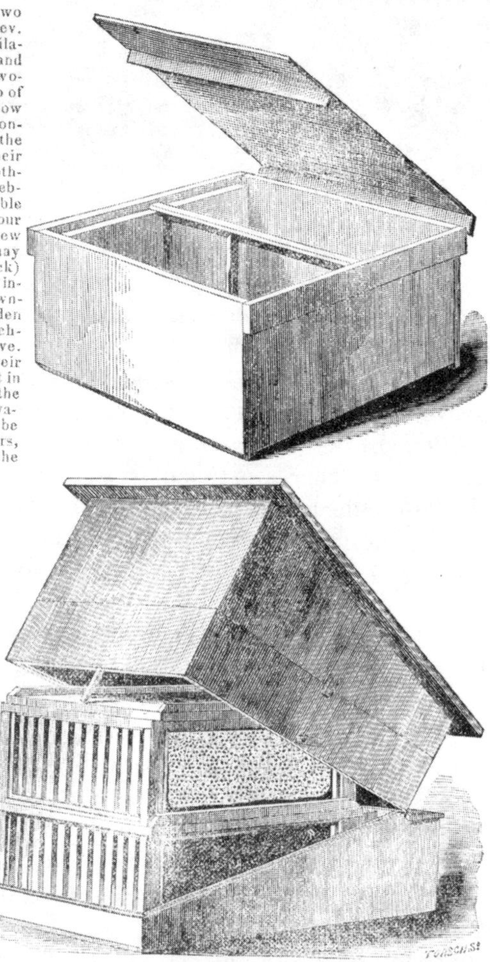

r. L. L. LANGSTROTH'S MOVABLE COMB BEE HIVE.

e cuts represent, two
ve patented by the Rev.
roth, formerly of Phila-
e of the simplest and
n, and the other a two-
glass Hive. The top of
aised, in order to show
rrangement, which con-
posts fastened on the
l, with railing on their
ng from one to the oth-
osts and rails are reb-
sides, and form double
glass is set on all four
ough which a full view
tions of the bees may
wo end (front and back)
rebated out on their in-
nd from the top down-
se rebates light wooden
spended (or rest) reach-
the bottom of the Hive.
nes the bees build their
as each comb is built in
ne, detached from the
ne frames are all mova-
d all of them may be
arately from the others,
d and replaced at the
he owner. The
partment or "BEE
covered with a
rests on the top
space above the
ames, and is also
that it may be
l put on at pleas-
oard is perforated
over which a sec-
third story (with
ll frames in it)
y receptacles, of
ion to suit the
y of the owner,
d, and in which
store their sur-
free from "*bee*
young brood."—
inner or glass
' and the outside
the Hive (which
wood) a few inch-
left, which, with
ween the double
dead air cham-
ne sides of the bee
serves to protect
their combs from
temperature.—
ng board" is cov-
oof, so that the bees are protected
n the moment they alight upon it.

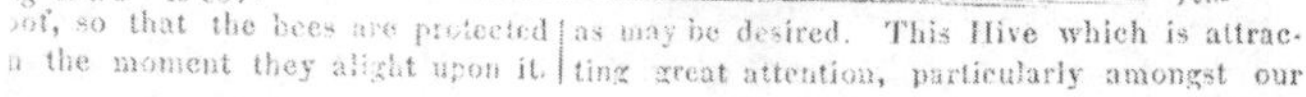

as may be desired. This Hive which is attrac-
ting great attention, particularly amongst our

Fig. 1-6. Advertisement for the Langstroth hive in *The American Farmer*, January, 1859 (courtesy, Smithsonian Institution, Photo No. 44547).

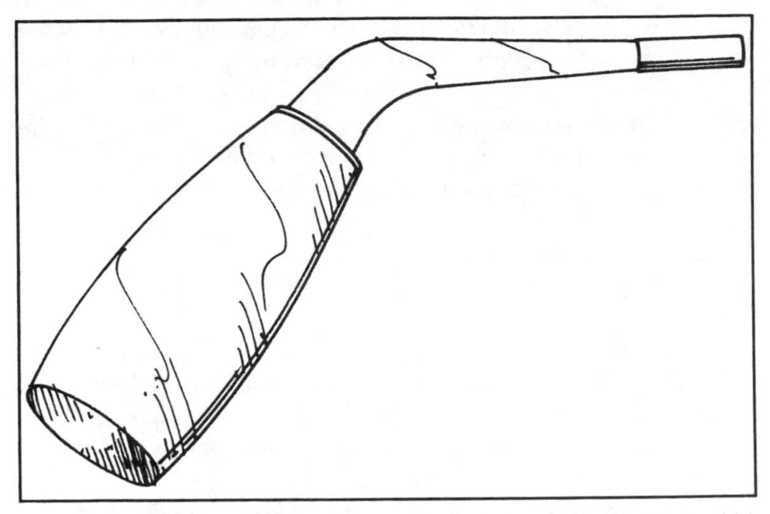

Fig. 1-7. Sketch of the briar pipe smoker, developed by Frank Cheshire, which won a prize at the Crystal Palace Show in London, 1874.

smoke could be driven out through the stem, won a prize in England as an innovative smoker (Fig. 1-7). Another early model included a simple metal tube with slow burning fuel, a mouthpiece for blowing, and a removable cap with a vent at the other end.

The first bellows-type smoker, forerunner of today's smoker, was invented by Moses Quinby of New York state, in 1870. Quinby is credited with being the first commercial beekeeper in the U.S.A. since his only income was from his honey production.

Other smoker refinements followed: the bellows and tube were separated, a ventilator was included, the nozzle angled, and the firebox enlarged to become the present day prototype.

Wax foundations, allowing for consistently straight combs of worker cells, were invented in 1857, by Johannes Mehring, a German carpenter. He developed a press with wooden plates for printing a pattern of worker cells on wax sheets. Better designs appeared in Germany, England, and the United States. A.I. Root of Ohio, founder of one of the first U.S. supply firms, had a machine built with embossed metal rollers, into which flat sheets were placed. They were made by hand dipping wooden boards into tubs of molten wax five or more times for the correct thickness, and then peeling the wax off when cool.

In 1896, E.B. Weed of New York, constructed a machine that fed a continuous sheet of wax on a spool through the rollers, thereby producing a uniform product.

Early frames to hold the foundation included devices like wide toothed combs fastened across the wax from top to bottom. They were removed when the combs were partly built. Wood supported wax was not accepted by the bees; they gnawed the wax down to the wood instead of building up on it. Other materials like paper, cloth, and cellophane did not meet with bee approval either and were eventually given up.

Captain Hetherington of Cherry Valley, New York, originated the use of wires passing through, and embedded in, the wax for support.

Better wiring plans were developed in the 1920s by both Root and Dadant. Dadant increased reinforcement with kinked or crimped wires, which prevented the wax from slipping. Root strengthened his foundation by pressing three sheets of wax together and tightly cross-wiring.

Early *queen excluders* were generally slotted wooden ones like those used in the Stewarton hives in the mid 1800s. In 1865, Abbe Collin devised a metal sheet of tin or zinc with slots of 9/50 inch wide. In 1907, Root perfected an excluder of galvanized wires through flat metal strips, thus eliminating the sharp burrs that had injured some of the bees passing through.

E.C. Porter of Illinois, introduced the *bee escape* invented by his father in 1891. It consisted of two flexible strips of metal designed to allow the bees to push their way from the hive. It closed behind them to prevent their return, thus facilitating honey removal a great deal. The Porter Bee Escape is still with us and practically unchanged.

Major Franz von Hruschka gets credit for applying the principle of centrifugal force to honey extracting. The story goes that he had given his son a piece of honeycomb in a basket and that the boy idly began whirling the basket around his head as he strolled along. Later von Hrushcka noticed that the honey had been emptied out. In 1865, he capitalized on his observation to build a honey slinger. His *extractor* was a cone-shaped container with a tap at the pointed end and ropes at the other end by which it was spun around.

At about the same time an Italian version called the *simelatore* was introduced. It consisted of a mesh bottomed box to hold combs and was twirled around a pole. The Americans Quinby and Langstroth both built and tried extractors along these lines. From the first Langstroth used gears and put his mechanism in a wooden tub. Quinby put his reel and gear in a metal can. A.I. Root, founder of one of the first United States bee supply companies, built the first all-metal extractor in 1868, using an apple paring machine to drive the reel.

With the help of an assistant, he established a record in honey extracting, 285 pounds in 7.5 hours. Upon hearing of this feat, a demand grew immediately for Root's machine, and he sold thousands of his Novice Honey Extractor. Another improvement was added by William Cowan, editor of the British Bee Journal. In other extractors, the frames had to be removed and turned around to remove the honey from the other side. Cowan constructed a reversible model in which the baskets of combs could be swung from one side to the other without handling.

Today's hobbyist has a choice of a simple, hand-turned two-frame extractor or a motor-driven reversible model. Commercial beekeepers have all the high-tech refinements available with totally automatic variable speed extractors requiring very little operator intervention.

LEARNING MORE ABOUT THE BEE

Not only has technology played a vital role in improving tools and equipment for beekeeping, but sophisticated investigative techniques such as microbiology, genetic engineering (including artificial insemination), and chemical analysis have added immeasurably to our store of knowledge about bee behavior and management.

Of the modern scientists who have contributed to our understanding of bees, one of the most reknowned is Karl von Hirsch, who spent more than 59 years conducting research into ways in which bees communicate. Results of his experiments and those of his colleagues are carefully documented and summarized in his book, *The Dance Language and Orientation of Bees.*

After countless tests and a series of training programs with hundreds of colonies of bees in Germany, he was able to unravel the way scout bees tell other bees how to find a nectar or pollen source. They communicate the distance and direction from their home base, their hive, by performing a series of movements, which von Hirsch calls a dance. He also explored the effect of scent and visual clues such as color, polarized light, position, and shape as elements of bee orientation and communication. (See Chapter 2.)

In 1973, Dr. von Hirsch won the Nobel Prize for his research in bee communication. Martin Lindauer, one of his students, carried on his work and added significantly to the interpretation of the amazing dances and other ways in which bees share their perceptions. A.M. Wenner and his colleagues later conducted experiments with different methods that led them to discount the von Hirsch theory of dance communication, claiming that bees transmitted and followed only odor clues.

In 1975, James Gould, now an associate of biology at Princeton University, found a way to deceive the bees and cause them to misinterpret the dances. In this way he hoped to measure whether the dance truly is a means of receiving clues about the direction and distance of the food source.

In perceiving direction and distance to a food source, forager bees will orient to the sun or to an artificial light if provided. The simple eyes of the bee, called the *ocelli* (Fig. 1-8), are important light receptors in the vision process of the honeybee.

Gould took advantage of this fact and covered the ocelli of the foragers. When the ocelli of the bee are covered, she either requires a much stronger light to orient toward or she reorients toward gravity in performing the dance. Therefore, by providing a light that would stimulate the recruits whose ocelli were not covered but not intense enough for the ocelli-covered foragers to read, Gould was able to fool the recruits into interpreting the dances incorrectly.

By moving the light, he was able to send recruits off in any direction. If only odor clues were read by the bees, then the angle of the light should have made no difference in their locating the food source.

All possible methods were employed to eliminate the odor signals. The bees were caught in such a way that they did not release the alarm pheromone and their scent glands were sealed with white enamel. An array of recruit stations were set up equipped with a photoelectric detector to count the arrivals. As they fed, carbon monoxide was released to anesthetize them and cause them to fall into a funnel so that the order of arrival could be monitored.

The ocelli-covered foragers were housed in an observation hive constructed to force them to dance on only one side of a frame, making it possible to videotape their dances.

The direction of the light was shifted every 30 minutes to indicate a new recruit station. The distribution of recruit arrivals shifted accordingly, showing clearly that the direction correlation in the dance is communicated and followed by recruits.

Gould's results definitely reaffirmed von Hirsch's dance communication theory. He is quick to point out that olfactory clues are

Fig. 1-8. Photograph of a foraging worker bee shows the compound eyes and *ocelli* (mask). James Gould covered the mask to fool bees into misinterpreting dances in experiments to test von Hirsch's theory of bee dance communication.

sometimes the only clues required, as when many nectar plants near the hive are in bloom. Therefore bees are able to communicate either with odor, dance, or a combination of both.

AFRICAN BEES COME TO AMERICA

One of the most notable events to affect beekeeping in the last decade is expected to create challenges into the twenty-first century. This is the importation of the African bee into South America. The African subspecies, *Apis mellifera adansonii* (also referred to as *Apis mellifera seutellata*), is noted for its potentially higher honey yield but also for its fierce defensive behavior. The adansonii bee will sting in response to almost any slight disturbance—a person walking near a hive, livestock grazing in a field. The guard bees come out in much greater numbers, travel further from the hive to sting, and persist longer than their European cousins.

In 1957, an accident allowed 26 African queen bees to be released at Rio Claro, in the state of Sao Paulo, Brazil. A geneticist, Warwick Kerr, was conducting research with selected stocks of the African bee in the hope that interbreeding with European races would result in higher honey production. He had placed special grids across the hive entrances to permit the workers to come and go but still contain the queens and drones.

A visiting beekeeper, uninformed of the experiment, removed the screens. This allowed the queen bees to fly free with departing swarms and established a feral population that has continued to reproduce and spread. In the following years up to 150 persons and many animals died as the result of bee stings, much more than the average number of 1 in 200,000 reactions in any given population.

One theory of the cause of the aggressiveness of the adansonii strain stems from their adaptation to intense plundering by animals and man. Swarms nesting in the crevices of the trees and cliffs were eventually discovered by animals or humans and destroyed for the honey. Only the hardiest and best-defended colonies survived to result in a population that is quick to defend itself.

At first scientists hoped that interbreeding would tame the African bee as well as yield more honey, but experimental results have been disappointing. Most experts now say that North American beekeepers cannot depend on a genetic barrier to water down or slow the African bees' push through Mexico into the United States.

Since 1972, active research into the behavior and management of the African bee has been conducted through the U.S. Department of Agriculture, mainly out of the Bee Breeding and Stock Center Laboratory Lab at Baton Rouge, Louisiana, plus valuable contributions of others like Dr. Orley Taylor of the University of Kansas. Based on his studies of the migration of the African bees in South America in 1975, Dr. Taylor prepared a map forecasting the possible spread of the species to various Central American countries (Fig. 1-9). His prediction has been amazingly correct with the bee averaging a migration of 300 miles per year.

Slowed by rains in Darien, in eastern Panama, the bees took 15 months to migrate 200 miles in 1981 and early 1982. But on March 3, 1982, a former member of the migration study team, Dr. Dave Roubik of the Smithsonian Tropical Research Institute spotted a swarm in a football stadium in the Panama Canal Zone, again fulfilling Dr. Taylor's forecast. At that time Dr. Taylor reaffirmed his belief that the African bee will reach Brownsville, Texas, in the United States, by 1988.

Efforts to combine the African with the European bees to obtain hybrids with behavior more like the European and the honey production capability of the African have met with poor results. While African drones will mate with European queens, European drones mate only with European queens. The African drones have an advantage of time and space distribution. They are produced by an African colony earlier in the spring than the European drones and

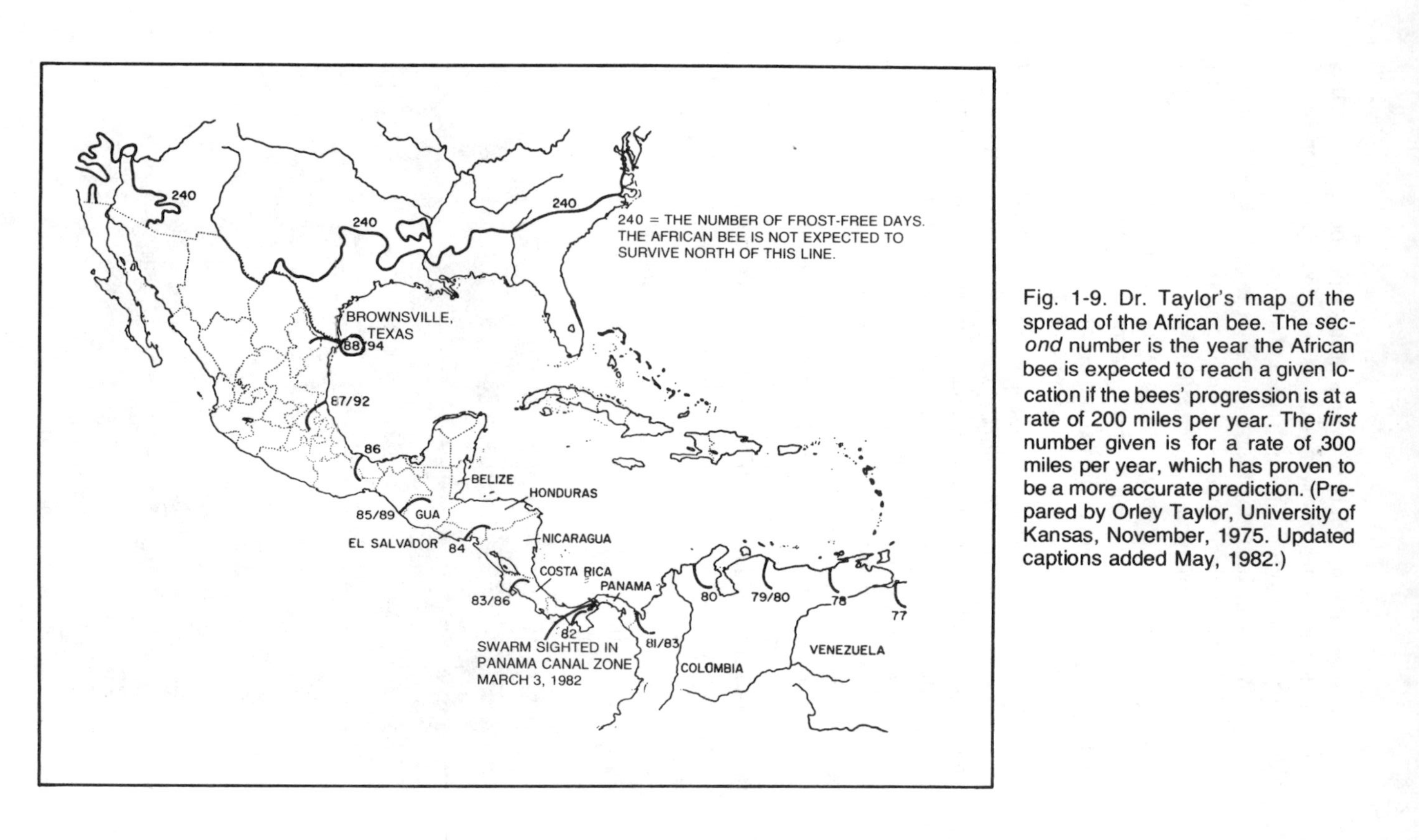

Fig. 1-9. Dr. Taylor's map of the spread of the African bee. The *second* number is the year the African bee is expected to reach a given location if the bees' progression is at a rate of 200 miles per year. The *first* number given is for a rate of 300 miles per year, which has proven to be a more accurate prediction. (Prepared by Orley Taylor, University of Kansas, November, 1975. Updated captions added May, 1982.)

are available in larger numbers over a greater period of time in the congregation areas where mating occurs. The hybrid bee appears to differ very little from the pure African strain.

Dr. Warwick Kerr and other leaders in the field report that the African bee has indeed increased honey production in southern Brazil and beekeepers are successfully managing these hybrid bees. He points out that the same hive in northern Brazil is four times more aggressive than a typical European hive. The reasons are not clear, but conjecture is that the problem could stem from the difference in humidity or the strength of infrared rays of the sun.

Two lines of research have been followed employing methods of aggression control and breeding out the unfavorable traits of the African bee (Fig. 1-10). The adansonii can be rendered stingless through the use of radiation to produce the split sting mutant. Brazilian beekeepers don't want stingless bees because of the easy accessibility to their hives by human robbers and by bees from outside the owners' colonies.

Those who have witnessed the African bee situation in Venezuela paint quite a different picture. The introduction of the African strain into that country in 1975 seems to have brought back the original fierceness both in managed hives and wild swarms to the effect that many beekeepers have abandoned their work. Professionals have left warehouses of supers abandoned. Housewives and students learning beekeeping on a part-time basis have simply given up because of the stings.

Fig. 1-10. Mackensen insemination apparatus.

Fig. 1-11. Removing semen from a drone.

Management problems are many. Very heavy clothing must be worn, larger smokers must be used, and honey removal sometimes must be undertaken at night under red lights (invisible to bees), when hives are located close to people or animals.

Research continues into the inheritable factors of the bee. Qualified apiarians, including Dr. Warwick Kerr, feel that the future of a thriving beekeeping industry lies in genetic engineering, not only to breed out the ferocious traits of the Apis mellifera adansonii but to breed in desirable traits of disease resistance, foraging capacity, and higher honey production (Fig. 1-11).

Because African bees do not cluster well to maintain brood in winter, Dr. Taylor's prediction is that they can survive only in areas that have 240 or more frost free days. This will limit them to the southern region of the United States, with little chance of their moving into the central and northern states (Fig. 1-12).

This is not to say that their migration into the United States will not affect other beekeepers. Most commercial and many amateur apiarists depend on southern suppliers for queens and package bees. If the advent of the African infiltration deters these producers, certainly other beekeepers in all climates could be adversely affected.

There is much more at stake than honey here. Large segments of agriculture in this country depend on pollination by bees. Leaders

Fig. 1-12. Inseminating a queen.

in the field are urging a crash program of increasing research on the Apis mellifera adansonii. If the beekeeping industry is seriously affected by the African bee's arrival in North America, the food supply could be curtailed and/or of much less variety. Many of the fruits, vegetables, and nuts plus several major seed crops depend on the honeybee.

Chapter 2

Getting to Know Bees

Honeybees, like all other insects, have three body parts—a head, thorax, and abdomen—and gauzy veined wings, six legs, single and compound eyes, and two antennae. But the honeybee, *Apis mellifera L.*, its botanical name, also has a strawlike tongue for nectar collecting, hairy combs on her legs for gathering pollen, and navigational and communication systems. These systems are so complex that not even today's scientists, with their sophisticated instruments and techniques have totally unraveled their mysteries. Bees as a specie have been around for 19 million years, and there are 5,000 species in the North American continent alone.

As a cooperative unit, probably no other animals are as organized as honeybees. Each adult worker passes through several phases, performing specific tasks for the survival of the colony during each phase. Bee colonies employed an air conditioning system long before man. They also have an intricate communication system, which enables the bees to interpret the direction and distance of nectar and pollen sources from the hive, to warn other bees of danger to the colony, and to tell if the colony has a healthy productive queen.

CASTES

A colony is composed of 40,000 to 100,000 bees who work together as a unit and are loyal to one queen. Three types or castes of bees are found in every colony and each is indispensable to its

Fig. 2-1. The three castes of bees, from left to right, worker, queen, drone.

survival (Fig. 2-1). Several thousand undeveloped females are the *worker* bees. There are a few to several hundred male bees called *drones*. A completely sexually developed female, the *queen*, is the third caste. There is usually only one per colony, but it's not impossible to have two or more.

It is important that the beekeeper learn to recognize the three castes of bees. The worker is the smallest, about ½ inch. They comprise the largest number of the colony. Her body is furry. The segmented abdomen appears striped or banded either yellow or brown with dark bands if Italian, or black with gray bands of hair if Caucasian. The wings, when folded, extended nearly to the tip of the abdomen. The worker has broadened hind legs with special, curved featherlike spines for pollen collecting. Usually when bees are out working, several can be seen at the entrance of the hive. Their hind legs are encased in pollen, like bright knee socks in colors from yellow-white to a deep golden brown. The worker is also equipped with a stinger carried inside at the rear or tip of her abdomen.

The queen is larger, with a long abdomen that becomes more elongated as she lays. The abdomen extends well beyond her wings, giving them the appearance of being considerably shorter than those of the worker or drones. Her abdomen has a smoother appearance—more like a beetle—and is pointed at the end. She is almost never seen outside the hive. She may be glimpsed taking off or returning from her mating flight; she will not be seen flying in or out.

Her business is egg-laying day after day, week after week (Fig. 2-2). Usually she can be found on the innermost frames of the hive surrounded by workers who groom and feed her. Workers do not walk on the queen as they do each other. As she lays, she first declines her head into the cell to check it with her antennae, then turns and drops her rear to deposit her egg.

When ordering queens from a supplier, you can request that they be marked. The supplier will paint a dot on her thorax so you can more easily spot her as she moves among thousands of workers and drones.

The drone is the same size as the queen. Newcomers to beekeeping often mistake a drone for a queen. The drone, however, has a wider abdomen, decidedly rounded and blunt, with a conspicuous brush of hairs at the end. His wings, when folded, cover his body as do the workers'. His eyes are a distinctive feature. Unlike the queen's or the workers' eyes, which are separated on the head by areas of hair, the drones large eyes are adjacent to one another on top of his head.

LIFE CYCLE

Like most other insects, the honeybee passes through three phases of growth before it hatches into an adult: the egg, larva, and pupa (Fig. 2-3). The eggs, up to 2,000 per day, are laid by the queen, one to each of the hexagonal cells that are joined vertically and horizontally to form the comb. In nature the comb is often seen as

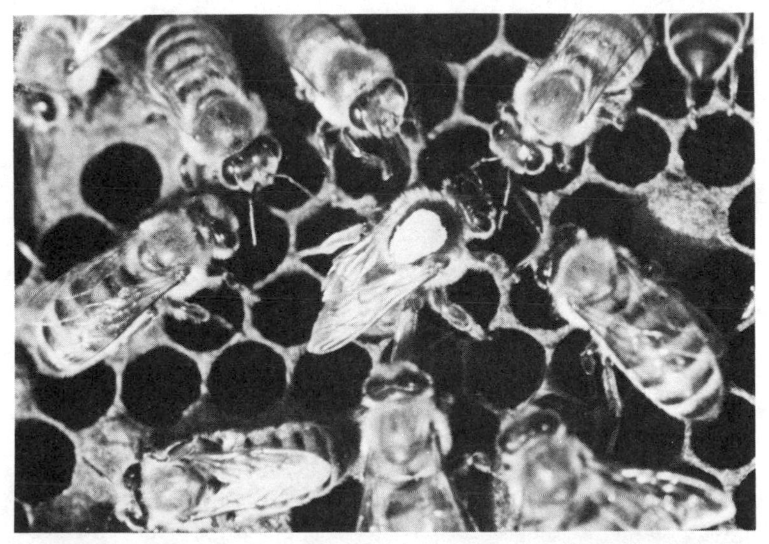

Fig. 2-2. A queen laying an egg. Note mark on her thorax and the circle of workers surrounding her. (Photo by W. P. Nye; reprinted courtesy Agricultural Research Service, Utah State University.)

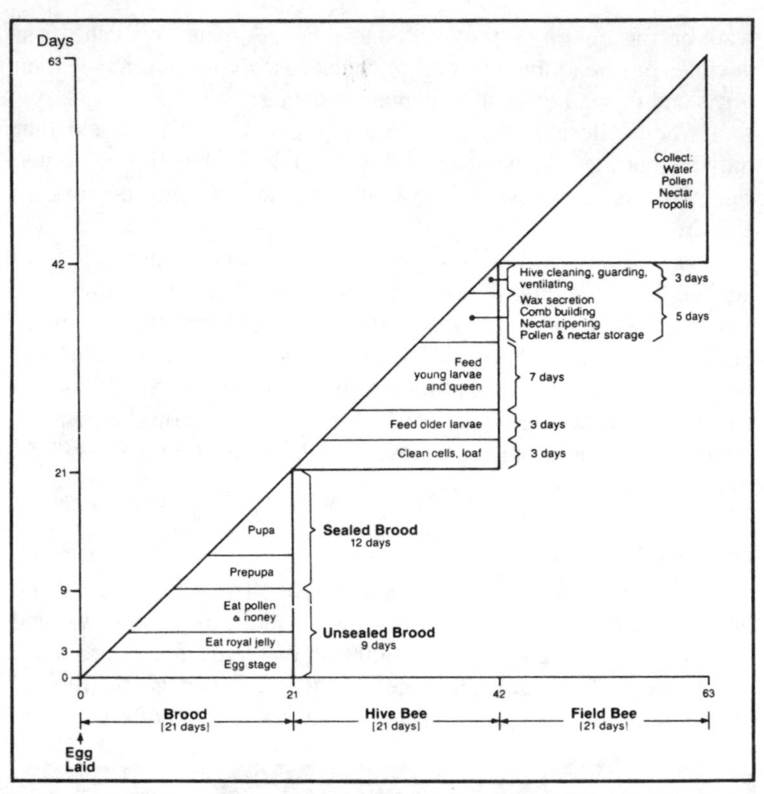

Fig. 2-3. Life history of the honeybee from egg through adult stages. (Reprinted from Agricultural Handbook, 335, USDA.)

large elliptical leaves hanging free or squeezed into the shape of the space available. In a man-made hive, the comb is built on a layer of imprinted wax, called a foundation enclosed in a rectangular frame. There are about 25 cells per square inch (2.5mm) on each side of the frame (Fig. 2-4).

The Egg

Each egg resembles a grain of rice or a wisp of thread, measuring about 1/16 inch (1.5mm). The queen attaches each egg to the bottom of the cell. As with all eggs, the nucleus cell starts dividing. By the third day, the embryo is formed and the head and body parts are discernible. Within the first 84 hours, the embryo moves about so that it forms a C shape with its tail and head touching. At this stage it looks like a small grapefruit segment, milky white in color (Fig. 2-5).

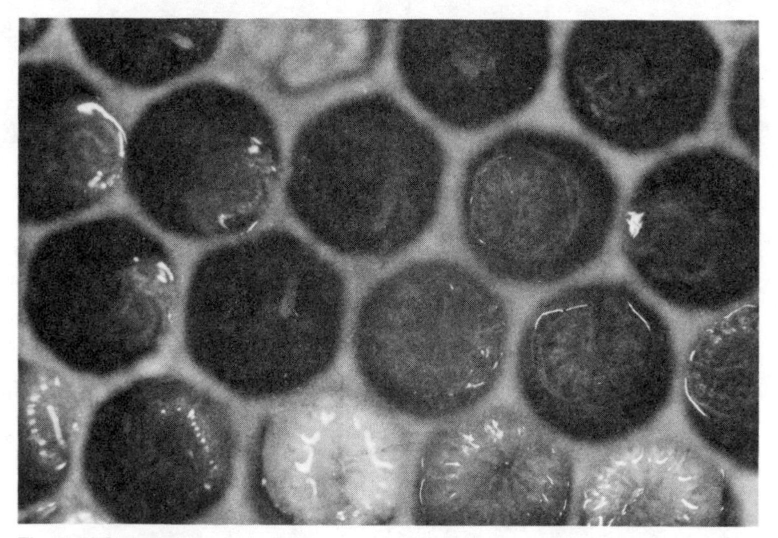

Fig. 2-4. Cells of brood, eggs, (third cell from left, top and second rows) larvae (especially clear, bottom row). (Photo by W. P. Nye; retired, apiculturist, Bee Biology and Systemics Laboratory, Logan, Utah.)

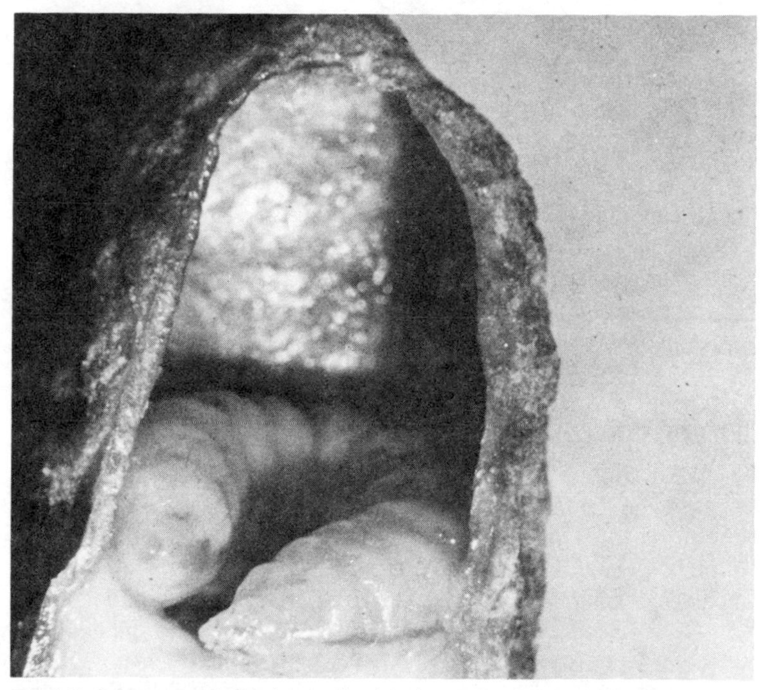

Fig. 2-5. Cut-away cell showing resting bee larva, 4 to 4½ days old. (Photo by W. P. Nye; reprinted courtesy Agricultural Research Service, Utah State University.)

The bee larvae are fed by the worker bees. At first they are given only royal jelly, an especially rich substance secreted from the glands of young workers. The larvae are then fed pollen and honey by older bees, known as nurse bees. Scientists estimate that 110,000 visits are made to each bee during its egg and larval stages. The larva moults (splits and sheds its skin) four times. By the end of the eighth day, its cell home is capped by the worker bees. The larva spins a cocoon of silk from a gland in its head. It goes into the pupal stage lying quietly on its back with the head toward the cell opening.

As a pupa, the bee moults two more times. After the fifth moult, color can be seen in the eyes. On succeeding days color appears in the abdomen, legs, wings, and finally the antennae (Fig. 2-6). The last moult occurs about the twentieth to twenty-third day. The pupa then reaches the *imago* stage and begins to chew its way out of the cell to emerge as a fully developed adult bee. Metamorphosis is complete.

Queen and Drone Larvae

A larva that is to become a queen is fed throughout its larval stage on royal jelly. It is provided a larger cell, which hangs vertically from the comb and looks somewhat like a small peanut. The exact process by which a larva becomes a fully developed female with all the queen characteristics is not completely understood but has to do with the quantity and quality of the food provided.

Drones develop from unfertilized eggs. Mature, fully mated queens can control whether they lay a fertile egg to become a worker or an unfertilized one to become a drone. Drone eggs are laid in larger cells that when capped appear to have a dome shaped top. Capped worker bee cells are in the same plane as the rest of the comb.

LIFE EXPECTANCY

A worker bee lives only about four to six weeks during the busy season when she must make thousands of trips to bring in nectar and pollen. She literally flies her wings to shreds and wears off her pollen brushes. During very cold winters, when she is confined to the hive for long periods, she may live for several months.

A queen can live up to five years. She is a prolific and dependable layer for only two years, so most colonies supercede her unless the beekeeper intervenes to provide a new queen. Most colonies

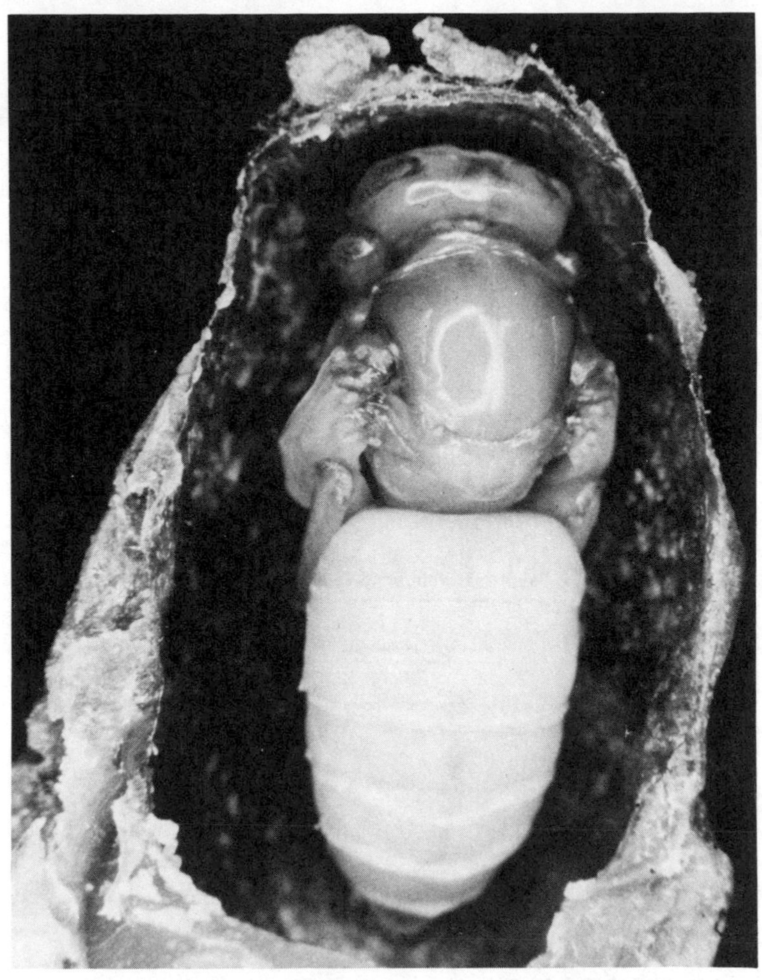

Fig. 2-6. Cut-away cell showing larva in imago stage before last moult. Note color beginning to show in eyes. (Photos by W. P. Nye; reprinted courtesy Agricultural Research Service, Utah State University.)

and many beekeepers replace a queen long before she dies naturally.

The drone that mates with the queen becomes paralyzed when he everts his genitilia into her vagina and sting chamber, falls backward and downward to his death. Otherwise he flies around the hive or in drone congregating areas waiting for a queen. His lifespan corresponds with the abundance of food. When nectar becomes scarce and the colony must depend on stores to survive, the drones are prevented from eating by the workers and forced out of the hive to starve or freeze to death. For quick reference facts, see Table 2-1.

THE WORKERS' ROLE

When an adult worker chews her way out of the cell, she is fuzzy and soft. She is unable yet to make wax, fly, or sting. She probably rests a couple of days while her body hardens. Then she begins her work—first feeding the older larvae and then the other larvae. At this stage, it is believed she serves as nurse bee because her hypopharyngeal glands in her head are producing brood food.

She will spend almost half of her life as a house worker. At about 10 days she begins to take orientation flights near the hive, sometimes called *play flights* because of the typical bobbing and weaving motions. House bees also clean debris like dead enemy ants or wax moths from the hive.

Table 2-1. Reference Facts on Bees.

Bees and the Numbers Game

Sometimes you want to remember number facts about bees and you can't recall where you saw it. Here's a quick and ready reference (figures are *averages*).

Bees per colony	45-70,000 plus
Size of eggs	1/16 inch or 1.6 mm
Length of worker larva	1.6 mm
Size of adult worker honeybee	1/2 inch or 1.2 cm
Development period required for queen (egg to adult)	16 days
Development period for drones and workers	23 days
Visits by nurse bees to each egg/larva until capped	110,000
Worker cells per inch of honeycomb	5
Worker cells per full depth frame	680
Eggs queen can lay in one day	1500-2000
Sperm queen receives during mating	5-6 million
Number of bees per pound (depending on amount of honey in honey stomachs)	6000
Number of flowers bees visit to fill honey stomach	1000
Flight speed of bee	12 mph
Wing beats, normal	250 cycles per second
Wing beats, buzzing	400-500 per second
Weight of honey on full depth frame	5 pounds
Weight of honey in a gallon	12 pounds
Temperatures at which bees no longer fly	50°F, 10°C
Temperature at which bees start fanning	95°F, 35°C
Temperatures at which bees cluster for brood warmth	57°F, 14C°
Number of nerve cells in bee brain	860,000
Number of species in North America	5000
Age of the bee species	19 million years

Fig. 2-7. Workers whose wax secreting glands become active hang in chains to build comb.

As the worker's brood food glands diminish, the wax secreting glands located in the last four anterior segments of her abdomen become active (Fig. 2-7). She starts working on the comb building "teams" with other workers. First, the members of the construction crew eat large amounts of honey. They then hang together with their feet locked. (You will often see them, as you attempt to pull out a frame, linked in a chain extending from the side of one comb to the side of the next.) Tiny flakes of wax gradually form in each of the eight wax pockets of each worker. She takes these with her hind feet and passes them to her mandibles or mouth parts. She will then manipulate several flakes together until they are soft and can be fitted in place.

Bees are very fast construction workers. Sometimes wax flakes form so rapidly, they drop to the hive bottom, where they look like dandruff.

The hexagonal shape that bees use is perfect from an engineering standpoint. Round would be economical of space but wasteful of wax; square would be economical of material but poor utilization of space and would not fit the developing bee.

Older house bees work with the pollen and propolis (bee glue) to place or store it. They relieve the field bees of their nectar by using their mandibles to carry and work the nectar. Eventually they deliver it to a cell for ripening.

Another important job of the house bee is fanning, both to carry away excess moisture for proper honey consistency and to cool the interior of the hive in warmer weather.

Field bees are the foragers for the colony. Scout bees go ahead to find nectar and pollen sources—suitable blooming plants from fields of weeds to groves of trees (Fig. 2-8). They also locate a new home or nest if the hive becomes overcrowded and the bees are ready to swarm. It is not known exactly how scout bees are developed or chosen to carry out this task. Possibly it is a matter of individual development.

Field bees also collect resin from trees to make propolis, which bees use like a glue to tighten and weatherproof their home. Propolis is believed to have an antibacterial property as well.

Another job of the worker is that of guard. Guard bees stay near the entrance of the hive and fly up to interrupt an intruder whether it be a wax moth, robber bee, or human.

Each worker passes through a job phase apparently in synchronization with the development of their glands. As they produce food substances in the first week or two, they tend brood. As they start to produce wax at 12 to 15 days, they work with comb. The guard phase most likely represents an intermediate step between house work and field work. The schedule fluctuates with the needs of the colony. When a good honey flow is on, more bees must serve in the field; when the queen is laying profusely (usually in early spring), then more bees are needed for nurse duties.

One researcher, Martin Lindauer, monitored a single marked bee day and night in an observation hive to see in what sequence she performed various jobs. Results showed that she performed several jobs as needed and did not necessarily stick to one continuously. Over a period of 24 hours, this bee cleaned cells, capped them, fed younger and older larvae, and built comb. She spent about one third of the time patrolling and many hours doing nothing. According to Landauer, the loafing does not diminish the bee's reputation as a busy creature. Rather, those idle workers form a backlog of reserves ready to buzz into any task as needed by the colony, insuring that emergenices are met expeditiously.

THE QUEEN'S ROLE

When a pupa destined to be a queen reaches maturity after 16 days, she chews her way out of her cell like the workers. At first she rests and the workers pay no attention to her. If a good productive queen is already "reigning," there is a strong possibility she will sting the newly hatched queen and kill her before she even starts. Queens, unlike workers, retain their stingers and can sting repeatedly. (Upon being stung, a worker bee pulls away from her

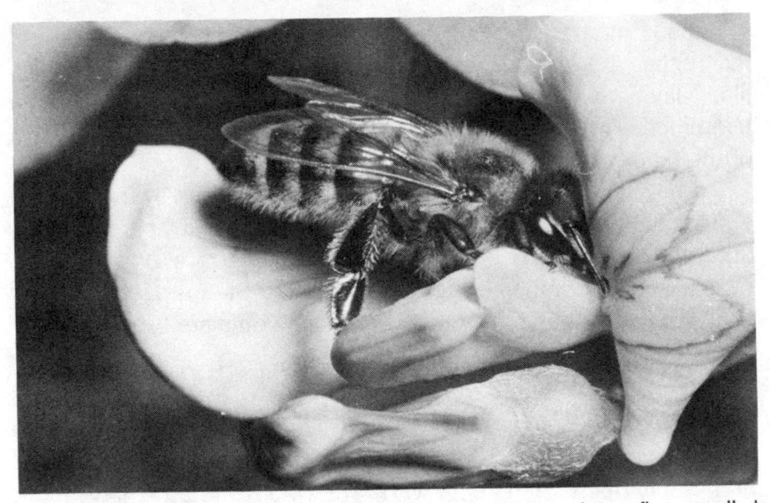

Fig. 2-8. A field bee foraging for nectar. Proboscis is deep into a flower called bladder senna, a leguminous deciduous shrub, which grows wild in desert areas. (Photo by W. P. Nye, Logan, Utah.)

victim and in doing so loses a portion of her abdomen and dies.) The queen's stinger is firmly attached so that she can sting as many newly hatched queens as necessary.

If the colony is without a queen or is not *queenright* with an old or poor queen, the new queen often works on in the same hive for a time. After resting a few days, the new queen is sexually mature and will take her first mating flight.

She leaves the hive and goes up to 50 feet, where drones have congregated for the purpose of mating with her. In order for the queen bee to have enough fertile material—six or seven million sperm—to last her lifetime, she must mate with several drones, as many as ten, usually in two or more flights.

After her final mating flight, she reenters the hive. In two to five days she begins her life work of laying eggs. For the first several months she will lay fertilized eggs that become workers. Later she will control whether the egg will be fertile or not, a worker or a drone. A queen can live up to five years but a beekeeper following good management practices usually replaces her after one year, and certainly within two when her production starts to decline.

The bees themselves will replace a queen who is not effective. They draw out one or more cells into the larger queen cup and feed a larva the right food to develop a queen. Sometimes they "ball" the old queen, clustering so tightly about her that she is killed.

But a good queen is given royal treatment. She is groomed and fed by the workers, who surround her in an oval ring as she moves along laying her eggs. She exudes a powerful stimulant called a pheromone, which the workers sense and communicate to the rest of the hive that the colony is queenright.

The queen's egg laying is controlled to an extent by the season. Following the summer's busy food gathering and honey storing (except in areas with mild winters), the queen tends to taper off by October. She resumes her egg laying some time in December or January when she is fed by the workers to stimulate brood production.

THE DRONES' ROLE

The drone's only job is to mate with the queen. One defender of drones say that they do help warm the colony during clustering in the winter. Since they are not equipped to gather nectar or pollen, clean cells, or feed larvae, and yet eat what they need from the honey stores, too many at the wrong time is definitely a drain on the food resources of the colony. Drones cannot defend the hive because they have no stinger. When food stores are short, the workers will refuse to allow the drones to eat and literally drag them out of the hive to starve and/or freeze.

Drones do have stronger wings than the workers. These carry them up 30 to 50 feet to the drone congregating areas where they wait to mate with the queen. Out of the many drones a colony produces, only five or six mate at each encounter.

BEE COMMUNICATION

When the scout bees return to the hive with nectar or pollen, they pass the word to their fellow workers by a certain pattern of movements called a *dance*. This dance system of communication was discovered by Karl von Hirsch, a German scientist who studied bee behavior for 50 years (Fig. 2-9).

Communicating the Direction

When the food source is less than ½ mile (80 M) away, the scouts move in a circular pattern—a round dance—with no indication of direction. Within a short distance of the hive, the dancers are "saying," is a food source (Fig. 2-9). When the plant with nectar or pollen is further away, the scout bees move in a straight line with a pattern of jiggling movements von Hirsch called the *tail waggling* dance. She will repeat this dance often, turning away from the top of

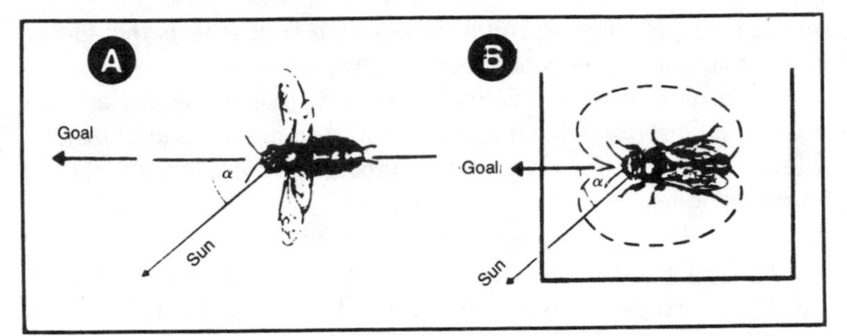

Fig. 2-9. The honeybee indicates the direction to a pollen source by dancing on a horizontal surface. First, a scout bee takes an angle on a food source (A) and then (B) performs a dance, upon return to the hive, to communicate the direction. This was called a "tail waggling" dance by Karl von Hirsch, who discovered the principle. (Reprinted from *The Dance Language and Orientation of Bees* by Karl von Hirsch, 1967, by permission of the publisher, Harvard University Press.)

her line in an elliptical curve somewhat like the shape of a wing. She returns to the base of her line and waggles her tail at the same angle over and over (see Fig. 2-10).

The line she traces represents the angle on the earth's surface between the sun and the food source and thus communicates the direction to her hive mates.

Bees can determine this angle because of their ability to perceive polarized light. Polarized light is caused by particles and moisture in the air and is seen by the bees as separate points of light with vibrating waves. As there is always some polarized light in the daytime sky, whether it is a bright day with full sun or a cloudy overcast day, bees are able to navigate most of the time using this natural phenomenon. (Fig. 2-10)

Transposing to the Vertical

The scout bee works in a dark closed hive on the vertical surface of a frame of comb. Not only must she "remember" what she perceived via the polarized light, but she must also transpose the information from the horizontal plane to a vertical plane. She is able to manage this feat through her gravitational sense organs located at the joints between her head and thorax and between her thorax and abdomen.

A tail waggling dance in a line parallel with the side bars of the frame, or straight up, means the food source is in the direction of the sun. A tail waggling run straight down translates to a food source opposite the sun. One at an angle of 60 degrees to the left of the straight line means 60 degrees to the left of the sun. Sixty degrees to the right, 60 degrees to the right of the sun. It is as though the worker bee uses the coordinates of the compass.

A professor at Princeton University, James Gould, and his associates discovered that bees have a trace of the mineral magnetite, the element used in making compass needles, located in front of the abdomen.

With the use of very sensitive instruments and by applying a strong field, a remanent or permanent magnetic field was induced in 15 of 18 test bees (see Table 2-2). The magnetic fields were oriented transversely and restricted to the horizontal plane of the bee. Although further tests must be conducted to prove that honey bees orient to magnetic fields by using the magnetic crystals in their abdomens, results show that the magnetic material is constructed in an orderly way that might make it suitable as a detector.

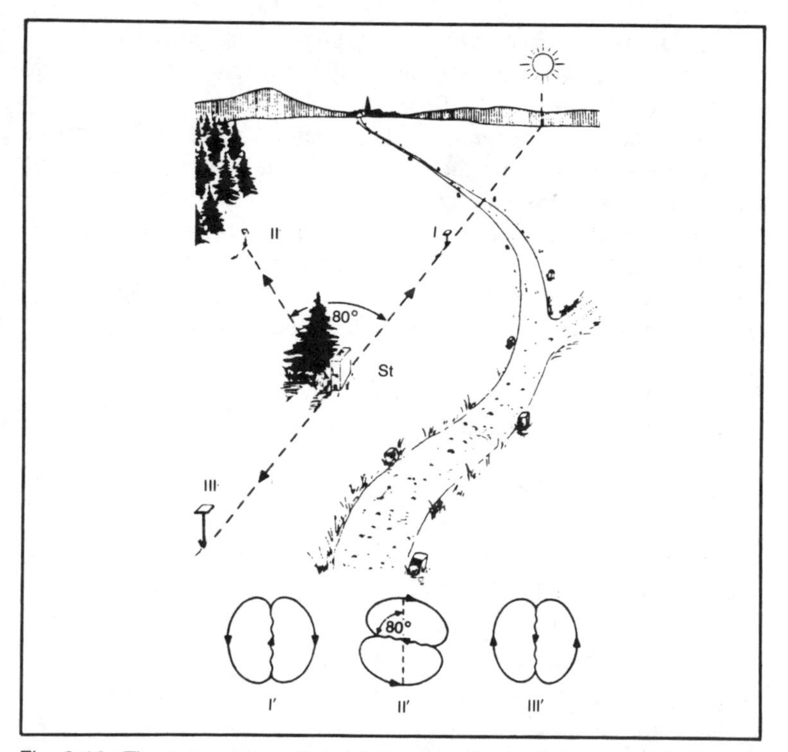

Fig. 2-10. Three examples of the indication of direction on a vertical comb surface beehive. Three feeding stations, I, II, and III, are located in three different directions; I′, II′, III′. The corresponding tail-waggling dances on the vertical comb are shown. (Reprinted from *The Dance Language and Orientation of Bees* by Karl von Hirsch, 1967, with permission of the publisher, Harvard University Press.)

Table 2-2. Effects of Magnetism on Honeybees.

Mean magnetic moments ($\times 10^{-6}$ emu $= 10^{-3}$ A • m^2) of samples before (natural remanence) and after (induced remanence) application of a strong magnetic field, and the standard error of the mean for each. *N* indicates the number of different measurements. In the case of induced moments, these include strong field applications in the horizontal plane of the bee (along and across the bee's axis) and in the vertical plane. The strongest induced moment was 5.1×10^{-6} emu, while the strongest natural remanence was 2.1×10^{-6} emu.

Sample	Natural Remanence	N	Induced Remanence	N
Empty sample box	0.2 ± 0.2	2	0.3 ± 0.1	6
Dead bees	0.2 ± 0.03	7	2.7 ± 0.2	41
Live bees	1.2 ± 0.2	12	1.7 ± 0.2	17
Older pupae	1.5 ± 0.4	4	1.5 ± 0.2	11
Young pupa, larvae, and egg	0.4 ± 0.1	2	0.5 ± 0.1	10

The experiment was conducted by James Gould and associates. Reprinted by permission of the author from *Science* Vol. 201 p. 1027, Table 1, 15 September 1978. Copyright 1978 by the American Association for the Advancement of Science.

Communicating the Distance

The dance tempo communicates the distance to the food source. With increasing distance to the goal, the tempo slows and the number of circuits per unit of time decreases.

The distance represented is not the actual time it takes the scout to get to the plants or the true distance between the hive and the food but rather the amount of energy she expended. Experiments with bees covering the same distance in headwinds versus calm air, and with lead weights attached versus unencumbered, showed that the bee demonstrated in her dance a longer distance than the actual measure with headwinds and weights.

Monitoring hundreds of dances, von Hirsch and his colleagues found that the bee dances gave more importance to the outward flight from the hive to the food plants in communicating the distance or energy expended.

The enthusiasm and duration of her dancing tells her hive mates something of the quality of the food source. The sweeter the nectar the more excited the movements she makes. She may emit a sound during the waggling as well.

Odor and Taste

The bee's sense of taste and odor are also important elements of orientation and communication. As the forager bee dances, she pauses from time to time to give an observer she is trying to recruit a drop of nectar from her honey stomach. The recruits who surround her feel her abdomen with their antennas to check the species of flowers visited, the scent of which has clung to her body.

Hive Ventilation

Hive ventilation is another process important to the health of the colony. Bees are able to start and stop ventilation by their interaction or communication. When the weather is hot, above 34 degrees Centigrade (95°F) fanning is not enough. Lindauer found that a system of begging and food transmission started and stopped forager bees bringing in water for cooling. As the hive becomes too warm, bees at the center begin to regurgitate the water in their honey stomachs, or 60 percent of the total amount. Now they are carrying only highly concentrated sugar solution.

As they move out toward the edge of a layer of workers, they stretch their proboscises and tap with their antennas, begging to exchange the contents of their honey stomachs with bees having the normal watery solution. Soon the begging extends to the entrance of the hive where foragers with the least concentrated nectar are met the most eagerly. Commonly, those with the richest nectar are relieved first. Experienced foragers are thus informed by lack of interest in their normal nectar load to start collecting water instead.

They begin bringing in droplets of water that are put on the cells by house bees and spread into a film with their proboscises. Hundreds of these thin droplets form a large evaporating surface.

Once the urgency has passed, how do the foragers know to stop bringing in water, especially since bees cannot store water in comb? According to Lindauer, the house bees do not relieve the foragers as quickly. When the hive is still too hot, the recipient bees react to the water carriers with what he calls "stormy begging." As the colony becomes cool, the foragers must try to find another bee to take it. When they are not relieved within three minutes, they stop collecting.

Pheromones

Bees, as well as other insects, exude chemical substances called pheromones that serve as a means of communication. In apiculture the documentation and analysis of pheromones is a relatively new area of research. One mandibular pheromone of the queen is simply a signal to the workers that she is present. This scent is constantly passed from one to another worker throughout the hive. If it is not strong enough or not present at all, the workers, usually undeveloped females, can start laying eggs. These eggs are all drones because they are not fertile. Their ovaries develop in response to the absence of the pheromone. Workers will also start

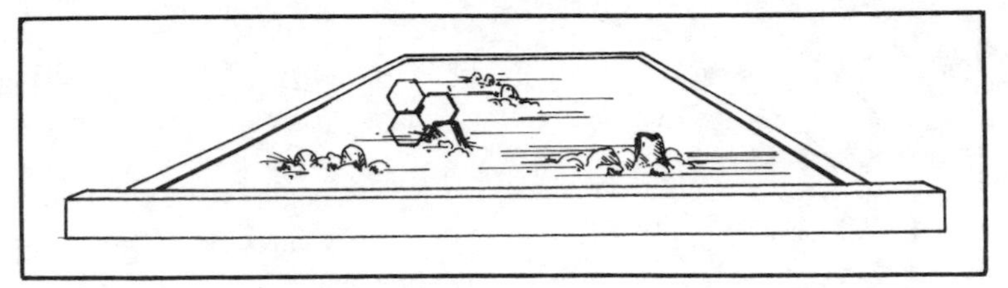

Fig. 2-11. Queen cells are built by the workers when they need to replace or supercede a queen. They are often on the bottom of a frame but can be anyplace. The lack of or weak pheromone signal is a clue to the bees that the colony is not "queenright."

building up queen cells or prepare to swarm in the absence of this pheromone (Fig. 2-11).

Worker bees produce pheromones as well. One of the most observable reactions to a pheromone is the use of the *nasanoff* or scent gland when a swarm is entering a hive. As bees are entering, some stay on the porch and fan. They turn their abdomens down and a white droplet can be seen on top at the end. The other bees respond to this pheromone and march right in.

Pheromones plus the food materials being gathered help to create a "colony odor," distinct and different for each colony. It is this odor that causes bees to fight and kill one another if an attempt is made to combine colonies. The problem is easily solved by placing a layer of newspaper between the hive bodies of the two colonies. By the time the bees have chewed through the paper, the colony odors have intermingled and a new colony odor is established for the new colony.

BODY PARTS

The honeybee is an insect. As such it shares all the common characteristics of this class of organisms. Its body is composed of three segments—head, thorax, and abdomen. It has both simple and compound eyes, six legs, wings, and two antennae. Because it has adapted to a particular lifestyle, however, the honeybee also has several uniquely specialized body parts.

Eyes

Like other insects, the honeybee has both simple and compound eyes. This gives the appearance of a "mask" on the face. The simple eyes, called ocelli are three small eyes situated in a triangle at the front top of the head of the worker and queen. They are lower

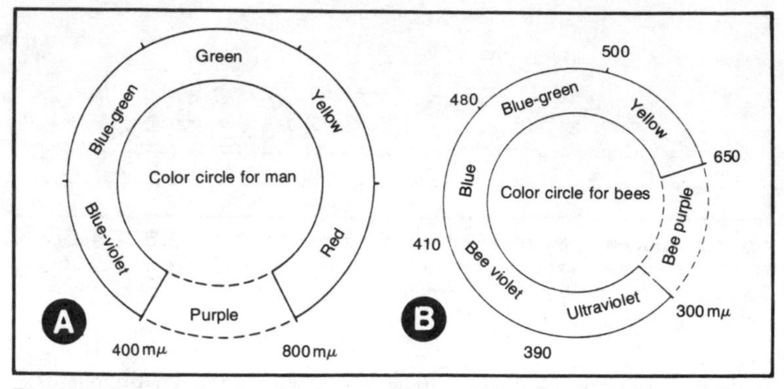

Fig. 2-12. Color charts showing the color ranges for man and for bees. (Reprinted from *The Dance Language and Orientation of Bees* by Karl von Hirsch, 1967, by permission of the publisher, Harvard University Press.)

on the face of the drone. The ocelli respond to degrees of light and do not throw an image on to the retina.

The compound eye is composed of a large number of ocular units covered by a cuticular cornea. The surface of the cornea has thousands of six-sided facets, the centers of which are transparent and comprise the lenses. The surface of the compound eye is covered with long hairs that wear off as the bee ages.

Bees see ultraviolet colors the most intensely. In the range of purple colors, bees can recognize several hues (Fig. 2-12). Yellow flowers that appear as the same shade to humans can be distinguished easily by bees because of the difference in the admixture of ultraviolet light. Leaves and other foilage look gray to them; therefore flower colors stand out all the better. The nectar markers, usually the throat of the flower, appears to have a sheen because of the ultraviolet reflection.

Bees do not have good form perception. Training experiments to get them to respond to a square, circle, or triangle have not been successful (Fig. 2-13). A much more important clue to them is the amount of breakage in a pattern or figure. This is the reasoning behind arranging colonies in an irregular pattern rather than the traditional straight row. Bees do get confused and will drift toward the end hives, increasing those populations to the detriment of the middle ones. (During heavy nectar flow, bees accept outside bees who are nectar laden regardless.)

Legs

The six legs of the bee are beautifully designed to handle pollen and propolis, collecting, carrying, and passing it to house bees. The first leg has long cyclindrical bristles that are used as a brush to remove the pollen rubbed on to the worker's body and head from the anthers or pollen producing part of flowers. The inner surface of the lower third, or last legs, is a carrying device dubbed a *pollen basket*. It is formed by the concave segment of the leg and the stiff hairs around it. These hairs are called *rastellum* or "little rake."

By scraping her legs together, she is able to push the pollen into the baskets. Scientific observers say the worker does this on the wing, hovering in the air with no forward movement. When the forager returns to the hive, she uses her middle legs to push off the pollen.

The honeybee has claws on her feet that enable her to cling to smooth surfaces upside down and to gain a firm foothold when she, along with many other workers, become the supporting layer for a swarm or a cluster.

Wings

The honeybee has two sets of wings. They are similar to most

Fig. 2-13. Bees cannot be trained to respond to shapes as visual clues, but they do receive visual orientation from the amount of brokenness in a pattern or figure.

insects' except that they are simpler in shape and veining pattern than most. The forewing is larger. When the wings are not in use, they lie folded over the back with no connection between them. In flight, the front wing extends over the hind wing. The hind wing is equipped with tiny hooks that fit into a fold of the front wing, allowing the two wings on each side to be connected and function in unison.

Brain and Nervous System

With more sophisticated processes and instruments such as the oscillograph, printed circuit microelectrodes, and videotaping, entomologists are now able to measure the extent to which a bee learns and how she learns. This dispels once and for all the theory that she responds strictly to blind instinct. A researcher in Cardiff, England, has electronically measured the learned nervous reaction to a given scent and has definitely determined that the bee has both short- and long-term memory banks. Exposure to a stimulus (flower) and the reward (nectar), in as few as three trips will reinforce the bee's memory pattern for life.

Both the bee's eyes and antennae have important nerve receptors that feed signals into the bee's brain. When bees are moved or their home environment is changed, they typically hover and circle the area before landing. It is now clear that they are referring the new visual impressions to their memory bank of imprinted patterns before deciding if it is all right to fly in to the entrance.

POLLINATION

The honey that bees produce was doubtlessly the primary reason for men to keep bees. But the bee's most important contribution to mankind is not as a producer of the golden sweet liquid, but as a pollinator of crops (Fig. 2-14). According to Dr. Roger Morse, a professor of entomology and director of the Dyce Laboratory for Honeybee Studies at Cornell University, more than 15 percent of our food comes from plants that are dependent on, or give extensively higher yields with, insect pollination.

Fifty major crops in the United States depend on insect pollination. They include tangerines, avocados, and berries; stone and pome fruits like plums, peaches, cherries, and apples; melons such as cantaloupes and watermelons; cucurbits like cucumber and squash; and nuts, particularly almonds and peanuts. Many valuable seed crops essential to the food chain need bees for pollination. Among them are alfalfa (food for both dairy and beef cattle) and

Fig. 2-14. A worker bee collects pollen from an alfalfa flower and increases the crop yield at the same time. Note the large amount of packed pollen on the hind leg, in her "pollen basket."

oilseed plants such as sunflower, cotton, and soybeans (basic components in salad oil and shortening). The production of hybrid varieties of corn, onions, and carrots are all aided by bee pollination.

Heavy pollination increases the likelihood of early yields, often permitting crops to be harvested before harmful insects infest the plants or before a siege of heavy rain or severe frost sets in.

Although flowers appear in nature in a great variety of forms, from the tiny clover floweret to the large sunflower head, from a peach blossom to the complicated tassel and ear of corn, the basic composition of a flower is universal. The sexual organs are the *stamen* (male) with the pollen producing anthers on the outer ends, and the *pistil* (female) comprised of the ovary, ovules, the style with the pollen receptor, the stigma near the end. Surrounding and supporting the sexual parts are usually colorful petals that form tube or crown called a *corolla*. The corolla is supported by more durable green petals called the *sepal.*

Most flowers have both male and female functional parts within one flower. Often the male and female parts mature at different times (Fig. 2-15). The stigma may not be receptive when the pollen is available, necessitating the transfer of pollen from one flower to another, where the stigma is ready. In other plants like the squash, some flowers are male, others female, again requiring a pollinator like the bee to insure fruit set (Fig. 2-16).

Pollination is actually a two-fold process: first, pollen is transferred from the anther to a receptive stigma, and then the pollen grain sprouts and there is growth down the style into the ovary, resulting in the union of the male nuclei with the female germ cells in the ovule. When a honeybee gets pollen from the anthers on her head and body as she enters the flower, she brushes some on to the stigma as she dips her head to take the nectar. Or she carries the pollen from one flower where the stigma is not receptive to a flower where it is.

Pollen is abundantly available. A single apple blossom may produce as many as 70,000 grains of pollen, of which only 10 grains are needed to fertilize another blossom. Bees can carry up to 50,000 pollen grains at the same time. Pollen is as diverse as the flowers

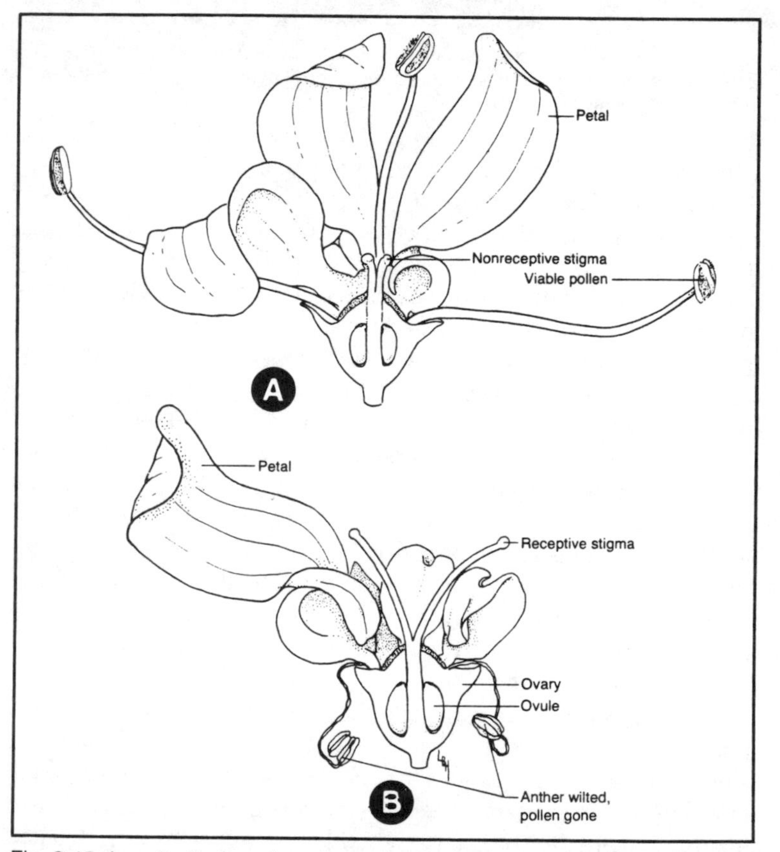

Fig. 2-15. Longitudinal section of a coriander flower (magnified) (A). Pollen is available but stigma are not receptive. This pollen must be carried by the wind or an insect, like the honeybee, to another coriander flower with receptive stigma, as shown in B. (Reprinted from Agricultural Handbook 335, USDA.)

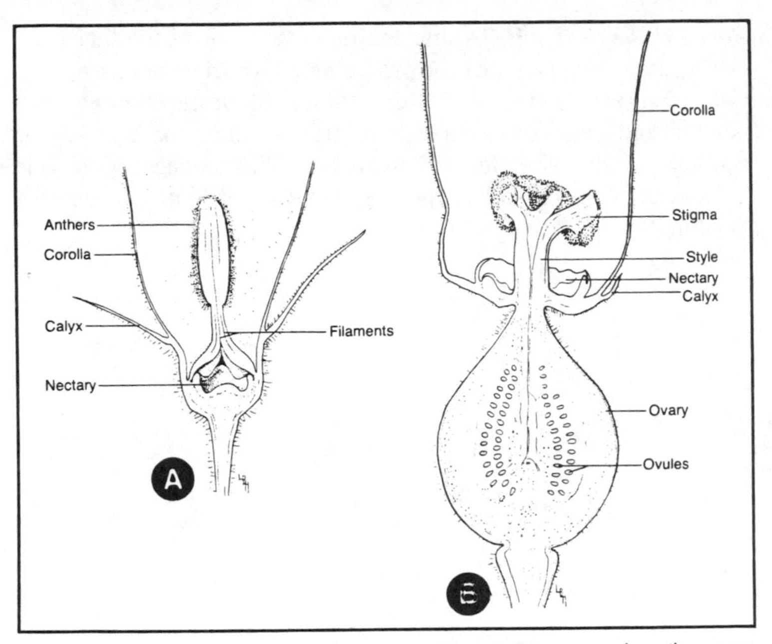

Fig. 2-16. Some plants have male flowers and female flowers, such as the acorn squash shown here in a longitudinal section. A is the staminate or male flower. B is the pistillate or female flower. (Reprinted from Agricultural Handbook 335, USDA.)

from which it comes, ranging in size from 6 microns (6/1000 mm or 1/4,000 inch) to 14/1000 mm, or 1/250 inch, and take a myriad of microscopic shapes.

Wasps, moths, butterflies, beetles, thirps, and midges are pollinators, too, but not as efficient as bees. Bees visit flowers methodically, and in large numbers until most of the nectar or pollen is taken (and a great deal transferred), from a given field. They do not harm the plant or flower in the process.

The honeybee does not always perform her pollinating duties as anticipated. Bees can find shortcuts through holes left by other insects. They may crawl between the petals rather than from the top and miss contacting the pollen anthers. Such is the case with the Delicious apple, where a study showed that as many as 86 percent of the bees were "sideworking" the apple blossoms. This resulted in a disastrously lower apple yield. Orchardists in this situation were advised to interplant with another species of apple so that the bee would be forced to change technique from row to row.

Wild bees, like the leafcutter bee and the alkali bee, are useful alfalfa pollinators, but their effect has been difficult to measure.

Research since the 1940s into the domestication of the leafcutter has resulted in guidelines for providing appropriate nesting materials, shelters, and cold winter storage to protect larvae from beetles and moths. Information is also available on building up artificial nesting sites for the alkali bee. The propagation of wild bees is most successful in the western United States, especially Washington, Utah, and California.

Chapter 3

Finding a Place for Your Hive

It is important to give careful thought to where you will locate your bees. It is much easier to plan and prepare in advance than to find your bees are collecting on the edge of your neighbor's fish pond to drink or winter winds are chilling them to death. Moving bees can be tricky, especially when you are new to beekeeping and have only minimum equipment (Fig. 3-1).

Bees are kept in a great variety of places. Hives can be placed in woods, fields, fruit orchards, near flood control sites, backyards, oil fields, and even on rooftops. Consider the following points when selecting a site for your beehive.

FOOD AND WATER

The prime need of bees is a plentiful source of food, nectar for making honey and pollen. This food must be available over as many months of your area's growing season as possible. Your bees can store excess honey for you when they have sufficient food stores to keep the colony strong.

You have two broad areas to consider. You can keep bees near your home—in your backyard or on your grounds—or you can locate them on the outskirts of town or in the country. If you think you might locate your hive in the country contact a farmer, a truck gardener, or an orchardist. Ask about the availability not only of cultivated crops but of weeds, wildflowers, and trees.

A city or suburban backyard often has a greater variety of

Fig. 3-1. These hives are located in the chapparal on a southern California mountainside. Availability of plants for foraging depends on winter rains, often very good in early spring and summer; diminishes in heat of late summer and fall to the point where the beekeeper must often provide water and supplementary feeding.

nectar and pollen plants, over a longer period, within bee foraging distance, or a radius of 3 to 4 miles.

If your home is in the middle of acres of concrete with only an occasional tree or well-trimmed shrub hugging apartment houses, your location is not favorable for beekeeping.

It's likely that you are surrounded by avid gardeners who keep something in bloom from the first crocus poking through the frost to the last rose of early autumn. Most neighborhoods have an abundance of flower gardens plus fruit, nut, decorative, and shade trees. Many common trees like the maple and willow are good early sources of pollen and provide food for bees. Weeds, wildflowers, and planted lawns in parks and highway, express, and freeway boulevards and access areas can also provide foraging areas.

Bees need a constant supply of fresh water. If your location does not have a natural source, then you must provide one. A bird bath with gravel and a plant (for bees to light on to get to the water) (Fig. 3-2) a drip hose and trough arrangement (Fig. 3-3), a dish pan with a sponge (Fig. 3-4) are all satisfactory.

It is important to establish a water source when you set up your beehive and to train the bees to use only that source. Otherwise they may choose another nearby watering place such as your neighbor's pool or fish pond. This may create difficulties from the start.

Watering units should be cleaned at least once every two weeks to prevent disease.

Fig. 3-2. If you have no natural source of fresh water, you must provide something. A bird bath converted to a watering "hole" for bees is one solution. The plant provides a walkway to the water and helps keep the water fresh.

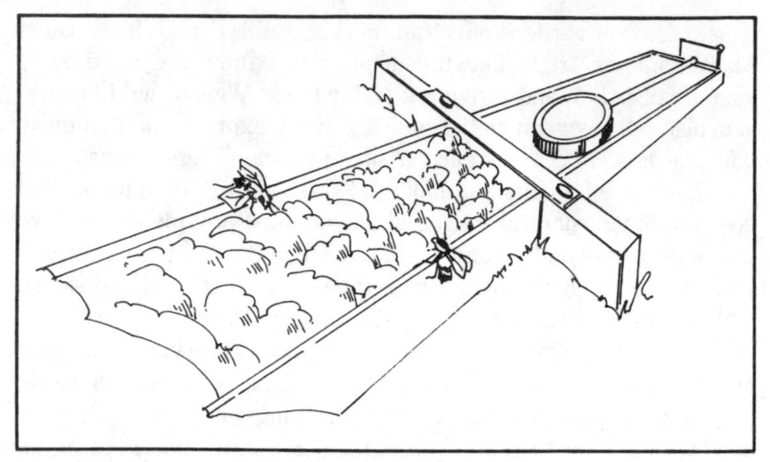

Fig. 3-3. A watering device can be constructed from 4-inch eaves trough filled with coarse gravel and equipped with a float water-level control. A drop hose is placed at the bottom of the trough.

ZONING REGULATIONS

Study the zoning regulations of your city and county. Many cities allow beehives in backyards only if they are located at a certain distance from a residence, usually 100 feet. In high-density areas such as Los Angeles or Chicago, this stipulation pretty well precludes having hives in yards.

If you decide the best place for your hive is near your home, get a copy of your city's zoning ordinance or go to city hall and see for yourself. If you merely call, the clerk who answers is very likely to

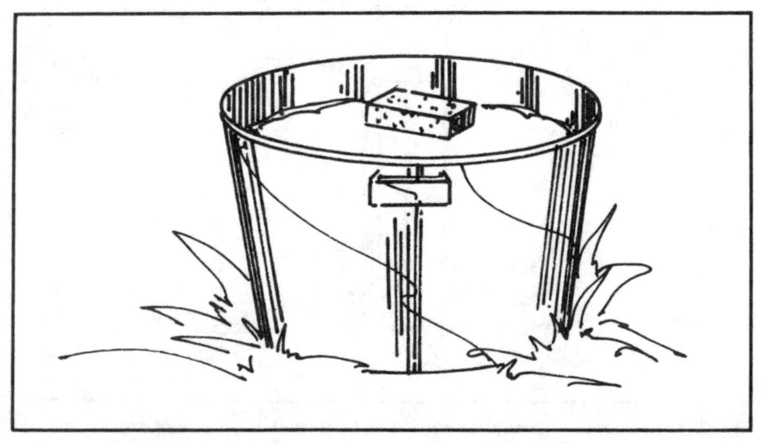

Fig. 3-4. A tub or dishpan with a cellulose sponge floating on top can be used as a source of water for bees.

say. "Oh sure, we have a zoning law about bees," when in fact there is none or none that is enforceable.

If your town hasn't any ordinances about beekeeping and your bees become a problem to your neighbors, you could be brought to task under a general nuisance law. If you want to keep bees in your yard, you should: check with your immediate neighbors—back, side, and across—to be sure no one is highly allergic to bee stings. (See Appendix F). Don't alarm them unnecessarily, but they are entitled to know some facts about bees before they have thousands of them living next door. Take a positive stand about the benefits to their garden caused by increased pollination. It never hurts to mention that you expect to share your honey.

You should also place your bees where their flight will be guided steeply upward such as near a 15-to-20-foot hedge or row of firs or a high roof line to prevent their landing in numbers in your neighbor's yard (Fig. 3-5). A 6-foot block wall fence will not be enough. (Some beekeepers put their hives up on their roof to insure that their bees' flight pattern is dispersed up and away. This obviously poses a few maintenance problems.)

Finally, be sure you commit the time to manage your hives carefully to prevent swarming. In northern areas this may be a problem for only a month or so. In warmer regions, where some plants are in bloom for most of the year, swarm-alert and control must be maintained for as long as three to five months.

Fig. 3-5. If you locate your hives in a residential area, you should place them near tall trees and /or a steep roof line to keep their flight pattern directed up and away from neighbor's property..

You should be aware that bees, like many of the higher animals, will not soil their nest. They are able to store their feces for several weeks through cold weather. On a warmer day they fly out for cleansing flights, voiding wastes on the wing. You can imagine the annoyance this may cause if their path is over a freshly polished car or clean laundry hanging out to dry!

PROTECTION FROM NATURAL AND ENVIRONMENTAL ELEMENTS

Your hive should be protected from winds, preferably with a windbreak such as a stand of trees, hills, fencing, or buildings (Fig. 3-6). A broken line is better than a solid wall that merely deflects the wind up and over into the bee yard. Temporary snow fencing makes an adequate windbreak. The hive entrance should be placed facing south or east to encourage workers to get out as early as possible to compete with other nectar-collecting insects.

It is seldom necessary to shade bees except in the extremely hot climates of the Arizona or Utah desert where temperatures may reach 110°F.

Protect your bees from harrassment, theft, and vibrations. If your site is near a busy street or highway, put your hives far enough back so that they will not be vibrated by heavy trucks passing by. Bees are especially sensitive to shaking and often react by swarming—leaving for a better site of their own choosing.

It is best to have your bee area out of sight. Unfortunately, there are those who do not respect private property and could throw

Fig. 3-6. Bees need protection from wind. This wind break of trees is in the bee yard operated for research at the University of Wisconsin. (Courtesy, Cooperative Extension Service, University of Wisconsin.)

rocks or try to overturn your hives. Beekeepers are also subject to theft, but usually only those with a profitable number worth the risk would be a target for bee burglars.

Do not locate your hives under power lines because bees are sensitive to negative ions in the atmosphere.

Finally, protect your bees from harmful pesticides. In considering a site, discuss the pesticide program with the person on whose land you will have your hive, or your neighbors. Be sure to communicate that pesticides can kill off your bees. Pesticides can also contaminate the hive with nectar and pollen from sprayed plants or trees not only in the immediate area but also in the vicinity of the foraging range. Pesticide applications are usually just as effective at night or early morning before bees are out. Or it may be necessary to cover your bees to protect them from harmful materials. (Read Chapter 7 for more details.)

ACCESSIBILITY

You will need to inspect and work your hives every two weeks during the heavy honey flow. Where the growing season is relatively short, this could be only two or three months. You should consider maintenance relative to distance. Even in the winter, it is necessary to inspect your bees every three to six weeks to see that they have adequate stores. If not, give supplemental feeding.

Consider in advance what the condition of road will be by a field or woods during rain and snow. It might be great when you set up your hive in the spring or early summer but impassable in a passenger car from January to April. Will you need a jeep, truck, or four wheel drive?

Another point of accessibility. If your hive is within the fences and gates of private property, you have less chance of intruders. Be sure you can get a key or have one of your own at all times. You might wait for just the right warm fall day to do serious work like requeening, make the trip out to your apiary, and discover that the good farmer has taken his family to town.

COMMON NECTAR AND POLLEN PLANTS BY REGION

A great variety of plants throughout the United States provide nectar and pollen for bees. Many weeds, trees, wildflowers, and crops serve as bee foraging sources with the end product being delicious honey for you to enjoy and sell. Some plants such as alfalfa and deciduous fruit trees like cherry and peach are common to nearly all regions. Some are unique to a particular climate zone,

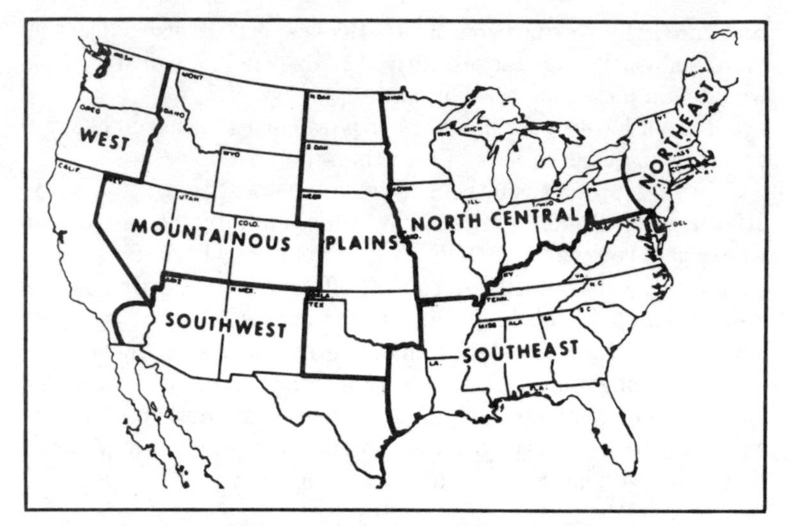

Fig. 3-7. Map of the United States showing the seven beekeeping regions according to William P. Nye, retired apiculturist, USDA. (Reprinted from Agricultural Handbook 335, USDA.)

such as the sourwood and tulip poplar of the Southeast. Sources often vary within a state from one climate zone to another (Fig. 3-7).

West. Alfalfa, buckwheat, citrus, cucurbits, deciduous fruit trees, locust, melons, mustard, rosemary, sage, willow, and wildflowers.

Southwest. Alfalfa, citrus, cotton, safflower, wild buckwheat, manzanita, mesquite, and other desert shrubs.

Mountainous. Alfalfa, arrowwood, ceanothus, mesquite, sweet clover.

Plains. Alfalfa, cucurbits, fruit trees, persimmon, spanish dagger, sweet clover, wildflowers.

Southeast. Citrus, clovers, cotton, cucurbits, fruit trees, sourwood, tulip poplar, and tupelo.

North Central. Alfalfa, aster, blackberry, basswood, black locust, goldenrod, mint, raspberry, smartweed, sweet clovers, soybean, and white Dutch clover.

Northeast. Alfalfa, apple, basswood, black locust, clover, birdsfoot trefoil, berries, wildflowers.

Chapter 4

Getting Your Gear

You will need special gear for beekeeping (Fig. 4-1). Following are lists of basics and a discussion on which types, styles, and quality to choose.

PROTECTIVE CLOTHING

You will need the following:

- Coveralls, overalls, or work pants, and a long-sleeved shirt
- Hat with a brim
- Veil
- Gloves with an elasticized gauntlet or sleeve
- Boots or sturdy shoes

The amount of protective clothing a beekeeper wears is a matter of personal choice. Established beekeeping and commercial operators who have 10, 50, or 500 hives, often work their bees in shirt sleeves with no hat or gloves. There are times when even they find a usually calm colony riled from an ant attack or a rain storm and don their protective gear.

Clothing worn around bees should be of hard finish, closely woven, smooth fabric, such as cotton or a cotton/polyester blend. Fuzzy or woolly clothes will bother the bees. When they land on you, they get caught up in wool hairs, become stressed, and sting.

What you wear should be in light earth tones—white, cream,

Fig. 4-1. Many firms offer a Beginner's Kit that includes most of the basic tools, protective clothing, and a complete hive body. (1) Full depth super, (2) bottom board, (3) reversible entrance reducer, (4) frame with foundation, (5) telescoping cover, (6) inner cover, (7) smoker, (8) hive tool, (9) veil, (10) "First Lesson on Beekeeping", (11) gloves, (12) boardman feeder requires an inverted jar to complete. (Courtesy, Dadant & Sons, Inc., Hamilton, Il 62341.)

tan, or light green. Because bees see in the ultraviolet range, avoid blacks, yellows, and reds.

A loose fitting coverall or jumpsuit type garment with long sleeves and pockets is very practical. It can be pulled over regular clothing for convenience and warmth when needed or worn by itself in hot weather. Bib overalls with a shirt or regular work pants or jeans and shirt can be worn as well.

The hat can be any brimmed hard hat (Fig. 4-2). It is more comfortable if ventilated and should fit fairly snugly so that it won't tip or jiggle and create a vision problem with the veil (Fig. 4-3). Most hats have an adjustable liner so that one size fits nearly everyone.

The veil protects your face from the bees. It is usually constructed of black wire mesh to form a frame around the face. A skirt of nylon mesh, open at the top and elasticized to fit closely down over the hat brim and also at the neck and shoulder area is attached. *Special note*—elastic wears out after a season or two. Check the elastic and replace it when necessary to maintain a protective fit.

Two types of veils are available, tie on and zippered. Both take a little practice to put on quickly and snugly. Both are about equally secure. The zipper-type aligns with a zipper around the shoulder area of a bee suit. This is available from suppliers, or you can sew in a zipper yourself. The fastener of the veil zipper hooks on to the fastener of the zipper on the suit and must be pulled from the front all around the back to the front again.

Where the zipper meets itself, there is always a small gap, which must be covered with masking tape. (Remember, bee space is only ⅜ inch.)

The tie-on-type has long cotton cords fastened to the bottom at the back and rings attached in the front. The cords are brought around from the back under the armpits, inserted through the rings, pulled taunt across over the chest in an "X," pulled to the back and tied around the waist, once or twice depending on your size (Fig. 4-4).

Gloves are available in canvas, plastic-coated canvas, and leather. For the difference in cost, leather with a ventilated gauntlet is by far the best. Bees can sting through canvas but hardly ever through leather. The leather will be serviceable for many years. Leather gloves with a long gauntlet are also handy for working around roses, berry bushes, or any thorny plants.

The mesh ventilation will prevent your hands from sweating in warmer weather. If you have your own gloves, the elasticized gauntlet or bee sleeve is available by itself.

Note: many suppliers are carrying women's sizes for those with smaller hands. Men's size are generally offered only in large and medium sizes.

It is very difficult to work around hives and not have a bee or two crawl up on to your shoe. Therefore it is advisable to wear sturdy shoes or boots. Bees will sting through canvas or open mesh sport shoes. They will also very readily crawl up pants legs. Secure your pants legs in your socks or boots, or with an elastic strap.

Fig. 4-2. A helmet with zipper veil with zipper style coveralls. (Courtesy, Dadant & Sons, Inc., Hamilton, IL 62341.)

Fig. 4-3. Ventilated helmet with tie-on veil (courtesy of Dadant & Sons, Inc., Hamilton, IL).

TOOLS

Some of these tools are unique to beekeepers. All are essential.

- Smoker
- Fire building materials
- Hive tool
- Bee brush
- Spray bottle with pistol grip
- Bucket
- Notebook or calendar

A *smoker* is a metal container with a hinged cover and spout attached to a set of bellows. A beekeeper builds a fire in the chamber with materials that give off a cool white smoke as the bellows are pumped. Usually you will want to smoke your hive before inspecting or working it. Bees react by moving down or up and by gorging themselves with honey. This is a protective instinct that calms them as you pull frames and work through the hive.

Smokers come in three sizes. Approximate dimensions are 3½ inches by 7 inches, 4 inches by 7 inches, and 4 inches by 10 inches (Fig. 4-5). The mid-size is good for the hobbyist, allowing enough space for materials to burn for some time. Suppliers also offer a shielded-type and an asbestos-lined smoker. Enthusiasts of the shield variety say they can carry the smoker under their arm, freeing a hand for other gear and allowing them to keep the smoker

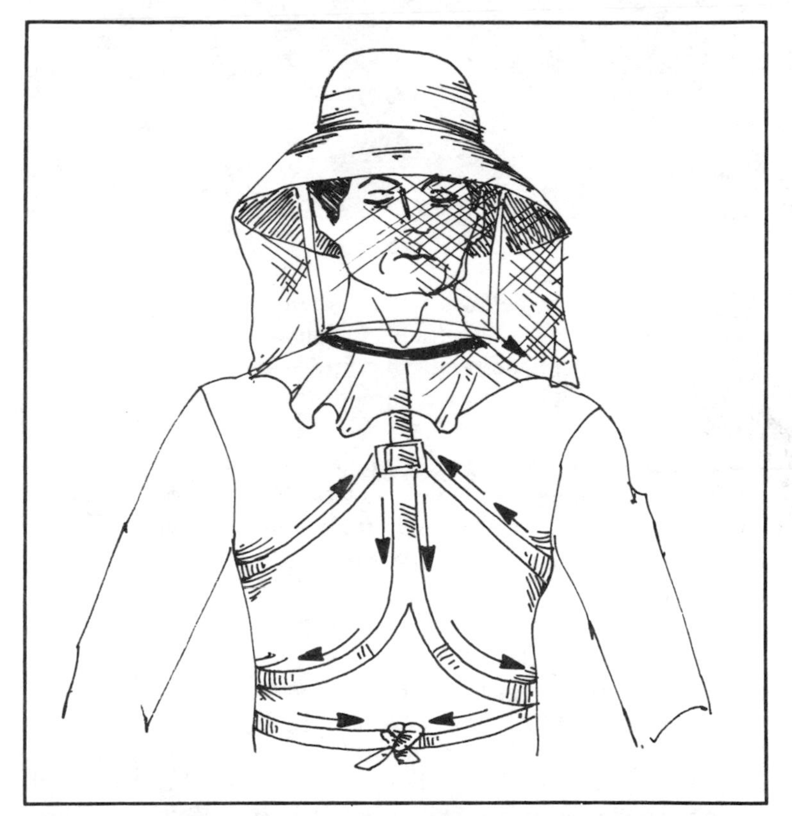

Fig. 4-4. To tie on the veil, bring the cords under the armpits through the ring(s) at the bottom of the front of the veil. Pull taut across the chest and around to the back, then around the waist, once or twice, according to your size, and tie.

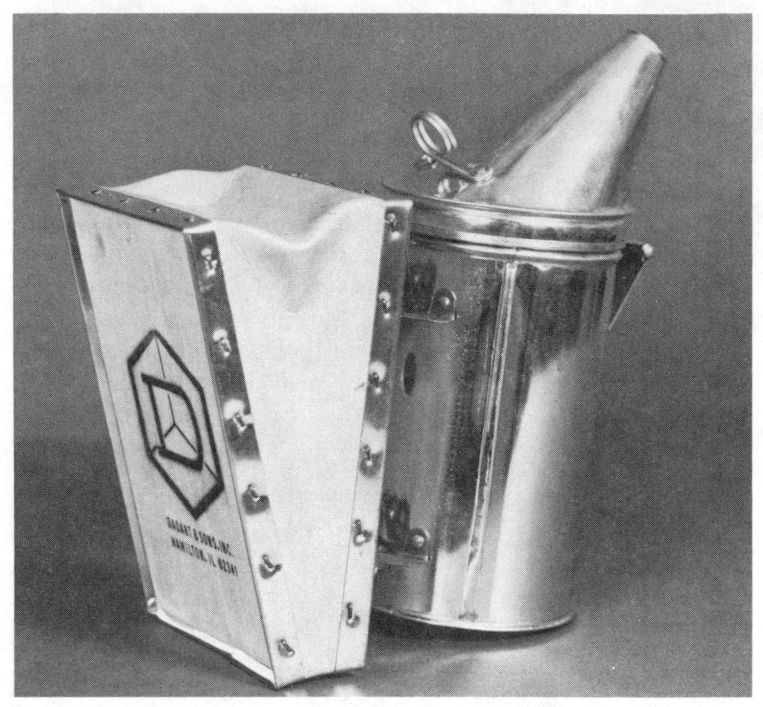

Fig. 4-5. A standard smoker, 4 inches by 7 inches.

going by pumping the bellows between their upper arm and side. Or you can hold it between your knees while doing other work (Fig. 4-6). The asbestos-lined removable fire chamber allows the inner container to be replaced when burned so that you do not have to replace the entire smoker.

The best fire building material for your smoker is burlap cut into strips and rolled into a medium wad. Gunny sacks are a good source of burlap and are available from feed and grain stores and from fish and bait shops. Torn sacks that can no longer be used cost little or nothing. Burlap cloth is also available at fabric stores.

Other materials that beekeepers use include dry pine cones, corn cob, leaves, and tinder size wood. Matches should be the strike-anywhere type. Store them in a moisture proof container such as a baby food jar or a metal bandage box.

The hive tool is used for prying off covers and supers, separating frames, scraping off propolis and burr (extra) comb, and pounding in and pulling out nails, brads or staples. Hive tools are made of tempered steel, come in 7-inch (pocket size) and 10-inch lengths.

They have a straight end and a curved end and a hole for removing nails (Fig. 4-7).

The hive tool looks very much like a paint scraper. (A heavy duty paint scraper can be used as a hive tool quite well, is less expensive, and locally available at a hardware or paint store.)

A bee brush is just what the name says, a tool for brushing off bees. It is very handy when harvesting honey from your hive. After smoking and then shaking off most of the remaining bees, the bee brush will enable you to gently remove any persistent ones before you take the honey frames to your vehicle. It is great, too, for brushing bees from your legs, shoulders, back, and head just before you jump in your car to leave the bee yard.

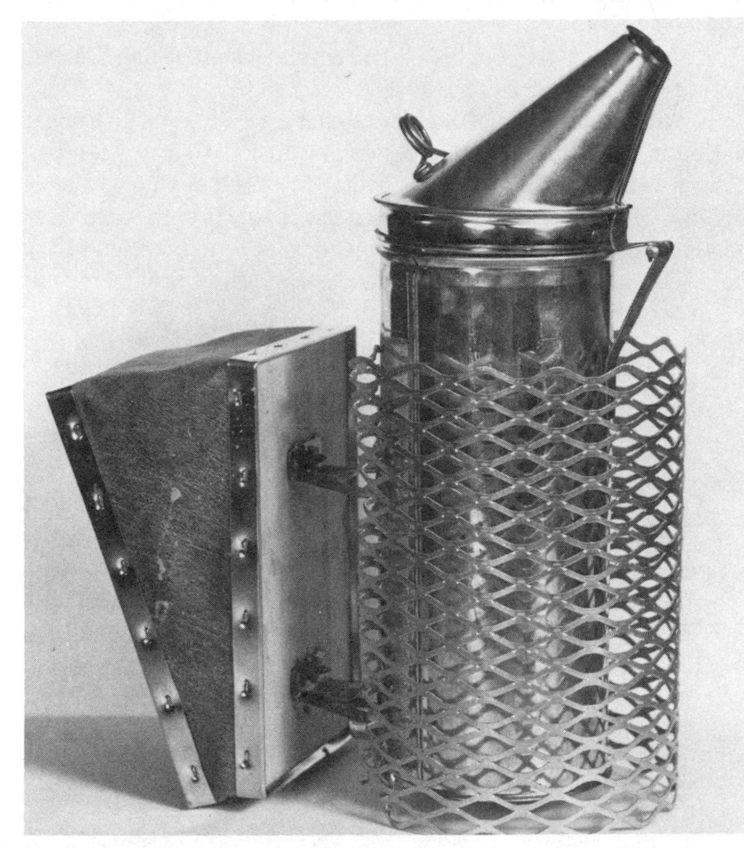

Fig. 4-6. A smoker with a shield for those who hold it between their legs while working, 4 inches by 10 inches. (Courtesy, Dadant & Sons, Inc., Hamilton, IL 62341.)

Fig. 4-7. A beekeeper using her hive tool to separate frames.

Bee brushes are single-rowed, curved handled flat brushes with plastic or horsehair bristles.

A pistol grip spray bottle, pint or quart size, filled with a sugar solution is useful for several beekeeping tasks. Use it when collecting a swarm (as discussed in Chapter 5), when mixing new bees with established bees, to feed new queens and workers in cages or package bees received through the mail, and to use in lieu of the smoker when extremely dry, fire danger conditions prevail in your hive area. Be sure it has a mist setting!

The sugar solution is composed of two parts water to one part regular table sugar. Boil the water and then mix in the sugar.

A bucket of water is important to have at hand for rinsing gloves or wetting down any areas on your clothing where bees have stung. The sting leaves an odor which attracts other bees.

A notebook, calendar, or both kept with your gear is a reminder to record your activities with the bees. Note when you hive a swarm, check for laying queen, date of first nectar flow, amount of honey taken off, when you switched supers to prevent a swarm, etc. Just a few notes and dates will help you make decisions and time operations in your next year of beekeeping. For prices on beekeeping essentials see Table 4-1.

HIVE COMPONENTS

You will need the items listed below for each hive. Purchasing information is given in Chapter 5 on obtaining bees (Fig. 4-8).

- Bottom board
- Hive bodies (2 or more)

- Frames per hive body with foundation (9 or 10)
- Queen excluder
- Lid or cover
- Hive stand(s)

Bottom boards are made of cedar, pine, or redwood. Two styles are available. A reversible board is used in areas where the honey flow season is short because it provides variably entranced space. The California or migratory style gives a tight fit when you move colonies for winter build up or pollination service. Bottom boards have a rim or lip on the sides to allow the hive body to sit into it. They extend beyond the hive body by 1½ inches to allow for a

Table 4-1. Relative Prices of Bees and Beekeeping Equipment.

Figures are average from a dozen representative suppliers' 1982 catalogs. Local prices may vary as much as $5.

Protective Clothing	
Hard hat (vented)	$ 7.00
Veil	11.00
Gloves (leather, ventilated)	13.00
Coveralls	22.00
Hive Components (unassembled)	
You will need at least three hive bodies, two deep and three medium, or two medium, and one shallow.	
Full depth hive body (9 5/8)	7.00
Ten deep frames	5.00
Ten sheets foundation	5.00
Medium depth hive body (6 5/8)	6.00
Ten medium frames	4.00
Ten sheets foundation	5.00
Shallow depth hive body (5 11/16)	4.00
Ten shallow frames	4.00
Ten sheets foundation	4.00
Queen excluder	4.00
Lid, telescoping with inner cover	$ 9.00
Lid, flat, migratory	5.00
Bottom board	6.00
Tools	
Smoker with shield	$13.00
Hive tool	3.00
Bee brush	2.00
	139.00
Bees	
Two pound with queen	$23.00
or	
Nuc	40.00
or	
Established colony (includes two complete hive bodies, frames, bees, queen, brood and honey)	50-150.00
Additional Equipment for Honey Harvesting	
Bee escape	$ 1.25
Uncapping scraper	
Rental of uncapping knife	3.00
Rental of extractor	10.00
Straining bucket	4.00
Straining cloth	3.00
Contaners (if you sell)	10.00 (for 3 dozen)
Lables (if you plan to sell)	3.00

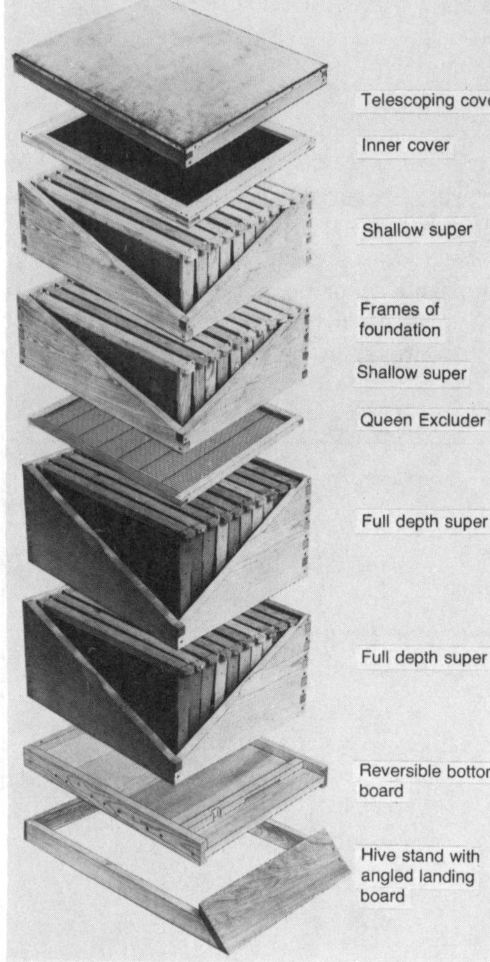

Fig. 4-8. Components of the hive.

porch on which the bees land and enter the hive. For longer wear, and to prevent moisture from getting into the hive, bottom boards should be treated with a wood preservative.

Hive bodies or supers are boxes, usually constructed of pine and are open at the top and bottom so that they may be placed at various positions in the hive structure. The bottom board is placed under the bottommost one and the top super is placed on the uppermost hive body. The best hive bodies are made of seasoned pine or cedar. They should be lock cornered to sustain hard use, have hand holds on all four sides, and a metal or wooden frame that rests inside a few inches from the top on which the ears or extended top bars sit. The frame rest allows the beekeeper to easily slide the frames back and forth for examining, switching, or removing them.

Modern standard supers are 20 inches long and 16¼ inches wide. They come in three depths: deep or full depth (called standard by Western beekeepers)—9⅝ inches; medium or three quarter—6⅝ inches; and the shallow or half depth—5¾ inches. Traditionally, the full depth supers have been used for rearing brood. Many beekeepers use them for honey too. They are heavy when filled with honey, weighing up to 90 pounds, and many people do not want to lift that weight (Fig. 4-9).

Fig. 4-9. This beekeeper uses shallow size supers and honey because she can handle them more easily.

More and more beekeepers, even commercial operators, are going to three quarter depth, especially for honey supers. A medium super filled with honey weighs 60 pounds and a shallow weighs 40 pounds. To minimize your labor, it is best to select medium depth for brood and medium or shallow for honey. You will need to plan on three medium depth or two full depth for brood and at least one full depth, two medium or three shallow for honey. Initially you can start with two supers for brood and obtain more supers as needed for honey.

Some beekeepers like to use medium supers throughout. You can move frames from one super to the other when you want to prevent swarming by switching empty frames from the honey super for filled frames in the brood chamber.

Although usually more expensive, with new equipment you can buy the mix of sizes you want and be sure that there is no possible problem with disease. You can hold the cost down on new woodware by choosing a commercial or budget grade. Because of the sky-rocketing costs of lumber, many suppliers are constructing supers, bottom boards, and tops with less than perfect boards, some with small tight knots or material defects occurring in cross cutting. Others are using narrow stock and gluing them to create the proper width. This grade is guaranteed, as are the better quality, and is quite serviceable.

New hive bodies must be painted on the outside. The traditional color has been white but more and more beekeepers are using other colors. If you are placing your hive in your backyard, it is a good idea to paint it the same color as your house and/or garage sheds. This helps to keep a low profile and to discourage children and others from disturbing your bees. Hives are often painted green, tan, gray, or other nature colors that blend in with the nearby foliage, fences, or out buildings.

Dark colors and metallic shades such as silver absorb a great deal of sun and are not usually suitable, especially in warmer climates or where summers are sizzling.

Any paint or enamel that will withstand rain or other precipitation is fine. Many beekeepers use a mixture of compatible (oil or water base) leftover paints they happen to have on hand or were able to find as bargains at their local paint, hardware, or discount stores.

It is a good idea to put some identification on your hive, either with paint or a branding tool for the convenience of the apiary inspector and to prove your case should a theft occur.

The standard hive holds ten frames, but many beekeepers

prefer to use only nine. This provides ease in moving, removing, and replacing them, allows "fatter" drawn comb and more honey per comb. Frames come in three sizes to match the three depths of supers: 9⅛ inches for the full or deep super, 6¼ inches for the medium size, and 5⅜ inches for the shallow super. Frames consist of a top bar with extensions, called *ears,* which sit on the frame rest inside the hive body, side bars, and a plain or grooved bottom bar.

Frames are constructed of wood or plastic. Wooden frames are traditional and proven but are subject to breakage and the wearing effects of weather. Plastic are more durable but have small spaces in the top bars where bees cannot enter to clean out wax moths and larvae. Some beekeepers call them "hotels" for wax moths. Some believe that wood is natural for bees and that they do not accept plastic as readily.

One major supplier manufactures a frame of both materials with wooden top and bottom bars and plastic end bars. It features a snap lock assembly without nails.

Each frame holds a sheet of foundation—a base layer of wax stamped with the bee's natural honeycomb design (Fig. 4-10). The bees build upon this flat sheet to form cells for brood rearing and for storing honey. This process is called *drawing out the comb.*

Foundation comes in different thicknesses and styles. Commercial operators use a heavy duty, very sturdy foundation to withstand the force of their high-speed extracting equipment. Hobbyists can do very well with medium-thick foundation.

Fig. 4-10. The bees are just beginning to draw out this new foundation. The small chunks of wax on top of the frame are called burr comb.

Foundation is composed of pure beeswax or a thin sheet of plastic with beeswax sprayed onto it. In recent years an all plastic foundation has been developed, but it is still considered experimental by many in the field.

If you get your frames already assembled, then plain beeswax foundation embedded into wired frames is fine. If you order your frames unassembled, it is much easier to use the crimp-wire type or plastic-reinforced frame. Crimp-wire foundation slips into the two piece bottom bar and is secured to the frame with steel hooks or support pins that you order as a separate item.

Plastic reinforced foundation is as easy or easier to install. Some brands do not even require any support pins.

With plain foundation, you must cross wire your frames. It is very difficult to get them strung tightly enough by hand. Suppliers and beekeepers with large numbers of hives employ a special wiring jig and electric wire embedder for assembling wired frames and plain foundation (Fig. 4-11).

Queen excluders are flat grids with spaces large enough for the worker bees to pass through but too small for the queen. They are placed between the brood chambers and the honey supers to prevent the queen from laying brood up in the honey super. Queen excluders are constructed of either metal or wood. Either is satisfactory.

Top boards or covers come in two styles—telescopic and migratory. The telescopic looks like a shallow box with sides that fit snugly down over the super. It is used with an inner cover. Beekeepers in colder areas use this type. The migratory cover is flat with cleats that hold it in place on top of the hive. It is used where winters are mild and where beekeepers move their hives to different nectar or pollination locations.

A hive stand is not essential but saves the bottom board and

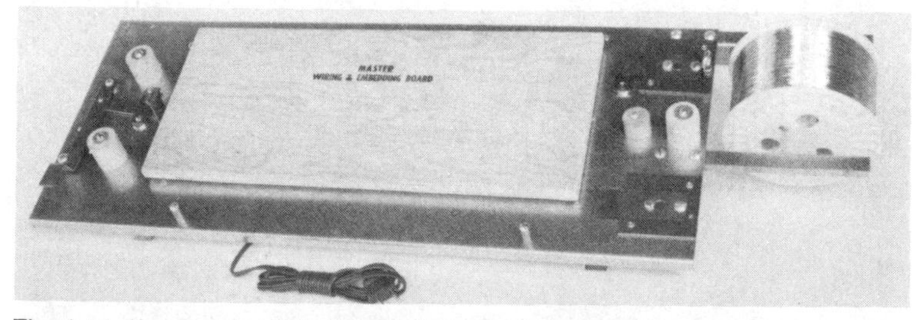

Fig. 4-11. If you order plain foundation, use a wiring and embedding board. To build one see Chapter 12. It is difficult to install the wires tightly enough by hand. (Courtesy, Pierce Manufacturing and Bee Supplies, Anaheim CA.)

Fig. 4-12. A two-hive stand can be constructed from tubular or box aluminum. This hive belongs to a beekeeping instructor who has moved one of his colonies from its usual location to a demonstration area. Note the boardman feeder in front to discourage the bees from foraging in a nearby orange grove where workers are picking fruit.

Fig. 4-13. A pair of concrete wall blocks make a good hive stand. Note the little stool this beekeeper has built to the right of the block. It increases the landing area for his bees.

makes it easier to control pests like ants or skunks that build nests under hives (Fig. 4-12). It also raises the hive up and makes it more comfortable for the beekeeper to work.

Hive stands can be constructed of wood or tubular aluminum. Stacks of bricks or cement, cinder, adobe, or fiberglass building blocks placed under each end of the bottom board make sturdy bases that withstand all weather conditions (Fig. 4-13). Whatever material, the stand must be able to support the weight of two brood chambers plus two or three supers of honey, or a total weight of about 320 to 350 pounds.

Chapter 5

Obtaining Bees and Establishing a Colony

There are four sources of bees: swarms, package bees, nucleus or NUC, and established colonies.

SWARMS

When nectar starts flowing heavily, hives often become overcrowded and the bees react by swarming. This usually occurs in late spring in areas with freezing winters and much earlier in milder climates. A swarm is one-half to two-thirds of the hive population who leave with the old queen to find a better, roomier location.

A swarm looks like a brown or gray quivering mass moving or resting as one unit with some bees flying around the perimeter. Sometimes a swarm is small, approximating a large grapefruit, or about 5,000 to 10,000 bees. Sometimes they are very large, as big as a bushel basket, or about 60,000 to 80,000 bees. In between swarms are described as football or basketball sized (Fig. 5-1).

Swarms of bees have been sighted on trees, bushes, surrounding and clinging to water meters, on car bumpers, in the walls and attics of houses, in sheds and barns, and even beneath a manhole cover.

Wherever the swarm lands or whatever its outside appearance, on the inside the swarm is organized. Loose chains of bees are hanging from one to another, leaving enough space for other bees to move in and out. They signal with their dances all information on the nesting sites the scouts have found. The queen is fed and groomed

Fig. 5-1. A medium- or "basketball-" sized swarm massed over a branch of a tree. To collect the swarm, trim away small branches and twigs, mist the bees with sugar water, and shake the swarm into a box or hive body.

and her pheromone scent is passed from bee to bee to keep them gathered around her.

If your area has a cold spring with trees late to bud and bloom, and frosts keeping early wildflowers like dandelions down, then swarms will not be available until April or May. With a milder spring, swarms will occur earlier. In colder areas, too, swarming tends to last only a month or two. In the southwest where spring is early and there is a long blooming season, swarming can go on for four to six months. It can begin as early as January and last as late as June.

Bees will fly out at 50°F (13°C) but are most active between 60°F (16°C) and 90°F (32°C). They will naturally be out in greater numbers on clear days but will fly in misting rain if nectar and pollen are available. Their activity is affected by winds of 15 miles per hour and stopped altogether by winds of 25 miles per hour.

Based on the weather, you can figure when swarming is likely to begin in your area.

Once a swarm is spotted, and if it is in an accessible place, it is not too difficult to get the bees into a box or hive body and proceed with beekeeping. Before bees swarm, they fill up with as much honey as possible for the trip and are likely to be fairly docile.

But they *are* unpredictable. Sometimes they stay put for only an hour. Often they remain in the first place they fly to overnight and into the next day or longer. It depends on what the scout bees find for a new home. (Your box fitted with frames, completely enclosed and safe will look pretty good compared to what nature has to offer.)

The same system of communication exists for locating and deciding on a new home as for recruitment of foragers. Scout bees return and dance the direction and distance. Different scouts will report different locations. Other workers will be recruited to check the suggested locations. The best places will be reported with the liveliest and longest dances. If only one good possibility is found by the scout bees, the weaker dances soon give way to that. but if two or three nearly equal sites are being scouted, the swarm may take three days before reaching agreement on the best one and finally leaving for the new home.

Locating a Swarm

How do you get a swarm if you yourself don't happen to see one? Most people know little or nothing about bees. Should a swarm come on to their property, they become quite anxious and want them removed! People who want swarms taken away call the police, fire department, city hall, animal control agency, beekeeping supplier, or agriculture extension agent.

You should call around to find which agency handles swarm calls in your area. Call those persons listed under Beekeeping, Honey, and Pest Control in the yellow pages of your phone directory. In some cities a professional beekeeper is under contract to collect swarms. He or she may or may not be willing to have you collect one or to accompany him. The city may not cooperate with anyone but a professional desiring a swarm. Many beekeepers want as many swarms as possible to build up their colonies. Others may be pressed with too many swarm calls and be glad for help.

If a beekeeper has an exclusive contract to collect swarms in your town, take heart. You can always buy disease-free bees from a supplier to insure a good start.

If you find you will be allowed to collect a swarm, then get ready to answer a swarm call. Before leaving your name, number, and other pertinent details with the fire department or whatever agency is responsible, you must be ready with the right equipment. You must decide in advance where you will put your bees.

You will need a cardboard box with the lid cut to open on three sides (Fig. 5-2). The kind of box that opens with four flaps is not suitable as it is too difficult to secure and keep the bees in. Heavy duty wine, liquor, or beer cartons make good swarm retrievers. A

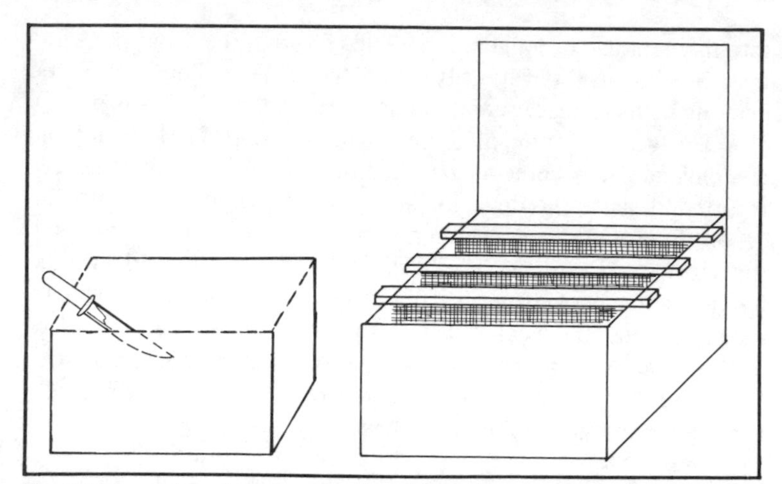

Fig. 5-2. A cardboard box can be rigged to retrieve a swarm. Cut the top as shown. Suspend two or three frames of foundation from holes near the top, and have tape, wire, or strap at the ready to secure the bees in the box for the trip home.

box approximating the size of a deep super (18 inches by 15 inches by 10 inches) will take care of most swarms adequately.

You will have a better chance of enticing the swarm into your box if you poke holes in it just below the top at the same point on opposite sides and suspend two or three frames of foundation through the holes. Tape around the holes, or they will be good bee escapes. Also punch some tiny holes in the top for ventilation. You can shake a swarm directly into a hive body but it is heavier to handle.

Other equipment you should have ready are:

- Bee suit, hat, gloves and veil
- Smoker, materials to start one, and matches
- Pruning shears, loppers, and a saw
- Ladder in case your swarm is on a tree
- A large piece of canvas or other smooth heavy duty material such as a ground cloth for a sleeping bag
- Masking tape, strap, or wire to temporarily contain a swarm
- A spray bottle with misting adjustment filled with sugar solution of one part sugar dissolved in one part hot water
- A deep or three quarter super with nine frames of foundation for final placement of swarm

After you leave your name with the agency or supply store that takes swarm calls, put a list by the phone and advise your family members or anyone likely to take phone calls of its importance. The list should include the name of the caller with a swarm, his phone number, the time of day the swarm was spotted and how long it's been there if known, location (tree, bush, building, etc.), and the address with cross streets or landmarks.

You should decide the limits of your swarm collecting and communicate that to the agency taking swarm calls in advance. If you haven't an extension ladder or the skill and nerve to climb up a 25-foot tree to retrieve a swarm, then say no. A beginner would be ill advised to attempt collecting a swarm in an attic or in the walls of a house. In that type of location the bees are no longer a swarm but often a colony with comb, honey, and brood and quite a mess to deal with.

Collecting the Swarm

If the swarm is on a bush or tree, get permission to trim any smaller branches, leaves, and twigs that prevent you from studying the swarm and getting a hand hold to shake it into your box.

If the swarm is high up, climb up the ladder with the box, sprayer, and tools in your pocket. Spray the swarm with the sugar mist, do any necessary trimming. Then shake the swarm into the box with several hard shakes.

If the bees fly back up, the queen has not come down yet. Try to smoke them toward the box. If you have the queen, the workers will be fanning with their rears up, from the edges of the box or the top of the mass of bees in the box. If they start flying back and resume clustering, you probably haven't caught the queen.

If the bees are on a low branch and there is no room to place the box under them, use the canvas. Shake them into that, then place the box near them, lay it on its side, with the opening toward the bees, and spray with the sugar water. The bees will probably move into the box and on to the frames.

It is not possible to get all the bees. After you have taped or secured your box with a wire or strap, you can spray the swarm with water to try to dispel the remaining bees. Without a queen they will soon leave.

There are some advantages to obtaining your bees from a swarm. It is free, you can get large numbers, and they are eager to build a comb.

It is also fraught with chance. Once you've decided to try beekeeping and have acquired your equipment, you want to begin.

You can wait and wait for a swarm and by waiting too long you could miss the colony build-up that you need to take advantage of the main nectar flow.

A swarm usually has an old queen and you may have to requeen in early summer. You will definitely have to requeen by late summer or early fall.

A swarm can carry a disease such as American Foulbrood (see Chapter 7). However, the use of foundation rather than drawn comb plus feeding sugar syrup with an antibiotic like sulfathiazole terramycin will curtail the spread of the disease. You must be sure to inspect the colony at least twice before adding another hive body.

PACKAGE BEES

Another way to obtain bees and the one favored by many beekeepers is by purchasing package bees. A package of bees consists of two to four pounds (approximately 12,000 to 24,000 bees) and a laying queen, guaranteed to be bred. They are shipped in a screened plywood cage with a can of sugar syrup for feeding during travel. The bees are raised in states in the southern sector of the country.

Producers of package bees are located in Alabama, California, Florida, Georgia, Louisiana, and Mississippi. (Names and addresses appear at the end of the book under Suppliers.) Usually they are available from March through June, depending on the supplier and his location. It is wise to place your order early in January.

As a beginner you probably have only foundation to offer your new bees. It is best therefore to order the three-pound package since it simply takes more bees to draw out foundation.

Local suppliers or branch offices of national suppliers often order package bees in quantity for several customers at once, at the lower rate for large orders. An advantage of dealing with the local supplier is that he will be receiving the shipment and will keep the bees in a safe place until you call for them.

If you order directly from the producer, your package will be sent via air mail. Talk to the local postal employees, both your carrier and the postmaster. Advise them when your shipment of bees is expected and something of the care of bees until they are delivered. They should not be placed in a warm room or near a radiator or furnace outlet, nor should they be left outside in freezing weather.

Your carrier may refuse to haul them in his truck with other packages or to handle them at all. Actually, it is probably best that you ask that they not be delivered to avoid any likelihood of their sitting in an exposed mail box or on your porch. Leave your phone number with the postmaster so he can quickly notify you of your bees' arrival.

Before the expected data of arrival, have one super with nine frames of foundation plus one extra hive body. Be sure your site is ready and cleared, with windbreak, water, and hive stand available. If necessary get your neighbor's consent and good will. (See Chapter 3.)

If nectar is just beginning or not available yet, it is mandatory that you feed the bees. You will need two gallon cans or jars with lids for feeding. Punch 5 or 10 holes in the lid. Use the extra container as an exchange while you clean the first one to guard against fermentation or contamination. Make a sugar solution of two parts granulated sugar dissolved in one part hot water and pour it into your container.

When your bees arrive, inspect them promptly before accepting delivery. If numbers of dead bees are lying on the bottom or you feel they have arrived in poor condition, refuse them and fill out a claim form with your postmaster. At home, put them in a dark cool place and check to see if syrup is still present in the feeder can. If not, you should mist or paint warm syrup lightly (you want to feed them, not drown them) on the sides of the cage two or three times a day. You should hive them as soon as possible.

Hiving Your Package Bees

Most producers send directions with their packages but the general procedure follows.

Feed them just before taking them to your hive location. Engorged with syrup, they will be more docile for your first beekeeping operation.

Choose late afternoon prior to sunset unless you have a source of artificial light at your site. Bees will not be as likely to fly as it grows dark and will settle in better. Put on your bee suit, gloves, hat, and veil. Fire up your smoker.

Take out four of the frames from the hive body and lean them against the stand or hive. Close the entrance with cleats, a handful of grass or weeds, or a piece of plywood lightly tacked in place. (Be sure to do the tacking before installing the bees; they don't like vibrations.) Leave about a two-inch opening until the bees get oriented. Have the extra hive body, cover, and the container of syrup at hand, or a boardman feeder.

Now you are ready to release the bees. Loosen the cover of the

Fig. 5-3. Hiving package bees. With hive ready and positioned, the hive tool is used to remove the cover from the top of the package cage. Keep the cover for subsequent use. (Courtesy, Dadant and Sons, Inc.)

package but do not remove it (Fig. 5-3). Take out the queen cage, which is usually beside the can of syrup. Remove the can. Replace the cover on the top of the bee cage (Fig. 5-4).

You will install the queen into the hive body first (Fig. 5-5). Remove the cork or any plastic covering from the candy end of the queen cage. The candy is now exposed for the bees to eat through and release the queen (Fig. 5-6).

Fig. 5-4. Bounce bees to the bottom of cage; then remove the feeder can and the queen cage. Place the cover back on the cage to confine the bees temporarily. (Courtesy, Dadant and Sons, Inc.)

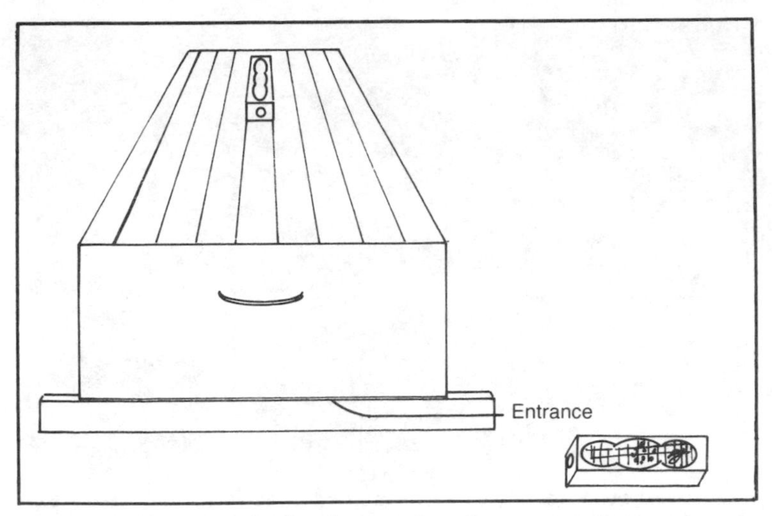

Fig. 5-5. A queen cage showing three sections for queen, workers, and candy.

Wedge the cage between two center frames toward the back of the hive and pointing down, as bees tend to crawl up. Pick up the bee cage, turn it upside down with the cover toward the open hive, slide the cover off and shake sharply to pour the bees into the empty space beside the frames (Fig. 5-7). You will probably have to shake them several times to get as many bees out as possible.

If your queen cage is sealed without candy, you will reverse the procedure, shaking bees in first. Spray the queen lightly with syrup to wet her a bit to prevent her from flying. Hold the cage down inside the box, take off the screen and drop the cage gently into the bees. Very gently and slowly slide the other frames into the hive

Fig. 5-6. Place the queen cage in the hive body, between two center frames toward the back of the hive.

Fig. 5-7. Next, bounce and shake the bees over the frames of the hive. Make sure a liberal supply of bees are shaken directly over the queen cage. (Courtesy, Dadant and Sons, Inc.)

body. If the bees are in your way along the frame rest, touch their backs with your hive tool lightly and they will move. As you lower the frames, pause and they will move (Fig. 5-8).

Turn your feeder container upside down over the hole in your inner cover or directly over the frames. Set the extra hive body on top and put the cover on. If your area is windy, set a large rock or a couple of bricks on the top. Lay the bee cage next to the hive at the

Fig. 5-8. While allowing bees to crawl down into the hive, place the entrance feeder in the bottom board entrance (if this type is used). Then gently put the inner cover on top of the hive. (Courtesy Dadant and Sons, Inc.)

Fig. 5-9. The telescoping outer cover is then placed on top of hive. The entrance reducer is in place in the bottom board. Be sure syrup is in entrance feeder. (Courtesy, Dadant and Sons, Inc.)

front with the opening toward the entrance to encourage any left to go in (Fig. 5-9).

Plug your smoker with a cork and gather your tools. Wait at least five days before disturbing your bees again.

Working the New Hive

Working a hive should be done during the warmest part of day, usually between 10 AM and 3 PM when most field bees are out. There are exceptions. The desert areas in Arizona, Utah, and California, are so hot in summer if you set frames out where bees can't cool them, the wax melts. In those locations work your bees during the cooler part of the day.

When you are ready to check your bees, don your gear except for gloves. Get your smoker going (Figs. 5-10, 5-11, and 5-12) then put on your gloves. To examine your hive, always stand at the side, never in front blocking the entrance.

Use your hive tool to pry up the hive cover at the corners (Fig. 5-13). In this short time, the bees have probably not propolised the cover on tight so it should come up easily. Lift the side away from you, keeping the cover between your face and veil and any bees that may fly up to greet you. Remove the feeder and inner cover if you've used one.

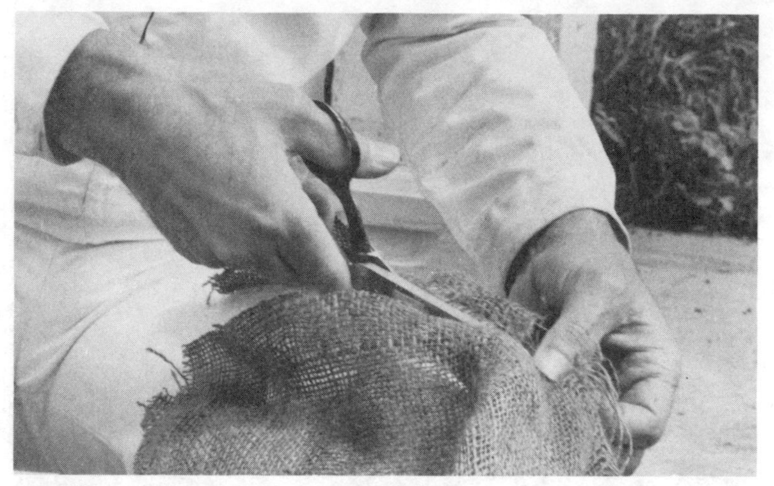

Fig. 5-10. A good material for the smoker is burlap cut into strips and rolled into loose wads.

Smoke lightly across the frames (Fig. 5-14). *Wait at least two minutes.* Give your bees a chance to think their home is on fire and start eating honey and calming. Waiting may be the hardest part because you are so anxious to see what is happening, but it is an important part of good smoking technique.

Before laying the cover on the ground, check the underside first just in case the queen is resting there. You are going to work your way toward the center frames to check for brood. Begin by loosening and prying up the ears of the outermost frame closest to

Fig. 5-11. Place burlap and some tinder, such as newspaper or wood shavings, in the smoker and light it.

Fig. 5-12. Pump the bellows until the material ignites.

you, one side then another. You can lift one ear with your tool, the other with your thumb and forefinger. Or stick your tool in your pocket and use both hands. Some beekeepers like to use a frame grip, available from suppliers.

Lift the frame slowly, holding it over the hive body. It is not likely the queen is here or even that this frame is drawn out well, but check. Then without blocking the entrance, rest it against the side of the hive or the porch. This gives you more space to maneuver the other frames.

Continue prying and lifting up frames working toward the center. Hold each frame vertically over the super. Look for the

Fig. 5-13. Use a hive tool to pry up the lid. (The flat, migratory type is being used here.)

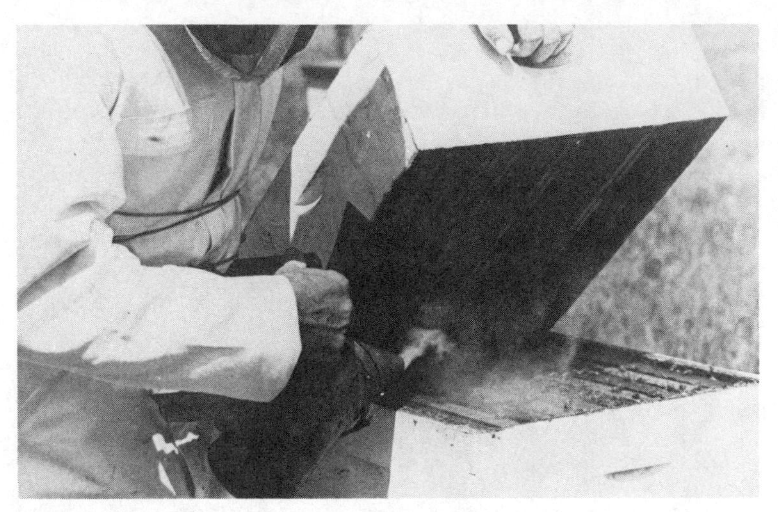

Fig. 5-14. Smoke lightly across the frames. (This lid is a telescoping type.) Note that the beekeeper is standing to one side and lifting the lid away from himself so that disturbed bees do not fly up into his face.

queen on one side then another. Your purpose is not necessarily to find her but to check for eggs and pupae, so don't spend a long while searching for her. If you cannot see the frame well enough with the bees on it, give the frame a sharp shake to get them off. If the queen is there, she will fall into the hive.

The eggs resemble grains of rice, one each at the bottom of a cell. The young pupae look similar to a small section of grapefruit curled on to itself in a C shape, milky white in color.

As you check through, return the frames with brood back into the super. Never leave frames of brood sitting out in the wind or hot sun.

If you do not see any eggs or pupae, you should order another queen promptly. Most producers guarantee their queens and will replace a poor layer with no extra charge.

Check the feeder jar and replace with clean fresh sugar solution if necessary. You can gauge how fast the bees are using the sugar solution and plan to return in time to replace it before the bees finish. As nectar becomes available, the bees will slow down or stop feeding from the sugar syrup. The early nectar flow may not be followed immediately by other plants coming on. You may have to reinstall the feeder. You can test for nectar flow by holding a frame horizontally above the open hive and giving it a shake. If present, thin nectar or unripened honey will drip out and be reclaimed by the bees.

NUCS

Another good way to get started is to buy a nucleus (NUC) which is a complete small colony. It contains three to five frames of brood, worker bees, and a queen in a box about one-third size of a regular hive body (Fig. 5-15). NUCs are available from some breeders, local suppliers, or established beekeepers. They are more expensive than package bees, but if you buy locally, you do avoid shipping charges. NUCs are a surer way than packages in that the queen is already laying. Your source will have checked for a good brood pattern. They are 35 to 45 days more advanced than a package.

Installation of a NUC is much the same as for package bees. You will use your protective equipment, have a hive body ready, and plan to feed the colony if there is no nectar or not enough available.

Begin by lifting the lid of the NUC with as little jarring as possible and smoke lightly. Wait two minutes; then proceed with the transfer. You will need to handle the frames with care, prying them up and removing them one at a time and placing them in the middle of your frames of foundation in your super.

Check the bottom of the NUC to be sure the queen hasn't run off the frame and is crawling around down there. If she is, mist her

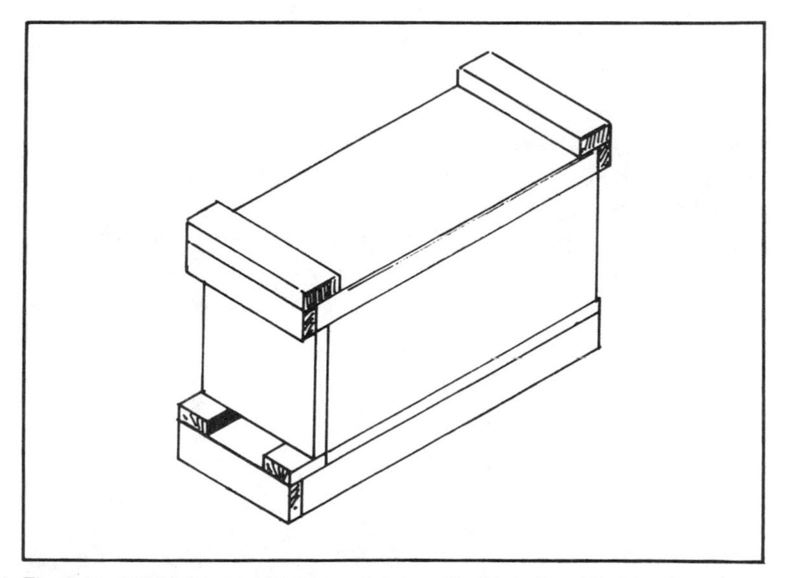

Fig. 5-15. A NUC (nucleus) is a complete small colony placed inside a box about one-third the size of a regular hive body. You can order one to be shipped to you from a supply house or you can buy one from a local supplier or from an established beekeeper.

lightly with sugar water and nudge her gently with your hive tool onto a frame. Then put it in the hive body. Any stray bees that did not get transferred with the frames can be shaken from the NUC box into the hive body.

Install the feeder following the directions given for installing package bees. Narrow the entrance with cleats, plywood strip, or handful of grass to prevent robber bees.

ESTABLISHING A COLONY

As part of their business, many successful beekeepers, hobbyists, and professionals alike, will sell colonies to beginners. A colony consists of one or two hive bodies complete with laying queen, worker brood, several pounds of workers, and about 10 to 20 pounds of honey plus some pollen. You should ask that your prospective hive be inspected before buying to insure that the bees are disease free.

In some states a purchased colony cannot be moved without an inspection and certificate from a county or state entomology inspector. In other states it is "buyer beware." If a seller wants to make a deal without an inspection, don't take the chance. If you get a diseased colony, it will not be worth your time or effort. It is sure to give you a very poor start in beekeeping. Foulbrood virus lives on and on. The bees must be destroyed and infected equipment must be burned or dipped in lye. (Read Chapter 7.)

Fortunately most beekeepers are anxious to see that beginners get started right and are very helpful and conscientious about managing their hives and medicating, and/or disposing of diseased colonies properly.

The cost of a colony will depend on the amount of honey, the current price for honey, the amount and state of the equipment, and the going rate for bees. It can range anywhere from $60 to $200. Buy wooden equipment in standard sizes so that the frames and hive bodies you add as you build up your hives will be interchangeable and fit together with this first hive. Hand crafted equipment is fine as long as it has been built to either full depth, medium or shallow super dimensions. (See Chapter 4.)

After you first check the bees for eggs and pupae, you will need to return at least weekly to read the activities of your colony.

Check the feeder. If bees are still taking syrup down, replace the feeder with a clean full jar or can. **Note**—it may be necessary to supply syrup for a month until there is enough nectar. The workers cannot produce wax to draw out the comb unless they have food.

If the bees have stopped taking the syrup, remove the feeder. When you open the hive inspect and check for nectar.

Watch your workers at the entrance. Are they coming and going regularly in large numbers or are there just a few now and then? Look at their legs for pollen. It can be any color from palest yellow to bronze or even red. Pollen is essential for brood rearing. If you see a good amount of it coming in, you can feel pretty confident you have a laying queen.

Can bees get into the hive through the entrance? Remember you narrowed or reduced it when you installed the bees. Now they may be crowded on the porch or the side of the hive waiting to slip in. If so, open the entrance another couple inches.

Now prepare to open the hive. Have the smoker ready, but if it is a warm sunny afternoon and you have seen good activity, you will not have to smoke very much. If on the other hand, rainy cool weather prevails and you must check your hive on a cool cloudy day, smoke more heavily.

Avoid getting into a hive as a thunderstorm is building up. The negative ions in the atmosphere are irritating to bees and they will be more likely to sting.

Remove the outermost frame as before, checking briefly for the queen, then shaking the workers back into the hive body or at the entrance. The frames should now be drawn out (on a NUC or package) and you should be able to see a brood pattern forming.

A good brood pattern is in the shape of an ellipse with the bulk of the brood on both sides of the middle frames (Fig. 5-16). The center part of the middle frames should be solid eggs, pupae, and capped larva with few or no misses. Outlining the brood should be a row of pollen, and the balance of the frame should be filled with honey with a sort of wrinkled appearance. Each frame from the center out will have less and less area filled with brood until the outer frames usually have only honey and pollen (Fig. 5-17).

In the winter, having the brood all together in this form enables the bees to cluster around them creating a warm blanket. However when the weather is warm, after all chance of frost, clustering is not essential and you can break up the brood pattern to prevent swarming.

As you're checking for brood, you want mostly worker cells, which are flat when capped. If you see nothing but raised dome-shaped cells, you have a problem—a *drone layer*. A drone layer can develop from virgin queen who flew out with a swarm before being bred, from an old queen of two or more years who has run out of

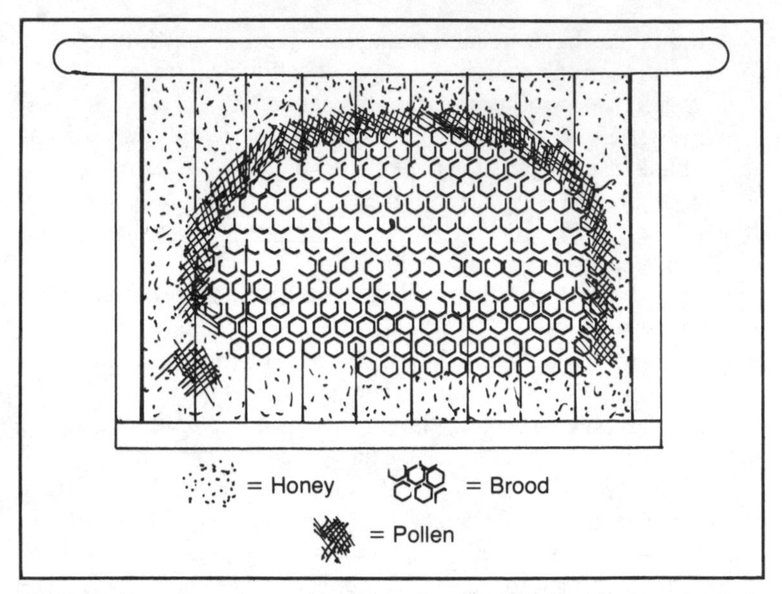

Fig. 5-16. A good brood pattern is ellipse-shaped with bulk of the brood on both sides of the middle frames. On the center frame the brood fills most of the frame, with pollen outlining the brood. The balance of the frame is filled with honey, which has a slightly wrinkled appearance when capped.

sperm and is laying unfertilized eggs, or from an an unfertile worker whose ovaries have been stimulated by the loss of a queen.

No matter what type of drone layer you have, the situation is bad and can only get worse. With no new workers being produced, there is no collection of nectar or pollen, no caring for eggs, and no work being accomplished. You will have to take this colony out and dump it. You must start over with package, NUC, or swarm. On the frames that have unhatched drones use your hive tool and dig out the pupa. The new bees will clean up the mess.

Once you have a frame of drone cells, the queen tends to lay only drone eggs in them. When you install your replacement bees, save those frames for honey storage and replace the foundation in the brood chamber. Stored frames must be protected against wax moth. (See Chapter 7.)

As pollen and nectar become available in greater quantities, the bees feed the queen more, and she is stimulated to lay more eggs increasing to as many as 1000 to 1500 eggs per day.

The number of cells on one side of a full depth frame averages 712 to 760, depending on the size of the bees. At the maximum rate of 1000 or more a day, this means the queen will fill up both sides of a frame or more in a day. Therefore, it is possible for her to complete the original nine frames in nine days or less.

Eggs take 21 to 23 days to mature to adult workers, which hatch leaving space for more eggs. The queen could be left without empty cells and slow down just when the colony needs to build a worker force for the main honey flow.

In the extreme, the bees keep packing in pollen and honey and the chamber becomes so crowded that the bees swarm. This is where the art of beekeeping is applied, where you take advantage of knowing the bees' behavior and patterns.

You must keep ahead of them by manipulating frames. By disturbing their design, you stimulate the bees to clean out cells. In the process of reestablishing their natural pattern, more space is created and swarming is checked.

When the frames in your first or lower brood chamber begin to fill up, it is time to establish a second or upper brood chamber. You must install more frames of foundation (Fig. 5-18). Transfer some frames that you have used to protect the feeder from the lower chamber into the hive body.

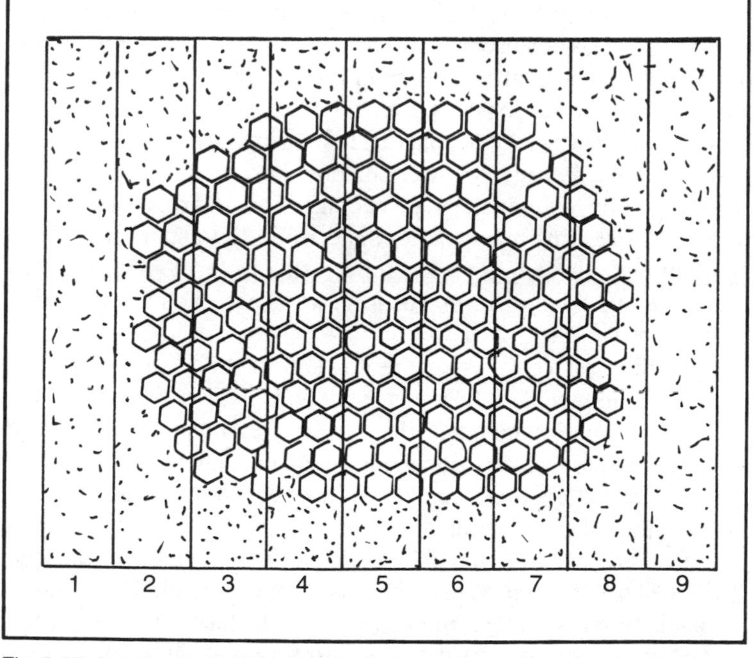

Fig. 5-17. A vertical "slice" through the frames showing the typical brood pattern in the whole chamber.

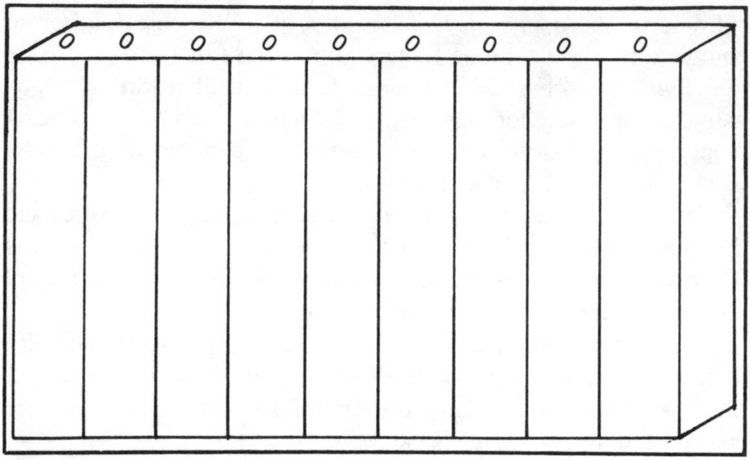

Fig. 5-18. A new super. Frames of the foundation are marked with "o."

At the same time you will be dividing the elliptical dome pattern by moving the frames most nearly filled with brood, now in the center, to the outside. Move the outermost frames filled with honey and pollen into the center.

To encourage bees to move up to work on the foundation, put a couple of frames of capped brood plus two frames of honey and pollen up into the center position of the second super. The second super is now your top brood chamber as the bees hatch, they become nurse bees for the pupae. Their vacated cells are now open space for the queen as the lower chamber becomes crowded again.

Hopefully, by now the main nectar flow is in progress or about to begin. After this manipulation, and while the upper chamber is being drawn out, it is time to prepare supers for honey—one full depth, two medium or three shallow, whichever you have decided upon.

In this first year, using the shallow depth for honey supers means another set of foundation for the bees to draw out before it is ready to receive nectar and then ripen into honey. If you have selected medium depth throughout, you can bring up three or four drawn combs of honey, capped or uncapped, to encourage the bees to move up and start working on the new comb. If the nectar flow is good, the bee population will be building up well and you want the shallow depth for ease in handling, use them instead. The bees fill the shallow sizes faster. You can take it off, harvest, and get the frames of drawn comb back to them to fill up again quickly.

At this point you may want to consider wiring and assembling your own frames (if you purchased assembled goods originally) to save on expenses. You will need to make jigs for wiring and embedding foundation. For greater efficiency, you might want to build a frame assembly outfit. (See Chapter 13.) In preparation for the honey flow, if you haven't procured one already, get a queen excluder.

As the upper chamber is drawn out, the queen starts working there. Frames fill up with brood, pollen, and honey. Now is the time to check for crowding! When you have the bottom and top brood chambers filling up, you may again need to maneuver the frames to avoid crowding and swarming.

One indication of swarming is simply a mass of bees covering each and every frame. Another definite sign is the appearance of queen cells. In preparation to leave with the old queen to find a new and roomier home, the bees start drawing out worker cells into the peanut-sized and peanut-shaped queen cell. Until they are capped or finished at the bottom, you need not be too concerned. But when new wax is added and the queen cup is completed (when the larva is about seven days old), beware. The virgin queen larva needs no further attention until she hatches, and your bees can swarm any-

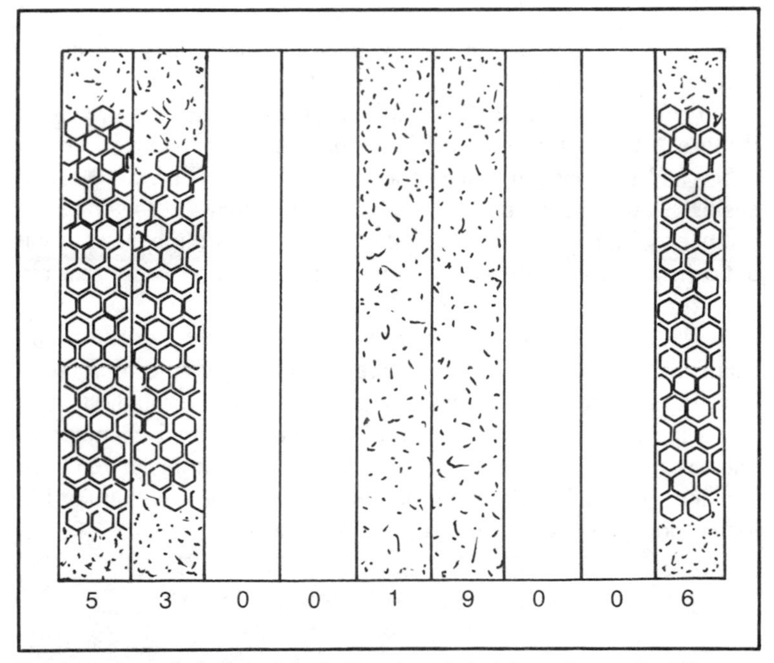

Fig. 5-19. A vertical slice of the bottom brood chamber after manipulation.

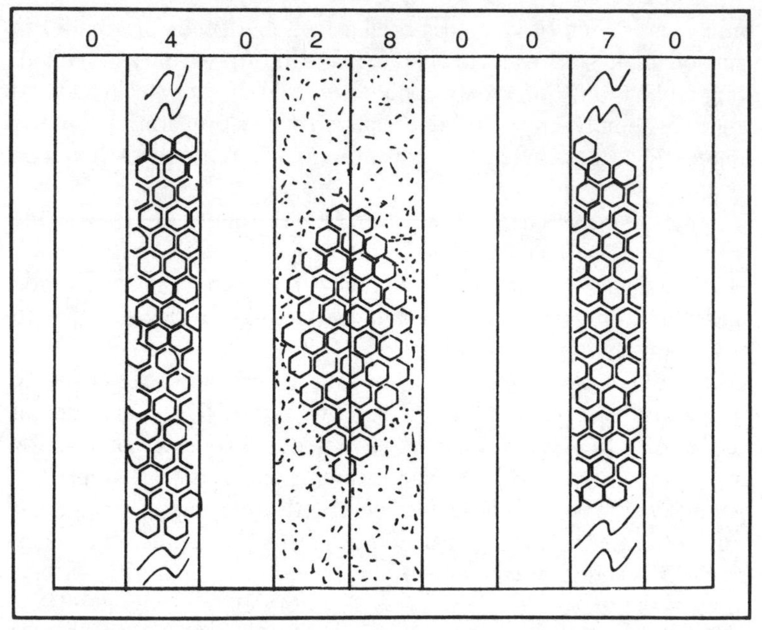

Fig. 5-20. A vertical slice of the hive body, second brood chamber, showing placement of frames of brood from bottom chamber and frames of foundation.

time. Pinch off any queen cells you see. Usually they are at the bottom but not always.

Provide more space! The pattern of brood covering two supers is more of an elliptic sphere with the top half of the sphere in the top super and the bottom half in the bottom super (Fig. 5-19). The easiest way to break up the pattern is to switch the lower brood chamber with the upper (Fig. 5-20). This causes the bees to clean out cells and re-establish the pattern. There will now be more room for more eggs.

When new white wax appears on top of frames in the brood chambers, it is time to put on a honey super with frames of foundation. If you have elected for the same size supers throughout, you can bring up some frames of honey from the brood chamber to encourage the bees to start drawing out the foundation. If you have decided on a shallow depth for honey and you have a medium or full for brood, then such interchange is not possible.

Chapter 6

Seasonal Management

Though season lengths vary a great deal from region to region in the United States, the beekeeper must be aware of the seasonal life cycles of the honeybee, whether spring comes in February or May. The colony activities from spring through winter occur in this general order: egg laying, brood rearing, brood expansion, large gains in worker force relative to nectar flow, tendency to move out and form new colonies (swarm), honey storage, slowing down and stopping of brood rearing, clustering activity, and decrease in population.

In the temperate areas, where there are four distinct seasons, the cycles of the bee colony are more pronounced. In milder areas of the deep South and the Southwest, where some plants are in bloom the year round, brood rearing does not stop in the winter. The nearly constant availability of nectar may preclude the need for large stores of honey over long periods. The honeybee colony's seasonal needs follow (See Table 6-1).

EARLY SPRING

Pollen must be available for feeding brood either from stores held over from fall or gathered from the first blooming trees and plants. This can be anytime from February in the southern states to late April or May in the northern states. Early spring is the time when colony build up occurs to rally the field force for the main nectar flow later in spring and summer. The beekeeper must sup-

Table 6-1. Annual Schedule for Beekeeping.

What the Bees Are Doing	What the Beekeeper Does
Early Spring	
Increasing brood rearing as nectar and pollen are available.	Remove insulation; open the entrance.
Gathering water to liquify stored honey	Give supplemental pollen or sugar feeding as necessary.
	Provide water.
Increasing work force	Check for disease; medicate. Put weak colony with a strong one, add a swarm or add a package of bees.
	Order queens for divides
Late Spring into Summer	
Colonies increase to peak size	Divide colonies
Make preparations to swarm	Break up brood pattern, pinch queen cells
Will readily draw out new comb	Add new foundation if needed
Increasing drone production	Bring up frames with drone cells into honey supers
Late Summer (or when major flow begins)	
Foraging at maximum with longest days	Guard against pests
	Provide ventilation
Filling, capping honey need space	Add honey supers, remove when capped, return for refill.
	Leave 60 to 90 pounds for bees
Slowing brood production	Order new queens
Fall	
Bring in last nectar, pollen	Leave ample stores
	Medicate after final harvest
Old queen slowing down	Requeen after nectar flow
Seal up cracks, openings with propolis	Reduce hive to two supers
	Store combs carefully
	Reduce entrance
Reduction in field force	Provide wind break
	Provide upper ventilation
	Insulate, wrap
Winter	
Eat stored food	On warm day, check amount and position of food
Cluster for warmth	Check for excess moisture
Keep drones from feeding	
On warm days, take cleansing flights	Clear entrance if blocked
	Check upper entrance
Stimulate queen by feeding (Late Dec. or Jan.)	Give supplemental pollen, sugar as necessary
Egg laying resumes	Prepare for busy season repaint, rewire, assemble supers

port colony build up. If there is too little pollen from the fall stores, a pollen supplement should be given the bees. They cannot raise brood without it.

Pollen substitutes containing no natural pollen are available but have come under question as the nutritional needs of bees have been more accurately assessed during the late 1970s and early 1980s. Some common pollen substitutes like expeller process soyflour and the lactose in skim milk powder contain sugars that have been found toxic to honeybees.

The pollen supplement should satisfy these requirements. It is attractive to them, stays palatable and of good consistency, and is readily available and inexpensive. One product that fills these needs is BeeFeast and Pollenex. Other products are advertised in bee periodicals.

A pound of pollen will feed a pound of bees (about 3,500 bees). For each frame of brood, considering normal pattern of about ¾ brood, a quarter of a pound is needed or a pound for each three or four frames of brood.

Feeding Sugar

If your colony is down to the equivalent of three frames of honey before the spring nectar flow has set in or they get low between the onset of early bloom such as dandelions or willow and the main flow, you have no recourse but to feed sugar. Remember that the best food for bees is honey, their natural food.

Many knowledgeable and seasoned beekeepers never give bees sugar except in dire emergencies. The prudent beekeeper always leaves at least one full super of honey for the bees in the fall for overwintering.

Sugar syrup in gallon containers placed over the inner cover (as described in installing bees, (Chapter 5) can be given. To prevent granulation, a solution with slightly less than two-thirds (66.6 percent) sugar and one-third water is recommended. One test showed that granulation stopped at 64 percent sugar, or 20 pounds of sugar dissolved in 9 pints of hot water.

Pour the solution into a gallon container with about 30 holes of 1/16 inch diameter punched in the lid. To keep the syrup warm until the bees can take it down, wrap the jar or can in foam padding, an old rug, layers of burlap, or cellulose attic insulation (Fig. 6-1).

Dry sugar is simpler and can be used when there is moisture present either from condensation in the top insulating super or water available and fair flying weather so the bees can bring it back

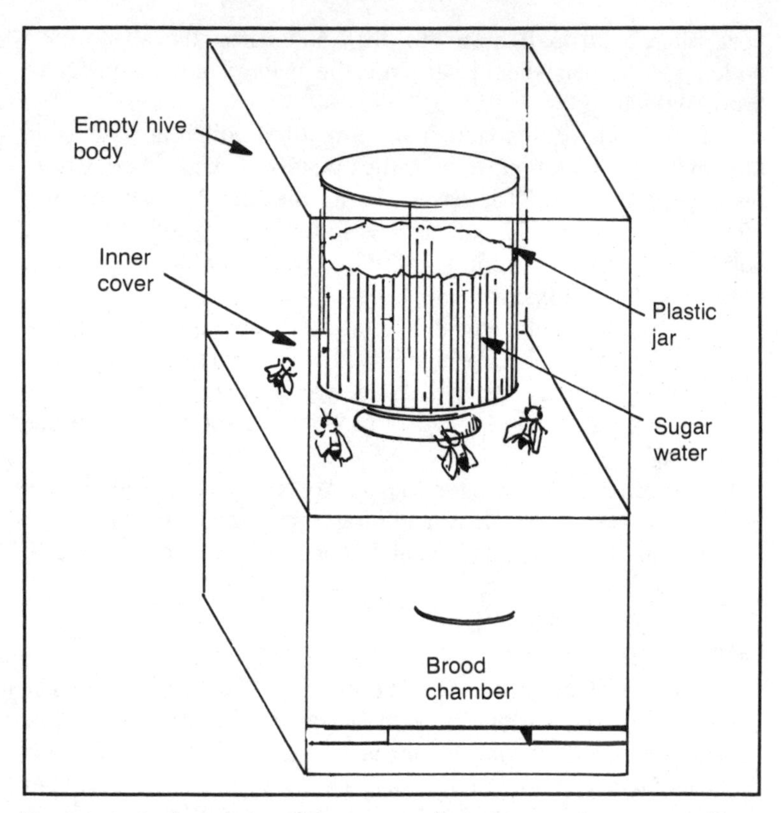

Fig. 6-1. A plastic container of sugar water turned over an inner cover with an empty super placed over it.

to the hive. Granulated sugar can be sprinkled on the bottom board, put in an open container above the frames, or spread around the hole of the inner cover.

If you are some distance from your apiary and want to give a quantity sufficient to hold them until your next visit, build up the rim of the inner cover to contain the sugar. You can tack on ¾ inch strips of plywood or use baseboard molding. Bees do not eat dry sugar, but the moisture coming up from the lower supers creates a sugar paste that the bees can take down.

When bees are flying and water is available, you can feed dry sugar through newspapers punched with two or three holes and placed over the frames. Pour three to five pounds of sugar on the papers and spread it around. The cover may not fit over the sugar so you may have to put on another super between the brood chamber and the lid.

If you have to set up a feeding arrangement, then you probably have removed the winter insulation or packing. As weather warms and danger of frost is past, the packing is no longer necessary. However, if you used a glass solar collector booster on the side of the hive, you could leave that on to conserve the energy of the colony.

Checking Up, Cleaning Up

Check your brood chamber carefully for signs of foulbrood or nosema. Wax moths may become a problem as temperatures rise, but where winters have long periods of freezing temperatures any eggs deposited in the fall will have been killed. If preventive medication is applied, give a dose of terramycin and/or sulfathiazole before the honey supers are put on (Fig. 6-2).

Fig. 6-2. In the spring, one of the first tasks is to check carefully for disease in the brood chamber.

While you are working with your brood chambers, you can clean off the bottom board and open the entrance either by flipping the board over if you are using a reversible-type or by sliding over the cleat or plywood strip.

Clean up the accumulation of leaves, sticks and other debris underneath the hive to deter insect pests. If you have used an oil can or jars of oil under the legs of your hive stand for ant control, replace or clean them out and put in fresh oil.

Robber Bees

During spring and fall, before the main nectar flow or between nectar flows, you must be on the lookout for robber bees when you have the hive open and combs of honey exposed. Robber bees are bees from other colonies, wild or beekeeper managed, who actually enter another hive and start sucking up the honey. They can be identified by their darting flight pattern around combs and open hives, usually with their legs hanging down.

Never put out a frame of honey not protected by bees when there is danger of robbing. Take special care with scrapings of comb or propolis where the scent of honey could attract robbers. Put them in a can and cover them with a board or wet burlap as you work. Do not allow honey to drip from torn comb or uncapped frames down the sides of the hive or onto the ground.

If you see robbing begin, close up the hive immediately. A weak colony can be overcome and killed by robber bees. Stuff grass or weeds into the entrance to reduce it temporarily and allow the guard bees to protect it more easily.

LATE SPRING AND SUMMER

As warmer weather prevails and there is a good nectar supply, colonies build rapidly and often become too crowded. Watch for queen cells and increased drone production and take steps to prevent swarming. It is usually a good time to make divides and start a new colony.

Adding Honey Supers

When you see new white comb deposited on top of your brood frames, it is time to add honey supers.

Some beekeepers advocate adding honey supers one at a time during the flow with the idea of stimulating the bees to fill up a super and cap it, thus concentrating the work force. If your apiary is not close by, this may not be practical. You can't check every other day, and you do not want the bees to run out of storage space during a heavy flow. Bees by nature tend to leave some work undone so that the top super usually has a frame or two left uncapped. If you find this is the case, simply switch the incomplete one with the one below it.

Two or three honey supers installed at the same time serve as insulation against heat. This is considered by some to be as efficient as providing shade. Remember to choose your lightest colored comb to put in the honey supers and use the dark stained comb in the brood chamber (Fig. 6-3).

If you are adding a super of foundation, it is best to add only one medium super or two shallow supers at a time. Bring up some drawn combs to encourage the bees to move up and start drawing out the foundation.

You will very likely receive requests for comb honey. It is popular with older people who grew up when most honey was sold in comb or chunk form. This was because it does not require extract-

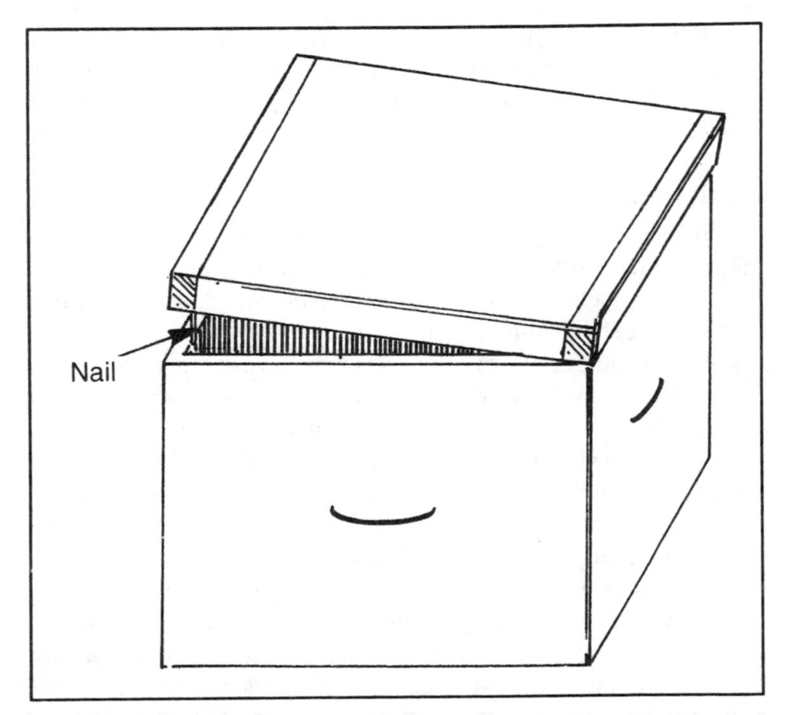

Fig. 6-3. In warm weather, you may need to ventilate your hive. A match or nail slipped under the lid will help.

ing equipment. *Comb honey* is honey in a self contained round or square of comb that has been set up for the bees to draw out and fill up. *Chunk honey* is a section of honey cut from a frame of drawn comb of honey. In either case the wax is kept with the honey, consumed with it, and not recycled back into the hive as with frames that are extracted.

It is *not* advisable for a beginner to attempt comb honey production. Bees are very reluctant to draw out comb sections. Nectar flow has to be excellent and the time and energy on the part of the bees to produce such honey is definitely out of proportion to the worth of the harvest.

A great deal of wax must be built by the bees for comb sections. For every 5 to 10 pounds of section to be drawn, the bees must consume 100 pounds of honey to have the energy to produce the wax (Fig. 6-4). The amount of honey contained in a frame of comb sections is less than the amount that can be stored in a frame. The average amount of honey extractable from a regular frame is 10 pounds or more, whereas the yield for a frame of comb sections is 8 pounds. You are losing two pounds of honey per frame of sections.

Before setting your honey super on top of the brood chambers, install a queen excluder. You want to know where your queen is, and you don't want to have to try to uncap pupae and larvae mixed in with honey.

Dividing a Colony

If you are enjoying a healthy colony increase to the point of taking swarm control measures, or if you started your colony with a swarm or an established colony, you can consider dividing your first colony and establishing a second one.

One advantage of two colonies is that you can bring over brood, honey, pollen, and/or worker bees from one to the other in case one is in trouble or loses a queen. If you should suffer some loss during the winter, you can then combine the two in the spring for a good work force in time for the nectar flow. Another advantage of two is a basis of comparison. You can see if one has much less pollen coming in or many more drones—both signals for you to take action.

The disadvantage is the additional outlay for equipment and the extra time needed to manage another hive, especially if you are still learning to work bees. If your area is having a poor nectar flow because of draught, cold spring, or rainy summer and your bees are building up slowly, it is best to concentrate on one hive and keep it going.

Fig. 6-4. Bees must consume a lot of honey to stimulate wax secretion. Here is newly drawn out wax.

If you decide to expand, the first step is to order a queen. You might like to try a different supplier for comparison. By mid-summer, some local beekeepers may have extra queens available. Many experienced beekeepers like to raise their own queens. Be sure there is a guarantee that you can return her if she turns out to be a poor layer.

Your queen will be in a small plywood cage with 6 to 12 attending workers (the same as with package bees), covered with a screen and plugged with a cork at one end and candy at the other for food. If you have her shipped, make the same arrangements with your postal personnel as described in Chapter 5. Keep the bees in a temperature room, below 80°F and above 50°F. Give the bees a drop or two of water each day. It's easiest to use the little bit left in the bottom after you yourself finish a drink.

Before taking the queen out to the apiary, you will need to have ready another hive body the same size as your present brood chamber with nine frames of foundation. Choose a pleasant day—your queen can be held in the cage up to three weeks if necessary. Set your new super about 2 feet away from the first hive, facing the opposite direction.

Take off the cover and place the hive body upside down on your work stand or on the ground. Remove the honey super(s), and set them on the cover. Take off the excluder. Check the underside for the queen before setting the excluder aside. Smoke lightly. Find two frames of emerging brood. Look briefly for the queen before shaking bees off *over* the hive body.

It is important that you have brood nearly ready to hatch or hatching—you can see them chewing out of their cells—for they are equipped to feed the new brood that the queen will be laying. Wedge the queen cage at the back of the hive between and at the top of the two brood frames. Spray the cage lightly with sugar water so that the bees from the first colony will accept her. Now choose two frames of honey and pollen with bees on them and place them on either side of the two frames of brood.

You will proceed with this NUC as you did with building up the first. It should build up faster with the drawn comb from number one instead of all foundation as before. The frames of honey and pollen are preferable to sugar water for stimulating bees.

Adding Swarms

Another way to build up your NUC is to add a swarm if you are fortunate enough to get one (Fig. 6-5). Put on a queen excluder and cover it with a sheet of newspaper. Make five or six slits for openings, then add a super for the swarm. By the time the bees chew through the paper (in a day or two) their hive odor is the same and there is no hostility.

The swarm's queen and drones are caught above the excluder. The workers will have moved down to get out for foraging, and you can remove the queen and destroy her.

You can mix the bees directly and immediately without news-

Fig. 6-5. To build up your foraging crew for the heavy nectar flow in late spring or summer, add a swarm. This one, on a window, will have to be smoked down into a cardboard box or hive body with a few frames of foundation to induce the bees to enter.

Fig. 6-6. When searching for the queen, smoke lightly.

papers by misting the old colony and the swarm with sugar water flavored with a little vanilla. Dump them from the box in which you caught them into the brood chamber through a queen excluder. The queen will be left on top and should be easy to catch and kill.

If you do not wish to build a second colony, a swarm can be added to strengthen your original colony. This will give you a larger foraging force for the nectar flow and insure good colony size for over-wintering (Fig. 6-6).

Another important consideration for bees during warmer weather is ventilation. As the bees process the nectar into honey, a large volume of water is withdrawn. The bees help this condensation process by fanning. They also fan to keep the hive cool when interior temperatures exceed 93°F. You need to provide another opening for heat and water to escape.

A matchstick or slim nail slipped under one or two corners of the inner cover will allow heat to escape without providing an easy entrance for robber bees. Beekeepers who use the simple flat or migratory cover often reverse it in extreme heat, leaving a space all around the perimeter. However, this is large enough for bees to enter and exit so beware of robber bees.

If you have two or more colonies and one has come through the winter in a weakened condition or has lost a queen, unite it with a stronger one. Usually at this time, with the onset of the first or early nectar flow, one colony will accept the other without the newspaper between. You can also collect a swarm and add it or order a package of bees.

One sign of a queenless hive in spring is the presence of drones. Normally to save honey supplies, the workers will have prevented the drones from eating and force them out so that by spring few or no drones are seen. Drones *are* allowed to stay, however, if a colony is queenless.

Providing Water

Remember to reestablish your water set up early. As bees start flying, they need water for liquifying honey that has granulated over the winter. This is especially vital if you have your bees in a residential area. You need to immediately train them to the source of water you provide even if it is a rainy spring and puddles abound. You do not want them to start getting water from a neighbor's pond, birdbath, or swimming pool. Once the bees have started using such a source, it is practically impossible to break them of the pattern.

Now that you have everything ready for nectar collection—plenty of space, a strong foraging force, queen excluder, honey supers in place—you are ready for nature to smile on you with an ample nectar flow. You can now think about harvesting!

AUTUMN

Many a wise old timer in beekeeping says: "What you do with your bees in the fall is your insurance toward a good honey crop the next summer." The following suggestions will allow a colony to get through a winter in the temperate states where there is two to five months of freezing temperatures.

At least 40,000 to 60,000 bees should be housed in a reduced hive of two supers. A diverse population including young bees and a young, vigorous queen should be present. To accomplish this you should requeen your colony in early fall. (If little or no nectar flow can be expected in the fall, then requeen in late summer). As old bees die off in the winter, a new queen will produce young bees to winter over and become the field force for the first spring nectar flow. A requeened colony nearly always means a superior honey yield.

Ideally the new queen should be introduced when the last nectar flow is on the wane or the "down" side. The interruption of a new queen should not occur at the peak of the flow but rather at a time when there is food with which to stimulate her to start laying.

There are three ways to requeen. You can first introduce the new queen into a NUC or a separate hive body. The idea is to get a relatively small number of bees to accept her, then join her and the new colony with the larger colony.

Reduce the original brood chamber to one hive body. Anytime you want to spot the queen, smoke very lightly so that she will not start running. A couple of puffs will do. If you spot her in one of the chambers, use the other chamber to introduce your new queen. First transfer up to the honey supers all but one frame of honey. Find two frames of emerging brood, checking to see that the queen is not working there. If you don't spot her, don't tarry. Simply brush off the bees gently over the open chamber in case she is on one. Put the brood frames in the center of the NUD. If there are no empty or nearly empty frames, exchange them with some from the other chamber and fill the super with them.

Place the NUC a few feet away from the parent colony, facing the opposite direction. Wedge the queen cage between the two brood frames, candy end up and pointing toward the front of the hive. Prop it up with burr comb or wax if necessary. Place a cover on the top. This method allows you to keep the old queen while the new one proves herself.

After a week check to be sure the new queen has been released from the cage. After another week to ten days, check to see if she is laying in a good pattern.

Then get into the original hive and start searching for the old queen. Start by looking on the center frames and glancing quickly around the edges first to be sure she isn't moving from one side to another. Then look toward the center. With your fingers, gently break up any clumps of bees you see. Remember that bees do not walk on the queen. Check the bottom and sides of the hive.

If you don't spot her the first time through, check frame by frame once more. After that, the bees will have become disturbed. Close up and come back the next day. When you find her, pinch off her head and set her on the porch or in front of the hive. Wait a day to be sure the colony knows it is queenless. Then bring your NUC over and install it over the old chamber. Spray the new queen and the bees around her lightly with sugar water or use the newspaper system.

The second two-step method involves removing the super with the old queen and setting it a couple of feet away. Move up most of the frames of honey to the honey supers first. The next day or so, return and introduce your new queen to the total colony. Again you have hedged your bet by keeping both queens until the new one proves herself.

The third method entails removing the old queen, killing her, throwing her in front of the hive, and installing the new queen within a couple hours. With direct introduction, it is best to remove the attendant workers, which the colony may not accept without antagonism. To do this, take the queen cage into the bathroom with the lights off. Open the cage and allow the workers and queen to crawl out a window. They will buzz but seldom sting. With your finger, gently herd the queen back into the hole of the cage, head first.

Of great importance in the autumn of the year is that you leave ample stores of honey and pollen for the bees to use during the winter. For a colony of 40,000 to 60,000 bees you must leave at least 60 pounds where there are mild winters and up to 90 pounds in areas with longer, harsher winters.

There should be a natural wind break close to your hives. A stand of evergreen trees or a hedge with spaces at least two inches apart is ideal. (A solid barrier lets the wind swoop up and over toward the hives.) If not, then you should put up a temporary wind break and get planting next spring (Fig. 6-7). Boards about 4 to 7 feet high placed 2 inches apart will work well, or you can use the simple slat cribbing (Fig. 6-8).

Good air drainage is important as well. Hives must not be situated where cold air collects around them. This is often the case near buildings or solid walls. It is a good idea to place them on a slight slope, facing away from prevailing winds.

Snow on the hives will not hurt the bees; it acts as insulation. Moisture collecting around and inside the hives will hurt the bees,

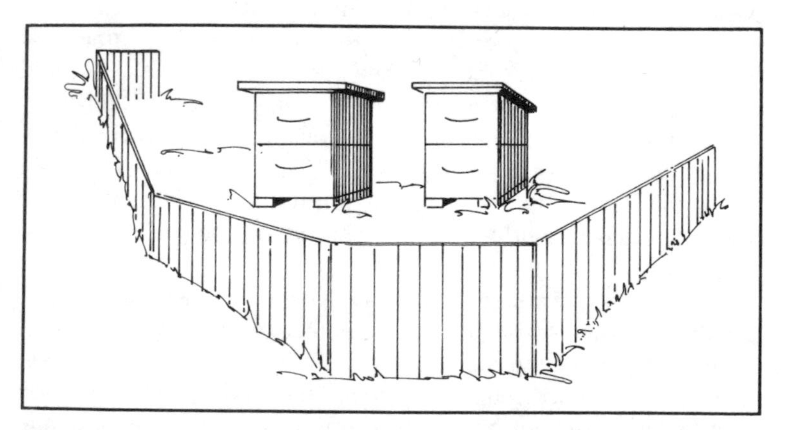

Fig. 6-7. In your first winter, if you have no other windbreaks, you can put up snow fencing.

Fig. 6-8. Another good windbreak is slat fencing. Allow about 2 inches between boards so wind sifts slowly through. Larger spaces allow wind to swoop up and over to chill the hives.

however. As the bees feed on winter stores, a great deal of moisture collects and must be ventilated out through the top of the hive. For each gallon of honey consumed, about a gallon of water is produced.

Insulating materials placed in an empty super above the brood chamber act as a wick and draw the moisture from the bees' living area. Hay, grass, wheat straw, fiberglass, or cellulose wall insulation can be used. Hives should not sit flush on the ground. Bottom boards will become soaked and create too much moisture inside the brood chambers. Put them up on hive stands of metal, treated wood, concrete blocks, or bricks (See Chapter 4).

Moisture and cold air can enter through the entrance. It must be reduced to ⅜ inch deep by 1 or 2 inches wide. It is a good plan to put up a narrow miniroof of tin or plywood over the entrance to keep ice and snow from collecting.

Another winter problem is mice. Even with the entrance reduced, a small mouse can still wriggle in, make a nest, and tear up the wax combs. A piece of ½-inch hardware cloth nailed tightly in place should deter a mouse and still allow bees to come and go, weather permitting. Interestingly, if the bees do break cluster to combat a rodent, they will propolize him so that his decaying carcass does not allow any bacteria to spread through the brood chamber.

Many beekeepers find their bees do well with only top insulation. Where winters are likely to be long and severe, however, many people provide additional insulation and warmth by wrapping them or by using some covering that will absorb and hold the sun's heat. Materials used include:

- Lightweight roofing paper
- Corrugated cardboard cases impregnated with plastic or tar
- Translucent corrugated plastic
- Glass or plexiglass, framed and fitted to the side of the hive
- Leaves secured to the side with wire mesh.

To wrap the hive in tar paper or roofing paper, cut a strip long enough to go all the way around the hive and wide enough to wrap two hive bodies. Drill an auger hole in the upper chamber near the hand hole for an alternate opening. Cut a matching hole in the paper.

You may nail cleats at the entrance and at the back with the nails left protruding for fastening the twine. Place insulating materials inside before you fold in the corners and secure them with nails. Cut another strip of paper to serve as a top.

Form the corrugated plastic sheets into a box with the sides slightly longer than the sides of the hives to allow for an air space (Fig. 6-9). Fold the tops like those of a box to open and close for winter checks. Push a pipe through the cover and the air space, into the auger hole in the top super. The bees can leave and reenter on cleansing flights by using the pipe.

You can purchase corrugated sheets at some beekeeping supply firms or from a local plastics dealer (check your yellow pages). Or order them from Western Packaging, 7451 Dogwood Park, Richland Hill, TX 76118. Request information on Tru-Dor, their trade name for the product.

The glass or Plexiglas plastic solar collector (Fig. 6-10), is cut to fit the side of the hive, and framed. It was designed by Frank Shaw, of Independence, MO. It can be held in place with a wire hooked to a screw eye on the frame and a screw on a cleat nailed to

Fig. 6-9. Corrugated plastic hive covers for winter protection are gaining in popularity. Research has shown that they protect better than many other materials.

the hive body on the opposite side. For best results, place it on the south side of the hive with the hive entrance facing east.

WINTER

During winter you will need to check your hives about once every three or four weeks. This is particularly important during your first year as a beekeeper when you don't know what to expect. Although you must use care and work as quickly as possible when exposing brood chambers to very cold temperatures, the value of making sure the colony has stores outweighs any possible problem from chilling.

Choose a period of thawing or the warmest day you can. When opening your hive, pry carefully so as not to crack the wood. If the

Fig. 6-10. The solar hive warmer devised by Frank W. Shaw of Independence, Missouri. Framed glass is hooked to the south side of the hive. (Photo by William David Gore. Reprinted with permission from the *American Bee Journal*, November, 1981.)

brood is all on one side of the super with no food adjacent to them, move the frames of honey toward them. They will not break cluster in freezing temperatures to crawl over empty frames to get to full ones. They will simply starve. If the honey supply is running low, you will have to feed them sugar.

When you close the hive, place a large rock or some bricks on top to keep it in place during wind and storms. The bees cannot propolize it back in place at this time.

Cold weather is a good time to repair and repaint stored supers, repaint or retreat extra bottom and top boards, and put together more supers and wire frames, embed foundation, and construct handier gadgets and equipment to make your beekeeping easier. (See Chapter 13.)

Winter is a good time to evaluate what you have done in beekeeping and where you want to go. Read through your calendar or notebook (Table 6-1). If you hope to expand, make a plan for purchasing or constructing more supplies and obtaining bees. Be positive and plan on a good honey crop your second year. Develop a marketing plan. (See Chapter 10.) Send for beekeeping supply catalogs. By now you may be on a number of mailing lists and have already received several.

Two good booklets on recordkeeping are available. One is a 4-H manual on advanced beekeeping methods published by the Cooperative Extension Service, Purdue University. It includes sheets on inventory, receipts, financial summary, labor, and apiary records. Send check or money order for $1.35 to: Agricultural Publications, Mailing Room, AGAD Building, Purdue University, West Lafayette, IN 47907.

The other is titled *Beekeeping Records* and covers capital, sales and purchases, operating income and expenses, inventory, and performance of colonies for a three year analysis. The booklet cost is $1.25 plus the cost of first class postage return. Address your request to Agricultural Bulletin Building, 1535 Observatory Drive, Madison, WI 53706.

MISCELLANEOUS TIPS

To avoid lifting the top supers to check your lower supers, try the following. Rock the whole hive carefully backwards and lower it to the ground. Now pry apart the super or brood chamber you want to inspect and pull it to one side as you might pull out a book from between book ends. Most situations can be appraised by looking up through the frames from the bottom—whether you have honey, queen cells, or brood. Obviously the supers need to be well propolized to hold together when you try this maneuver.

You can also tip a top super or two over onto a stack of empty supers, lumber, or even a sturdy portable camp table to avoid lifting the top third or fourth one from a height above your head and down to ground level.

At some time you are probably going to have to move your bees. You can move honeybees a few feet or several miles, but if you attempt to move them less than two miles, they will return again and again to the old site rather than adapting to the new location you have selected.

The best time to move bees is after honey harvesting when you have lightened the hives and are down to as few hive bodies as possible. A two-super stack is ideal for moving—the lighter the load the better for you and the greater the chance your frames to remain intact. Never move hives of over three stories.

Before moving bees it is essential that you secure the whole hive structure together. You can use staples or nails to hold the bottom board and fasten the supers together with staples, bailing wire, plastic strapping, or overlapping wooden cleats.

The best time to move bees is in the evening when all foragers have returned and when they are not impelled to fly out. If your destination is less than one hour's travel time you can put screen across the entrance(s). Blocking the entrance for much longer could cause bees to suffocate.

If you are moving a longer distance in warm weather, you can use empty shallow or medium supers with screen tacked on at the top in place of the lid. The bees can come up to cluster and ventilate the colony through the screen. Also provide water.

When you have the equipment ready to move, smoke each colony heavily. Be sure all chinks and holes where bees could exit are plugged or taped. Hive lifters, something like tongs, are available through suppliers, or you can slide a two super hive on to a hand truck. Tie the hives securely on to the truck bed, station wagon or van to prevent shifting and disturbing the bees even more.

Chapter 7

Diseases, Pests, and Pesticides

Just as with pets and livestock, honeybees are subject to diseases. The beekeeper must always be on guard, checking each time he or she visits the apiary to catch early signs of trouble. Take preventative measures before the infectious organism spreads, weakens the colony, and contaminates other hives.

AMERICAN FOULBROOD

By far the most worrisome infection for beekeepers to deal with is American Foulbrood (AFB). The *bacillus larvae* bacterium that causes it is impervious to extreme heat or cold and to chemicals. The spores remain viable in combs and on equipment as long as 50 years. Once a colony is infected, it cannot be cured. Most states require that the bees infected with foulbrood and all the frames of brood and comb be destroyed by burning. The contaminated woodwork must be sterilized with a blow torch or in a lye bath. A new method of sterilization by irradiation is proving successful in experimental tests in California, and the process does not damage or weaken the woodwork.

A comb infected with AFB has a peppered appearance with some normal cells, cells with the remains of diseased larvae, and empty cells. The normal slightly raised capping of a worker larva sinks inward. The capping is often punctured, but be aware that a healthy cell that has not been completed can appear to have holes in the capping as well.

The infected larva loses its pearly white, glistening appearance and turns first to a creamy brown, then to a dark brown. The remains become ropy. One test of possible AFB is to use a toothpick or matchstick (something you can burn later) to poke in a suspect cell. When you do so, the pupa or larva with AFB will collapse. As you draw out the stick, a gluelike thread will adhere to the end. Frequently a strong animal glue smell can be detected (Fig. 7-1).

Eventually the remains of the dying larva dry and form black scales, which adhere fast to the lower sides of the cells. To distinguish these scales from a normally darkened cell, hold the frame up to the sun. If the cell is infected, you can see a faint outline of the scale and slightly raised head. Often the tongue or mouth parts adhere to the upperside of the cell stretching in a thin thread to the mass at the bottom. This is a definite symptom of AFB (Fig.7-2).

Although the incidence of AFB runs only about 3 percent of those colonies inspected, it is readily communicable to healthy colonies through robber bees or infected combs or honey. As a beginner, if you suspect American Foulbrood, or learn that other colonies in your area are infected, get hold of your apiary inspector or agricultural county extension agent at once. Usually the reaction is prompt and helpful.

In 16 states, the inspector is required to assist in disinfecting the equipment. In 40 of the 50 states, beekeepers are subject to penalties for maintaining colonies with AFB (Table 7-1).

Two drugs, oxytetracycline HCl (terramycin) and sodium sulfathiazole are used by beekeepers as a retardant to American Foulbrood. Many commercial operators, whose hives number in the thousands, follow a set preventative routine of medicating. One of the largest commercial beekeepers in southern California has his colonies medicated *after* each time honey is removed following a major nectar flow, or three to four times a year. This has cut the incidence of AFB from 6 percent to 1 percent.

Medications should never be given during the nectar flow as they are processed by the bees into the honey, making it unsuitable for human consumption.

An antibiotic is fed to bees in powdered sugar. The formula for sulfathiazole is one-to-one by volume or one cup of powdered sugar to one cup of sulfa. The dose is *½ teaspoon* per colony.

Terramycin is available in three different concentrations, and the formulas vary accordingly. Follow the directions on the package for mixing it with the powdered sugar. The dose is *3 teaspoons* per colony. For smaller colonies, give less. In using either mix,

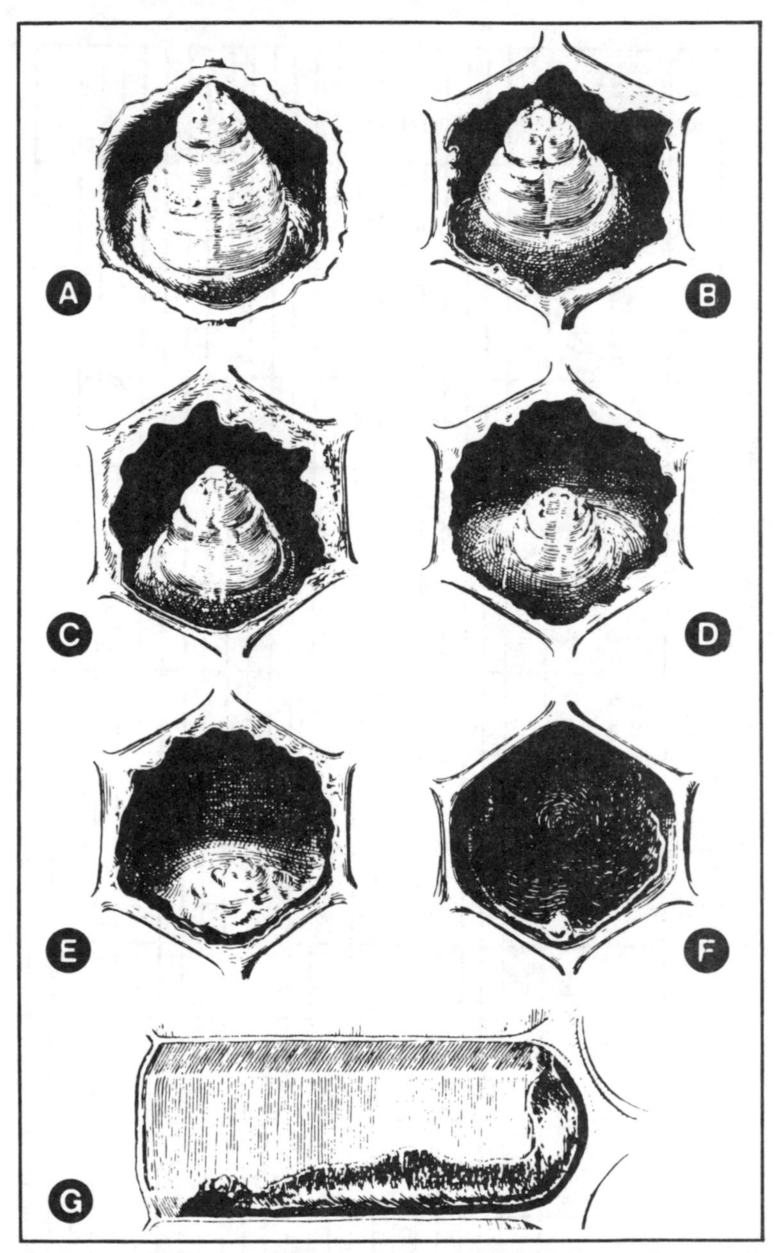

Fig. 7-1. Honeybee larvae killed by American Foulbrood, as seen in cells: (A) Healthy larva at an age when most of the brood dies of American Foulbrood; (B-F) dead larvae in progressive stages of decomposition (the remains in F are scale); (G) longitudinal view of scale. (Reprinted from Agricultural Handbook 335, USDA, rev. October 1980.)

Table 7-1. Intrastate Regulations Pertaining to American Foulbrood.

State		Owner			AFB Diseased Colonies or Equipment					Drug Treatment		Hives
		Subject to										
	Must be Notified	Tax	Fees	Penalties	Must be Quar-antined	Must not be Con-cealed	Must not be Exposed	Must not be sold or Transferred	Must be de-stroyed	Permitted for Control	Permitted for Prevention	Must have Movable Frames
Ala.	x		x	x	x	x	x	x	x		x	x
Alaska												
Ariz.	x				x		x		x	x	x	x
Ark.	x			x	x	x	x	x	x		x	x
Calif.	x		x	x	x	x	x	x	x		x	x
Colo. (1)				x				x	x	x	x	x
Conn.	x		x	x	x			x		x		
Del.				x	x	x	x	x			x	x
Fla.	x			x	x		x	x	x		x	x
Ga.			x	x	x			x	x			x
Hawaii										x	x	
Idaho	x	x			x			x	x	x		x
ILL.	x			x	x			x	x		x	x
Ind.						x	x	x	x	x	x	x
Iowa		x		x		x	x	x		x	x	x
Kans.	x	x	x	x	x				x	x	x	x
Ky.			x	x	x				x		x	x
La.				x	x			x	x		x	x
Maine			x	x				x		x	x	x
Mass.	x			x			x	x	x	x	x	x
Md.	x			x	x		x	x	x	x	x	x
Mich.	x		x	x	x	x	x	x	x		x	x
Minn.	x		x	x				x		x	x	x

Miss.				x	x		x	x			x	
Mo.	x		x(2)		x					x	x	x
Mont.	x		x	x	x				x		x	x
N.C.					x		x	x			x	x
N. Dak.	x		x	x	x		x	x		x	x	x
Neb.			x	x	x	x	x	x	x		x	x
Nev.	x	x	x	x	x	x	x	x	x		x	x
N.H.	x			x	x	x	x	x	x		x	x
N.J.	x			x	x	x	x	x	x	x	x	x
N. Mex.	x	x	x	x	x	x				x		x
N.Y.	x			x	x	x	x	x	x		x	x
Ohio			x	x	x			x	x		x	x
Okla.	x			x	x	x	x	x		x	x	x
Oreg.	x		x	x	x	x		x	x		x	x
Pa.	x	x		x	x	x	x	x	x	x	x	x
R.I.	x			x	x		x	x		x	x	x
S.C.				x	x		x	x				
S. Dak.	x		x	x	x		x	x	x			x
Tenn.	x	x		x	x	x	x	x	x	x	x	x
Tex.				x	x		x	x	x	x	x	x
Utah	x		x		x	x		x	x			x
Va.	x			x			x	x	x		x	x
Vt.	x			x		x	x	x	x	x	x	x
Wash.	x			x	x			x	x			x
Wis.		x		x			x	x		x	x	x
W. Va.	x			x	x	x	x	x	x	x	x	x
Wyo.	x			x		x	x		x		x	x

(1). Beekeepers with 25 hives or under are exempt from **all** provisions of the law unless they declare they are selling honey.
(2). Only on requested inspections.

From Michael's 1979 Summary of Bee Disease Laws of the United States courtesy Bioenvironmental Bee Laboratory, Agricultural Research Science and Education Administration, USDA.

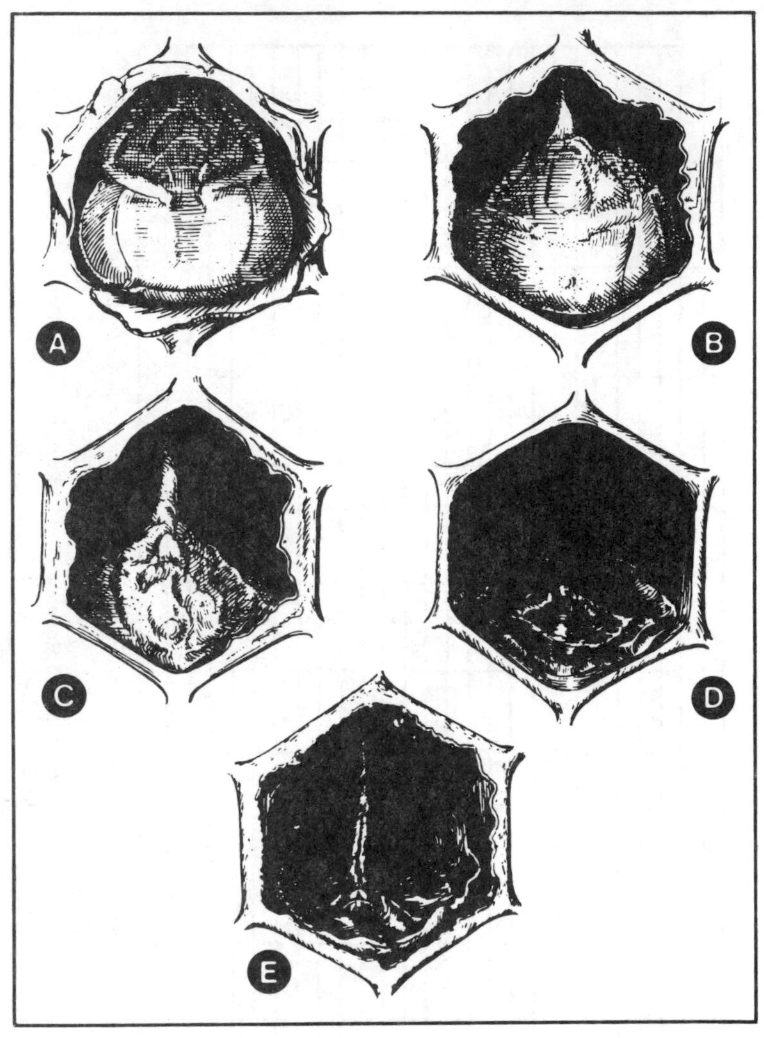

Fig. 7-2. Honeybee pupae killed by American Foulbrood, as seen in cells: (A-C) Heads of pupae in progressive stages of melting down and decay; (D-E) scales formed from drying of dead pupae. In B, C, and E, the tongue is shown adhering to the roof of the cell. (Reprinted from Agricultural Handbook 335, USDA, rev. October, 1980.)

sprinkle it on the frame rest at the back of the hive. Take care not to spill any directly over the brood as it can kill developing larvae and pupae.

Remember antibiotics are not cures for foulbrood. If you see any signs that the disease is active, by all means contact your apiary inspector or agricultural extension agent and follow his advice on destroying the bees, combs, and honey, and sterilizing the equipment.

EUROPEAN FOULBROOD

Some of the outward signs of European Foulbrood (EFB) are similar to AFB in that the comb has a mottled look, there is ropy consistency to the remains, and sometimes a sour odor. The larva color change goes from the healthy glistening white to dull white then to yellow and finally brown. As the larva turns brown, you can detect fine silvery tubes, which are the trachae or breathing apparatus of the bee. Also the scales left after death of a larva are loosely connected to the cells in contrast to the tightly adhering scales of AFB.

EFB is caused by a bacteria, *streptococcus pluton* but is not spore producing and does not usually kill the colony; nor does the colony have to be destroyed. It can drastically affect the honey production.

SACBROOD AND CHALKBROOD

Two other brood diseases are common but not as threatening as AFB or EFB. One is chalkbrood, caused by a fungus, *ascosphaera apis*. It also affects larvae three or four days old. Infected larvae dry up and look like hard white (hence the name) mummies. They can also become mottled, gray, or black. The mummies are removed from the cells by the nurse bees and can be seen on the combs, at the entrance, or on the bottom boards. They have a faint yeastlike odor. Chalkbrood can be transmitted by adult bees and contaminated equipment.

Sacbrood, is recognizable by the tough skin enclosing the watery contents of the dead larva like a sack. The sack eventually shrinks to a scale with the elevated head of the dead larva visible in the cell. This scale, as with EFB is easily removable from the cells (Fig. 7-3). Once in a while a susceptible queen produces especially large numbers of larvae prone to sacbrood and should be replaced with a queen of a different genetic make up.

Brood do die from starvation or chilling, not always from disease. These will be found on the outside of the brood with none of the signs as described above (Table 7-2).

NOSEMA

A very common adult bee disease is nosema, caused by a protozoan, *Nosema apis*. It affects workers, drones, and queens,

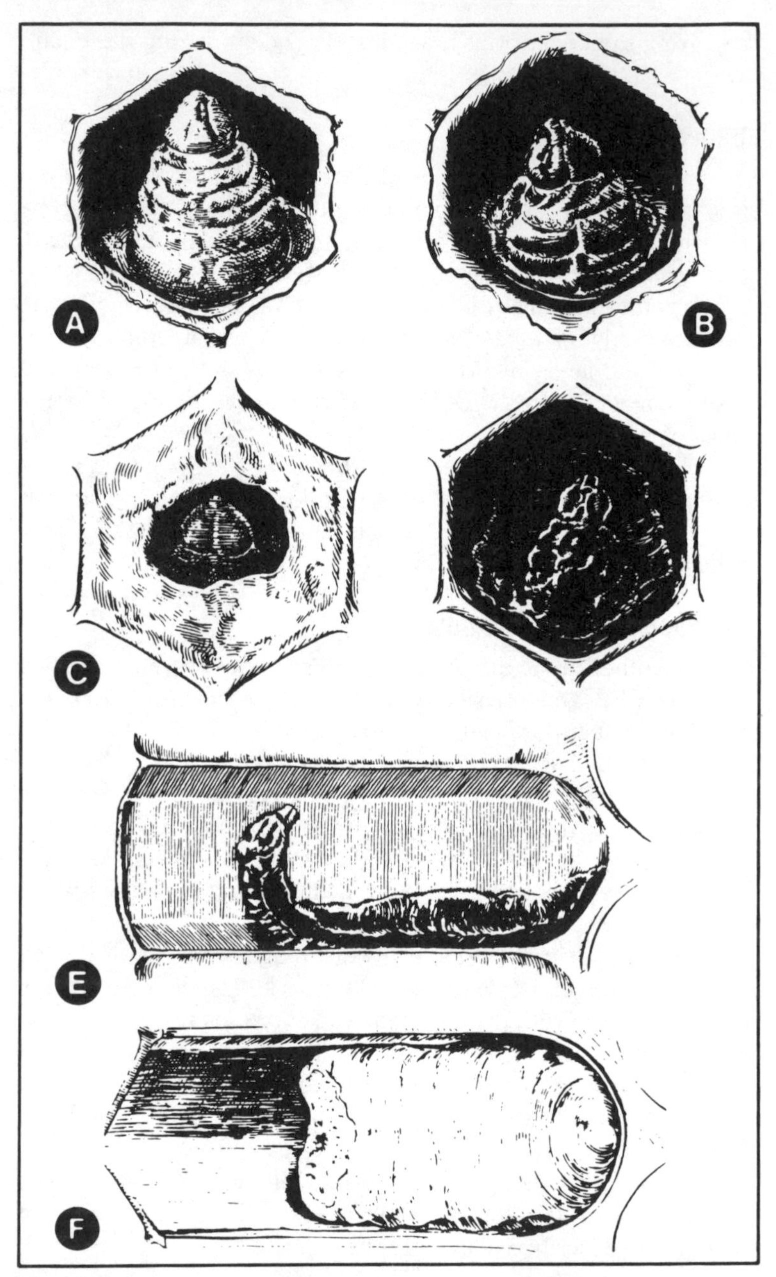

Fig. 7-3. Honeybee larvae killed by Sacbrood as seen in cells: (A-B) larvae in different stages of decomposition; (C) erect head of dead larva showing through opening made by bees in capping; (D-E) views of scale (note how head remains erect); (F) remains of larva, the head has been gnawed away by bees.

Table 7-2 Diseases of the Honeybee.

Symptom	American Foulbrood	European Foulbrood	Sacbrood	Chalk Brood
Appearance of brood comb.	Sealed brood. Discolored, sunken, or punctured cappings.	Unsealed brood. Some sealed brood in advanced cases with discolored, sunken or punctured cappings.	Sealed brood. Scattered cels with punctured cappings, often with two holes.	Sealed and unsealed brood.
Age of dead brood.	Usually older sealed larvae or young pupae. Lying lengthwise in cells.	Usually young unsealed larvae; occasionally older sealed larvae. Typically in coiled stage.	Usually older sealed larvae; occasionally young unsealed larvae. Lengthwise in cells.	Usually older larvae. Lengthwise in cells.
Color of dead brood.	Dull white, becoming light brown, coffee brown to dark brown, or almost black.	Dull white, becoming yellowish white to brown, dark brown, or almost black.	Grayish or straw-colored becoming brown, grayish black, or black; head end darker.	Chalk white. Sometimes mottled with black spots.
Consistency of dead brood.	Soft, becoming sticky to ropy.	Watery; rarely sticky or ropy. Granular.	Watery and granular; tough skin forms a sac.	Pasty.
Odor of dead brood.	Slightly to pronounced putrid odor.	Slightly to penetratingly sour.	None to slightly sour.	Yeastlike, nonobjectionable.
Scale characteristics.	Lies uniformly flat on lower side of cell. Adheres tightly to cell wall. Fine, threadlike tongue of dead pupae may be present. Head lies flat. Black in color.	Usually twisted in cell. Does not adhere tightly to cell wall. Rubbery. Black in color.	Head prominently curled towards center of cell. Does not adhere tightly to cell wall. Rough texture. Brittle. Black in color.	Mummified. Does not adhere to cell wall. Brittle. Usually chalky white in color. Sometimes black fruiting bodies are present.

Reprinted from Agricultural Handbook 335, USDA, rev. 1980.

attacking their digestive systems, the hypopharynegal glands (which produce the brood food) of the nurse bees, and the ovaries of the queens. The infection is often present but does not become serious except under stress, as when the bees are confined for long periods or when involved in manipulations such as moving. Symptoms are not definite nor discernible without a microscopic examination of 400× power of the abdomens or alimentary tracts of infected bees.

The disease is chronic—almost always present—with highest level occurring in the spring and the lowest level occurring in the fall. It cannot be cured but it can be controlled with the use of fumagillin (the trade name is Fumidil-B), sold at beekeeping supply stores. Fumidil-B is given to bees in sugar syrup. The recommended formula is 1½ teaspoons (5 grams) to one gallon of syrup.

Again, do not feed any medication to bees during the nectar flow because it gets into the honey. A good time to dose with Fumidil-B, if nosema is a problem in your area, is in the fall after the last nectar flow. Many beekeepers feel this prevents nosema problems the following spring.

Other adult bee diseases of lesser impact include dysentery virus paralysis and septicemia. To prevent the spread of serious diseases and pests to bees in the United States, the U.S. Department of Agriculture forbids the importation of any live bees from other countries except Canada.

DISEASE ANALYSIS SERVICE

If you feel your bees are suffering from some disease, which you or a knowledgeable person or inspector cannot diagnose, you may send a sample for analysis to: U.S. Department of Agriculture, Science and Education Administration, Bioenvironmental Bee Laboratory, Building 476, BARC-E, Beltsville, MD 20705. Remove a 4-inch square of infected brood comb *without any honey* and take care to leave the comb intact. If the problem is with adult bees, send a sample of 200 sick or recently dead bees. Mail the samples in a strong cardboard box or a foam bubble insulated jiffy sack. Poke in ventilation holes to prevent the contents from molding. Include your name and complete address.

Bees, like animals and man, are not only subject to disease but are also troubled by pests, both insect and animal. The beekeeper needs to keep alert to encroachment by pests before they become a serious problem and demoralize the colony. Pests include wax moths, ants, termites, skunks, and bears.

WAX MOTH

The wax moth is a pest unique to bees because it lives in wax and eats the protein bits of the fecal matter of the larvae, the shed skins, and pollen (Fig. 7-4). In warm weather, left unchecked, it can totally wreck combs in a short time.

Wax moths can create the most damage in stored combs left unprotected and in a weak hive where the colony cannot cover all the frames and kill the larvae before they start tunnelling through the comb.

Two species exist, the greater and the smaller. The greater is about the size of a half dollar; the smaller is about the size of a quarter. Like other insects, it passes through three stages: egg, larva, and adult. The adult female lays large clumps of eggs (but small or nearly invisible to the naked eye) in any crevice or crack within the hive structure, as in a groove of a split frame bottom, between supers, or in any worn hollowed spot. In warmer weather, 75°F to 80°F (24°C to 27°C), eggs hatch in five to eight days; at lower temperatures it can take up to thirty-five days.

When the eggs become larvae, they are white, very small and begin moving toward the wax almost immediately. They eventually work a crisscross of paths through the combs and create a mass of tunnels and webs. In the next stage, the larva spins a cocoon and attaches itself to a solid part of the hive like the frame, side, or inner cover.

The best defense against the wax moth is a strong, healthy colony. Bees will carry out the moths, preventing egg laying and interrupting the cycle of destruction. A beekeeper can help by cleaning up extra burr comb on tops, frames, sides, and bottom board where eggs can be hidden.

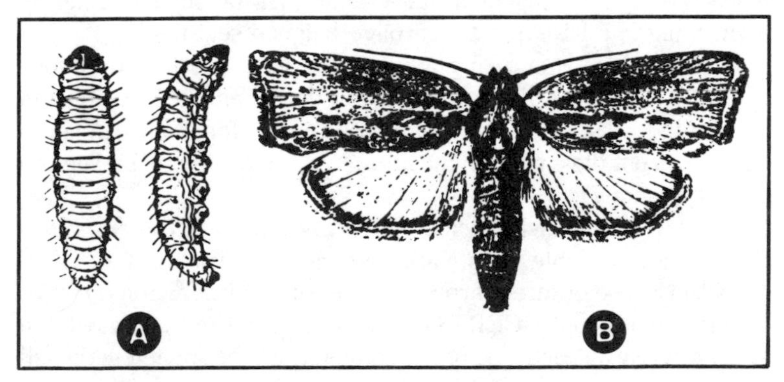

Fig. 7-4. Greater wax moth: (A) larvae and (B) adult.

Wax moths take their greatest toll on stored, used combs. Rarely do they attack new foundation. The simplest way to protect stored combs is to put them in the freezer. At 20°F eggs, larvae, and adults are killed. Seal them inside a plastic bag to keep the honey from dripping. Handle the combs carefully after they are frozen because the wax is brittle and can crack. If you lack space to do this, three products can be used on frames when off the hive. Two are strong chemicals and should be used with caution; the third is a natural biological product developed early in the 1980s.

Paradichlobenzene commonly known as PDB, the chemical used in moth balls, is a white crystalline substance, nonflammable and nonexplosive. If you cannot get PDB from your beekeeping supplier use crystals or flakes from a market or hardware store, be sure they are the type without naptha.

To use PDB, stack frames of comb and place the crystals on a paper plate on top of the frames. Enclose everything in a large plastic garbage bag and seal the bag tightly. Check the bag periodically and replace the PDB when all the crystals have evaporated. Because PDB kills only the adults and larvae, not eggs, keeping the chemical constantly available will kill the larvae that hatch during storage. Supers of frames can be stacked, no more than five high, with PDB on the top and covered with plastic paint drop cloths or tarps.

Another chemical that is very strong and kills the eggs as well as the larvae and adults is *ethylene dibromide* (EDB). It is marketed in liquid form. EDB is carcinogenic and must be used with caution. It can blister your skin and is irritating to nasal passages and lungs. In many states it is necessary to get a permit from your agricultural extension agent to use EDB. Pour the EDB in a shallow dish and place the dish on top of a stack of frames or supers. Enclose everything in a large plastic garbage bag and seal the bag.

Remember when using any chemical to read the directions carefully and then read them again. Follow them step by step. In using either PDB or EDB, air fumigated combs for at least 24 hours before you put them back on the hive. *Never* use either substance on combs of honey.

A new biological pesticide utilizing *bacillus thuriengiensis Berliner* is now available. It is marketed under the trade name, CERTAN and can be ordered through A.I. Root, Dadant & Sons, Inc. or Strauser Bee Supply. CERTAN is mixed with water and used as a spray directly on each side of the combs. It can be applied in the fall before storage or in the spring before returning supers for the honey flow. CERTAN is nontoxic to people, pets, or beneficial insects.

OTHER INSECTS

The other principal insects that pose problems for honeybees are ants and termites.

Various species of ants, namely fire ants, sweet ants, carpenter ants, and most commonly, the Argentine ant will try to gain access to hives. They will build mounds near or under hives and make trails into the entrance seeking droplets of honey or grains of pollen.

The best control is maintaining a clear area around the hive and putting the hive on a stand. During warm weather and into the fall, when ants are storing up food for the winter, get into the habit of taking clippers or pruning shears and a small shovel (army supply trench-type is handy) with you. Keep the weeds trimmed away from, around, and under the hive. Dig up any ant mounds you see. Pour oil into the area where nests are being built and along trails. You can also pour boiling water over the nests.

A very effective, inexpensive control that is not harmful to the bees is placing cans or jars of oil under the legs of the hive stand (Fig. 7-5). One Farm Bureau instructor offers a good suggestion. Get the discarded oil cans from your local service station. Often a layer of oil is left in the bottom of the can; you can collect more cans than you need and pour the leftover oil into the number of cans you need for your hives.

The carpenter ant will actually attack the wood of the bottom boards. Sticky barriers like tanglefoot can be applied to the underside of the hive. Treated bottom boards will also repel carpenter ants.

If ants are found in large numbers and persist in your bee yard, you may have to resort to an insecticide like Malathion or one of the granular powders like Last Bite. *Use with them extreme care*. A spray should be applied at night when the bees are not flying and only on the ground. Do not spray any blooms or water source.

In warmer states like Florida, termites can become a problem as they can build up tunnels as tall as 7 inches to reach the wooden bottom of the hive. Again, a metal hive stand or concrete blocks will help deter their activity. If termites are serious pests in your area, you will have to have the bottom boards treated with a wood preservative such as pentachlorophenol, creosote, or carbolineum. Be sure the material is not toxic to bees!

Other insects that prey on honeybees but are of little conse-

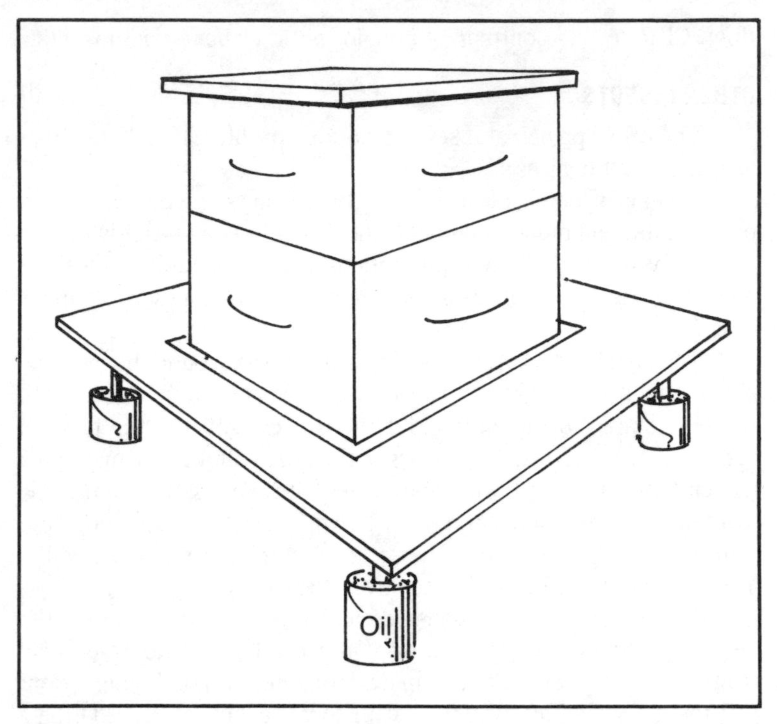

Fig. 7-5. An economical and easy deterrent to ants are oil cans or jars with oil placed under the legs of the hive stand. It works best if the legs are well under the hive stand top to prevent the oil from being diluted with rain.

quence are the dragonfly, praying mantis, some species of wasps, and robber flies.

The Varroa mite, *varroa jocobsoni*, which feeds on the blood of the honeybee adults, larvae, and pupae is a very serious pest in Europe, Asia, and South America (Fig. 7-6). Every effort is being made to stop its introduction into the United States by forbidding the importation of any live bees into the country. Even so, the possibility of the mite eventually being carried across from Mexico on natural swarms does exist.

A major problem in control is that early infestation is extremely difficult to detect. The male mite and the undeveloped larvae live inside the brood cells underneath the cappings and leave no visible evidence of their presence. Additionally, the mite is spread easily from one colony to another as the female adult attaches itself to foraging bees or drones.

Varroa infestation causes adults to be badly deformed and/or results in failure of the pupae to hatch into adults.

Apiologists of several countries are carrying out research efforts to control the Varroa. Today, no chemical has proven totally effective. One problem is that any acaricide—a substance that kills mites—tends also to be toxic to bees.

Low concentrations of Malathion brought about a measure of control in experiments in Greece. Certain fumigants like chlordimeformhydrochloride used in tests in Germany have shown promise, but it appears that a great deal of research must continue if the Varroa is to be conquered.

The side effects on the bees, development of resistance by the mite to chemicals, and the contamination of honey with the acaricide must be dealt with. In the meantime the only sure way to get rid of a varroa infestation and prevent it from spreading is to destroy the colony.

ANIMAL PREDATORS

If you are a suburban beekeeper you may chuckle at the idea of skunks or bears bothering your hives. Still, as suburbia expands into the foothills, canyons, and wooded areas where wild animals make their homes, more animals are being seen in cities and towns. Certainly the probability of animal intrusion into apiaries is greater in an outlying area, but it's not impossible for a city dweller's bees to be invaded by a bear or skunk.

Those lovely little mammals with the black and white coats and the repugnant defense system have another interesting trait. They enjoy a bee feast whenever they can manage it. Their *modus operendi* is night raiding. They scratch on the front of the hive and eat the bees that are aroused. They tend to pick on weaker colonies or NUCs.

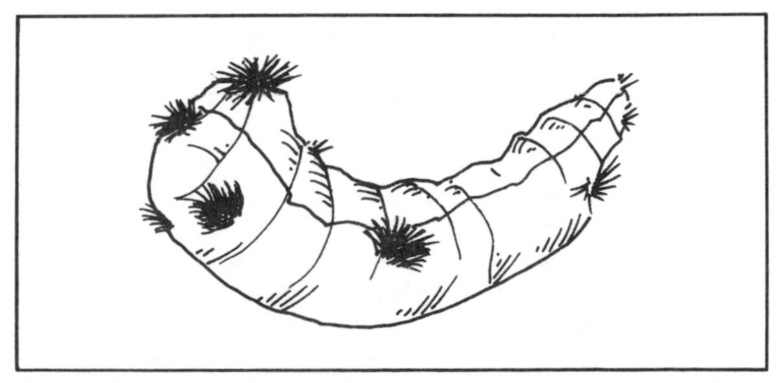

Fig. 7-6. Varroa mite on Honeybee larva.

If you see paw marks or dung tracks near the entrance or scratch marks on the front of the hive, you can suspect a skunk. Call your county agricultural agent or animal control agency before taking action. In many states the skunk is a protected species, and you may need a permit to use poison or a trap.

When a bear discovers a bee yard, it is usually devastating for the colonies. The bear can rip apart a hive, pull out the comb, eat the honey, and completely demoralize the bees in a very short time.

In a survey reported in August, 1981, in the American Bee Journal, a bear problem existed in the 32 states that have viable bear populations, mostly black bears. Five northwestern states have significant grizzly bear populations also. In most states bears are a protected species, and permits to set traps or hunt them must be obtained before trying to catch or kill the bears. If defense of personal property is involved, permits usually will be granted. Sometimes proof, such as a photograph of the bear in action in the apiary, may be necessary.

Where bears are likely to be a problem, beekeepers rig up electric fences. Other methods of control include dogs, poisoning, and chemical repellants. Government wildlife agencies in many areas carry out a bear control program and will assist in the removal of problem bears. However, beekeepers claim that relocating is often not an answer because bears will travel great distances to get back to their home territory. Once a bear develops the habit of taking honey, he will persist. As more and more bee foraging areas give way to weed abatement, housing, and industrial development, beekeepers must seek apiary locations farther and farther away. The bear-bee problem is likely to grow.

PESTICIDES

Possibly the most pervasive problem that beekeepers have is the loss of bees from pesticides. Disease and pest problems can be fairly well handled by the beekeeper and apiarian inspectors. The widespread use of pesticides by everyone from the truck gardener to the giants of agribusiness falls beyond the scope, and certainly the control, of agencies and organizations that support beekeeping.

When a farmer uses a pesticide to control weeds, insects, and/or plant diseases, he is trying to get the highest yield and get his product to market in the most palatable and attractive form. He is probably unaware of the damage his spray can cause honeybees, possibly uninformed of the presence of colonies, and may or may not be amenable to listening to the facts and altering his pesticide program to help the beekeeper.

Beekeepers who take their bees to pollinate large areas like acres of soybeans or miles of almond groves are the most likely to have serious problems with pesticide loss. In 1967, an Indemnity Program was established, administered through the USDA Agricultural Stabilization and Conservation Service to help beekeepers recoup some of the losses of bees killed through pesticides. The program was terminated in 1979, due to lack of funding.

Representatives of various government agencies including USDA Research Service, Animal, and Plant Health Inspection Service; Environmental Protection Agency; Office of Pesticide Program; Office of Environment Quality; and the Cooperative State Research Service have formed a Bee Protection Work Group. The group is responsible for surveying beekeepers on the facts of bee loss and the type of insecticide responsible. It also educates the public on the importance of bees to pollination and thus to food production, and establishes the monetary importance of bees to agriculture to justify ongoing bee protection measures.

As a hobbyist, you need to be knowledgeable of the types of pesticides and their potential toxicity to bees. Be aware of the kinds of foraging situations in which bees can come into contact with pesticides and the safest time and means of application. Basically, you took the responsibility for choosing a place as safe from pesticides as possible, but situations change. The farmer on whose land your bees are located may try a new crop or may be hit with a new insect invader, like the medfly in the citrus groves of California, in 1981. In the suburbs or city, you may get new neighbors or your present neighbors may decide to convert their grass to garden and use sprays they hadn't needed before.

It is your responsibility to inform them of the potential problem to your bees. This can be done in a diplomatic way. You will want to talk it over with the proprietor of the land where your apiary is located or with your neighbor. Give him some written guidelines (such as Table 7-3) that he can refer to when he reaches for his powders and sprays. Ask him to post it near his garden supplies. Many of the materials on the market are injurious to pets, fish, and birds as well as bees. You can point out that prudent use of a pesticide is in the best interest of the family pet or for the colorful cardinals they love as well as your bees. You can emphasize the natural biological controls like bacillus thuriengiensis (the same one

Table 7-3. Optimum Times for Pesticide Applications.

Crop	Time Bees Are in Fields	Best Time to Apply Pesticides
Alfalfa Seed	7 AM to 8 PM	9 PM to 6 AM
Avocado	9 AM to 7 PM	8 PM to 6 AM
Cantaloupe	7 AM to 7 PM	8 PM to 6 AM
Cotton	5 AM to 7:30 PM	8 PM to 4 AM
Ladino Clover	9 AM to 8 PM	9 PM to 6 AM
Milo	6 AM to 12 noon	2 PM to 4 AM
Onions	7 AM to 7 PM	Several days before bloom or after bloom has passed
Peach	6 AM to 5 PM	6 PM to 4 AM
Safflower	6 AM to 2 PM	4 PM to 4 AM
Sweet Corn	5 AM to 1 PM	4 PM to 4 AM

Based on a study by the Cooperative Extension Service, University of California, Riverside.

that kills the wax moth). It is sold as Dipel or Thucide and is harmful only to the caterpillar phase of an insect. Dimilin, a urea compound that inhibits the cuticle formation in insects, kills only larval stages. (See Table 7-4 Group III). And don't forget to remind them of the value of your bees' pollinating service to their melon, berry, or bean crop.

With the advent of microencapsulated types of pesticides, honeybees can be killed not only upon direct contact, but can also be affected by its residual properties. A substance like Pencap-M looks like pollen and is carried by the bee with real pollen into the hive where it is stored on combs and remains toxic for a long time. Brood that feed on the material are killed as well as emerging adults.

Unfortunately for the bees, microencapsulation has a couple distinct advantages to the grower: the toxicity to livestock is reduced over other types and the poison is released slowly and continues to foil the harmful insect over an extended period. Although a written application is required to use these substances and guidelines are provided by the manufacturers, it is still a tricky business to analyze the total picture of potential harm to bees. For example, a question on the manufacturer's guideline sheet is, "Are bees foraging on the plants to be sprayed?" The grower answers, "No, bees don't forage on apples, only on apple blossoms." So he or she sprays away, thinking he is doing no damage to any bees. But your bees are foraging on the weeds blooming in the field adjacent to the apple orchard and many are killed by the drifting spray.

Early each spring it is a wise idea to talk with the person(s) near or on whose property you have placed your bees. Discuss his or her plans for insect, weed, and plant disease control. Give him a copy of the following guidelines developed by the extension service of the University of California, Riverside, through studies conducted over the period 1950 to 1980.

1. For bees, the safest time to apply pesticides is during the night or early morning hours. For specific crops and bee foraging patterns, see Table 7-3. Treating crops with pesticides when bees are in the field is the most hazardous time, and treatments in hot weather when bees are clustering on the outside of hives may also cause large bee losses.
2. When you treat a nonblooming field, check adjoining areas for blooming plants like weeds and wildflowers that honeybees visit.
3. Sprays are safer than dusts.
4. Emulsifiable or water soluble concentrate formulations are usually safer than wettable powder mixes.
5. Fine sprays are less toxic than course sprays. Diluted sprays are safer than full strength sprays.
6. Granular-type materials are usually safest over all other types.
7. Ground applications are safer than aerial applications.
8. Combinations of pesticides are less hazardous than the same pesticides each used separately.
9. Specific pesticides are better than a high dosage of a broad spectrum pesticide.
10. Spot treatments are better than broadcasting materials over large areas.
11. Repeated applications increase the chance for damage to bees.

You should also make a copy of Table 7-4, showing the degree of danger of various substances, to honeybees, for anyone near your bees or near your bees' foraging area.

Fortunately, new equipment design and techniques for applying pesticides, herbicides, and other potentially dangerous materials to bees allows for a maximum spray with minimum drift. Another promising development in aerial spraying is the practice of "fly-ins" or test runs using a dye or chemical reagent. Analysis then shows the proportion of spray on target and the consistency of the distribution of droplets across the path. If there is too much drift, adjustments to the nozzles, the position of the spray boom, and other mechanics are altered and another test run is made.

Table 7-4. Relative Toxicity of Pesticides to Honeybees Determined by Laboratory and Field Tests.

GROUP I—highly toxic: Severe losses may be expected if used when bees are present at treatment time or within a day thereafter, except where noted to the contrary.

Pesticide (trade name and/or common name)

aldrin[2]
Ambush®[2,18], permethrin
arsenicals [1,2]
Avermectin®[17]
Azodrin®[1,2], monocrotophos
Baygon®[2], propoxur
Baytex®[2], fenthion
Bidrin®[1,2], dicrotophos
Bux®, bufencarb
carbosulfan[2], FMC-35001
Cygon®[2], dimethoate
Cythion®[2,4], malathion
Dasanit®[5], fensulfothion
DDVP®[2], dichlorvos
Dibrom®[2,3], naled
Decis®[2], decamethrin
De-Fend®[2], dimethoate
diazinon[2], Spectracide®
dieldrin[1,2]
Dimecron®[2], phosphamidon
Dursban®[2], chlorpyrifos
Ekamet®, etrimfos
EPN[1,2]
Ethyl Guthion®, azinphos-ethyl
Famophos®, famphur
Ficam®, bendiocarb
Folithion®, fenitrothion
Furadan®[2,5], carbofuran
Gardona®[1,2], stirofos
Guthion®[1,2], azinphos-methyl
heptachlor[1,2]
Imidan®[2], phosmet
Lannate®[2], methomyl
Lorsban®, chlorpyrifos
malathion[2,4]
Matacil®, aminocarb
Mesurol®, methiocarb
methyl parathion[1,2,11,12]
Monitor®[2], methamidophos
Nemacur®[5], fenamiphos
Nudrin®[2], methomyl
Orthene®[2], acephate
parathion[1,2]
Pay-Off®
Phosdrin®[1,2,3], mevinphos
phosphamidon[2], Dimecron®
Pounce®[2,18], permethrin
Pydrin®[2], fenvalerate
resmethrin, Synthrin®
Sevin®[2], carbaryl
Spectracide®[2], diazinon
Sumithion®, fenitrothion
Sumithrin®, *d*-phenothrin
Supracide®[2], methidathion
Tamaron®[2], methamidophos
Temik®[1,2,5,7], aldicarb
tepp[1,2,3]
Vapona®[2], dichlorvos

GROUP II—moderately toxic: Can be used around bees if dosage, timing, and method of application are correct, but should not be applied directly on bees in the field or at the colonies

Insecticide (trade name and/or common name)

Abate®[2], temephos
Agritox®, trichloronate
Bolstar®, sulprophos
Carzol®[2], formetanate hydrochloride
chlordane[2]
Ciodrin® crotoxyphos
Counter®, terbufos
Croneton®, ethiofencarb
Curacron®, profenofos
DDT[1,2,10]
Di-Syston®[1,2,6,18], disulfoton
Dyfonate®, fonofos
endrin[1,2]
Korlan®, ronnel
Larvin®[2], thiodicarb
Metasystox-R®[2], oxydemeton-methyl
Mocap®, ethoprop
Perthane®, ethylan
Pyramat®
Sevin® 4-Oil[2], carbaryl
Sevimol®[2], carbaryl
Systox®[1,2,18], demeton
Thimet®[1,2,6], phorate
Thiodan®[2], endosulfan
Trithion®[2], carbophenothion
Vydate®[2], oxamyl
Zolone®, phosalone

GROUP III—relatively nontoxic: Can be used around bees with minimum injury.

Insecticides and Acaracides (trade name and/or common name)

Acaraben®, chlorobenzilate
allethrin, Pynamin®
Altosid®[17], methoprene
Baam®, amitraz
Bacillus thuringiensis[17], Bactur®, Bactospeine®, Bakthane®, Dipel®, Thuricide®

Insecticides and Acaracides (trade name and/or common name)

Birlane®, chlorfenvinphos
Comite®, propargite
cryolite[2], Kryocide®
Delnav®, dioxathion
Dessin®, dinobuton
Dimilin®[17], diflubenzuron
Dylox®[2], trichlorfon
ethion
Fundal®, chlordimeform
Galecron®, chlordimeform
Heliothis polyhedrosis virus
Kelthane®[1], dicofol
Mavrik®[2], fluvalinate
methoxychlor[2], Marlate®
Mitac®, amitraz
Morestan®, oxythioquinox
Morocide®, binapacryl
Murvesco®, fenson
nicotine[2]
Omite®, propargite
Pentac®, dienochlor
Pirimor®[2], pirimicarb
Plictran®[2], cyhexatin
pyrethrum (natural)
rotenone[2]
sabadill[2]
Sayfos®, menazon
Sevin®, SL[2], carbaryl
Sevin® XLR[2], carbaryl
Smite®, sodium azide
Tedion®, tetradifon
Tetram®
Tokuthion®, prothiophos
Torak®, dialifor
toxaphene[1,2]
Zardex®. cycloprate

Fungicides (trade name and/or common name)

Afugan®[2], pyrazophos
Arasan®, thiram
Bayleton®, triadimefon
Benlate®, benomyl
Bordeaux mixture[2]
Bravo®, chlorothalonil
captan[11]
copper oxychloride sulfate
copper 8-quinolinolate
copper sulfate
Cuprex®, dodine
cupric oxide
cupric hydroxide, Kocide®
Delan®, dithianon
Dessin®, dinobuton
Difolatan®, captafol

Fungicides (trade name and/or common name)

Dithane® D-14, nabam
Dithane® M-22, maneb
Dithane® M-45, manzeb
Dithane® Z-78, zineb
Du-Ter®, fentin hydroxide
Dyrene®, anilazine
ferbam
glyodin
Hinosan®, edifenphos
Indar®, butrizol
Karathane®, dinocap
Lesan®, fenaminosulf
Morestan®, oxythioquinox
Morocide®, binapacryl
Mylone®, dazomet
Phaltan®, folpet
Plantvax®, oxycarboxin
Polyram®, metiram
Ridomil®
Sisthane®, fenapanil
Smite®, sodium azide
sulfur[2]
thiram, Thylate®
thyfural
Vitavax®, carboxin
ziram, Zerlate®

Herbicides, Defoliants, and Desiccants (trade name and/or common name)

AAtrex®, atrazine
alachlor
Alanap®, naptalam
Alopex®, clofop-isobutyl
Amex® 820, butralin
Amiben®, chloramben
amitrole
Ammate®l, AMS
Aquathol K®, endothall, dipotassium
Avenge®, difenzoquat
Balan®, benefin
Banvel®, dicamba
Basagran®, bentazon
Basalin®, fluchloralin
Betanal®, phenmedipham
Betanex®, desmedipham
Bladex®, cyanazine
Blazer®, acifluorfen
butachlor
butam
cacodylic acid[1]
Cambilene®[1], 2,3,6-TBA
Caparol®, prometryn
Casoron®, dichlobenil
Chloro IPC®, chlorpropham
Cotoran®, fluometuron
2,4-D[1,2]

Herbicides, Defoliants, and Desiccants (trade name and/or common names)

DEF®[8]
Desiccant L-10®[1,9], arsenic acid
Devrinol®, napromamide
dichlorprop[1], 2,4-DP
dinoseb[9], dinitrobutylphenol
diquat[8,9]
Dual®, metolachlor
endothall, sodium salt, Accelerate®
Eptam®, EPTC
Eradicane®, EPTC + safener
Evik®, ametryn
Evital®, norflurazon
Folex®[1,8], merphos
Garlon®, triclopyr
Goal®, oxyfluorfen
Hoelon®, diclofop-methyl
Hydrothol 191®, endothall
monopotassium salt
Hyvar®, bromacil
Igran®, terbutryn
IPC®, propham
Karmex®, diuron
Kerb®, pronamide
Lasso®, alachlor
Lorox®, linuron
Maloran®, chlorbromuron
MCPA[1]
Methar®[1], DSMA
Milogard®, propazine
Modown®, bifenox
MSMA[1]
Mylone®, dazomet
Nortron®, ethofumesate
Paarlan®, isopropalin
paraquat[1,9]
Planavin®, nitralin
Pramitol®, prometon
Preforan®, fluorodifen
Princep®, simazine
Probe®, methazole
Prowl®, pendimethalin
Ramrod®, propachlor
Randox®, CDAA
Ronstar®, oxydiazon
Roundup®, glyphosate
Sancap®, dipropetryn
Sencor®, metribuzin
silvex[1], 2,4,5-TP
Sinbar®, terbacil
Smite®, sodium azide
Surflan®, oryzalin
Sutan® +, butylate
2,4,5-T[1,2]
Telvar®, monuron
Tenoran®, chloroxuron
TOK®, nitrofen
Tolban®, profluralin
Tordon®, picloram
Treflan®, trifluralin
Turf Herbicide®, endothall, disodium
Vegadex®, CDEC
Zorial®, norflurazon

Nematicides and Miscellaneous (trade name and/or common name)

endothall[13]
Exhalt® 800[14]
gibberellic acid[13]
Mocap®[5], ethoprop
Mylone®[5], dazomet
N-Serve®[15], nitrapyrin
Polaris®[16], glyphosine
Smite®[5], sodium azide
Sustar®[13,16]

Continued on page 130.

Table 7-4. Continued from page 129.

Number-keyed Notes on Pesticide Uses

1. California state regulations require permits for most uses of these chemicals, also for 2,4-D and 2,4,5-T as herbicides but not as sprays on citrus.
2. Laboratory- and field-tested mainly on alfalfa, citrus, cotton, ladino clover, milo and sweet corn; all other chemicals were laboratory-tested only.
3. Dibrom®, Phosdrin®, and tepp have such short residual activity that they kill only bees contacted at treatment time or shortly thereafter. Usually safe to use when bees are not in flight; not safe to use around colonies.
4. Malathion has been applied on thousands of acres of alfalfa in bloom without serious loss of bees. However, occasional heavy losses have occurred, particularly under high temperature conditions. If applied to alfalfa in bloom, it should be only as a spray, and application should be made during the night or early in the morning when bees are not foraging in the field. Undiluted technical malathion spray (ULV) should not be used around bees.
5. Nematicide.
6. Di-Syston® (disulfoton) and other systemic pesticides used as seed treatments have not caused bee losses.
7. Temik® (aldicarb), although highly toxic to bees as a contact poison, is used only in granular form, and extensive field usage has not caused bee losses.
8. Defoliant.
9. Desiccant.
10. DDT has been withdrawn for most uses in the U.S.A.
11. Field dosages have caused brood damage.
12. The microencapsulated formulation of methyl parathion, known as Penncap-M®, is highly toxic to foraging bees, young hive bees, and brood. Overall, it is 13 times more hazardous to honey bees than the EC (emulsifiable concentrate) formulation. Penncap-M® is too hazardous to be applied to any area at any time when bees are present in the field or within one mile of the area to be treated.
13. Plant growth regulator.
14. Sticker/extender.
15. Nitrification inhibitor.
16. Chemical ripener.
17. Insect growth regulator.
18. Honey bee repellent.

Based on tests conducted in California, 1950 through 1980. (Reprinted from Leaflet 2883 of the Division of Agricultural Sciences, University of California, written by E.L. Atkins, D. Kellum and K.W. Atkins.)

Studies are being conducted to check out bee repellents to see if their use in sprays will keep the bees from foraging for a day or two among the treated plants. Some of the materials used in the experiments are permethrin and synthetic pyrethoroids, BAY-FCR-1272, and Mavrik.

If all your best BPR (Beekeeping Public Relations) does not deter someone from applying a pesticide in a way and time that is harmful to your bees, at least get him to let you know before he begins spraying so you can cover the hives. Tarps of burlap or dark plastic can be put over your colonies in a tent fashion. Burlap can be kept over hives for two or more days if it is kept damp. Gunny sacks, thoroughly soaked in water for a few hours, can be draped over hive entrances. The sacks do not prevent bees from flying but disorients foragers to the point of cutting their flights to a minimum to nearby pesticide-treated fields.

Chapter 8

Honey Harvesting

As the supers begin to fill up you will want to gather your honey extracting equipment and decide where you will extract. Commercial operators have a separate large building with a great deal of high-speed, automated equipment. Side-liners who have up to 100 colonies usually have a separate shed or outbuilding that they use as their "honey house."

CHOOSING A PLACE TO EXTRACT

Most hobbyists and beginners deal with 30 to 100 pounds of honey at a time. You may use some part of your house. The site for extracting can be an area of the basement (carrying heavy supers down steps may discourage this idea), a corner of the garage, a screened-in porch, or the kitchen. The area you choose should be secure against insects, especially bees, free of dust, and relatively clean. An open patio or porch is not a wise choice if bees have access to it, which they definitely will if your colonies are located on your property.

An extracting place needs space for an uncapping container, a small two-to-four-frame extractor, a 5-gallon bucket, and a countertop, table, or stand to put these pieces of equipment on. You will also need a *grounded* electrical outlet. Ideally, there should be hot water available to facilitate the clean up of drips of honey and sticky hands as you work. If you don't have plumbing in your extracting area, you can use a bucket, a vacuum bottle, or air pot of hot water that can be replenished. It is best if the extracting site has a cement, linoleum, or tile floor to facilitate cleanup. A piece of heavy duty plastic can be used to protect a carpeted or wooden floor.

EQUIPMENT AND TOOLS

The equipment and tools you will need are:

- An uncapping knife (Fig. 8-1) and a table or cooking fork
- An uncapping tank—a container with a screen covering or grid
- An extractor, hand- or power-driven
- Container for catching honey from the faucet of the extractor
- Filtering material over the above container
- Tables, counters, or stools on which to place all equipment
- Jars or bottles, glass or plastic, for the strained honey

You can make use of kitchen containers and utensils you have on hand for extracting a small amount of honey and to save on costs. Taking the time and making a modest expenditure to construct more efficient equipment pays off in the long run. Different options will be suggested and you can choose what suits you best.

The first tool you will need is an uncapping knife. Heated with steam, hot water, or electricity, the knife is used to slice off the top of the cappings on a frame of honey (Fig. 8-2). A fork is handy for scraping off the wax in low, uncapped spots when you bring the knife across the frame (Figs. 8-3, 8-4, and 8-5).

A deep pan, bucket, or box with a screen or grid is set under the frame to catch the cut off cappings and the honey that drips out as you are slicing. To begin with, for a small amount of honey, you can use a large broiling pan (Fig. 8-6). Most of the cappings stay on top of the perforated cover. To keep a clear working space, you must lift off the cut cappings quite often. Put them in a colander over a deep pot or mixing bowl to drain them more completely. The honey that drips from the cappings will need further straining to produce a nice clear product.

Fig. 8-1. Plain uncapping knife to be used with hot water. Usually two are kept going, one in hot water, one in uncapping. (Courtesy, Pierce Manufacturing and Bee Supplies.)

Fig. 8-2. An electric uncapping knife. (Courtesy, Pierce Manufacturing and Bee Supplies.)

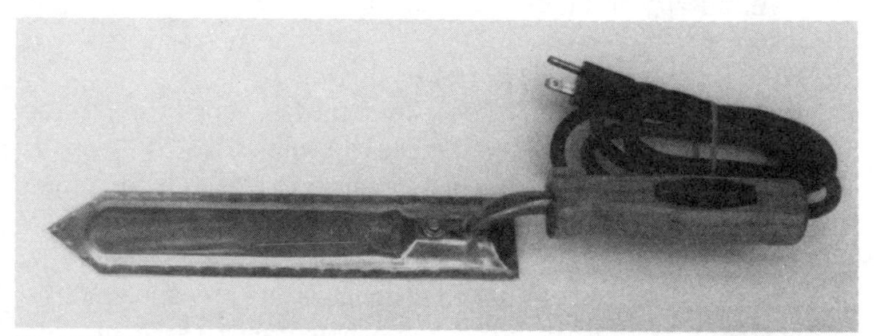

Fig. 8-3. Electric uncapping knife with thermostat. (Courtesy, Pierce Manufacturing and Bee Supplies.)

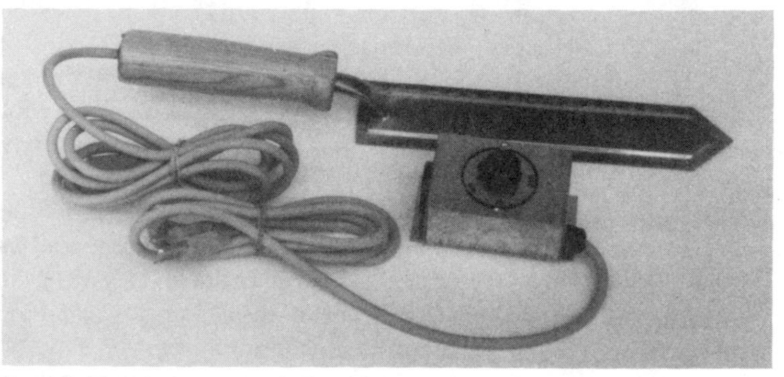

Fig. 8-4. Electric uncapping knife with control box. (Courtesy, Pierce Manufacturing and Bee Supplies.)

Fig. 8-5. Uncapping knife for use with a steam generating tank, where no electricity is available. Hoses at the base of knife attach to hoses on generator. (Courtesy, Pierce Manufacturing and Bee Supplies.)

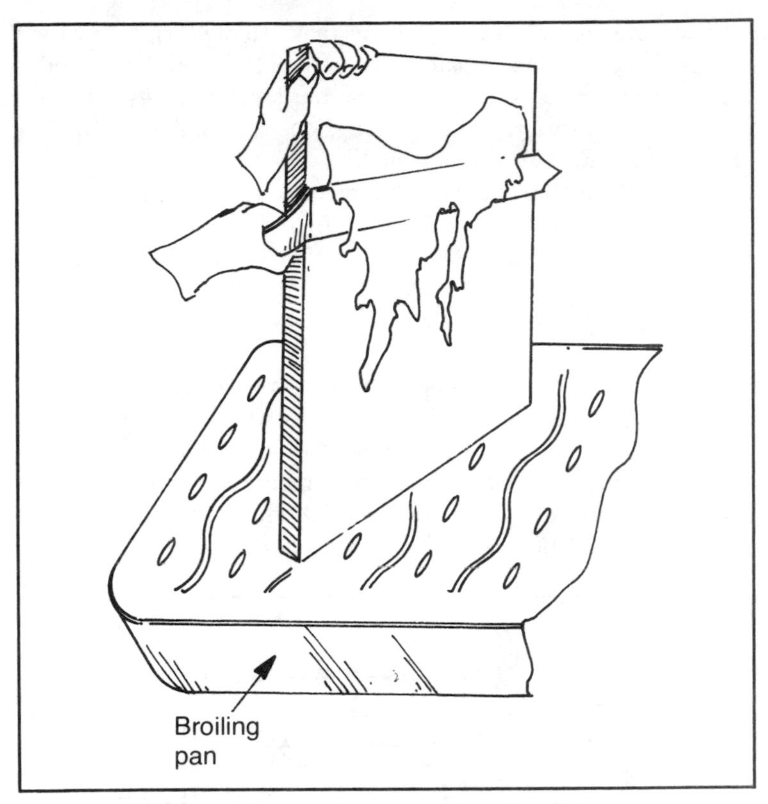

Fig. 8-6. A broiling pan may be used as an uncapping "tank."

The cappings are valuable. They can be rendered into blocks of wax to sell or turned in to your supplier for credit on new foundation or other beekeeping supplies. See Rendering Wax in Chapter 12. Cappings can be put in clean half-gallon milk cartons, sealed with tape or stapled shut. Store them in the freezer or pantry until you have collected a batch to render.

You can put together an uncapping tank rather cheaply and simply with the use of a tub or two supers, wooden cross bars, and screening. See Chapter 13 for details and illustrations.

Extractor

An extractor is a stainless steel or plastic tank fitted with baskets or wire frames into which the uncapped combs are placed. A shaft runs through the center with arms connected to the baskets on the inside and fitted with gears and a handle on the top. As the handle is turned, centrifugal force throws the honey out from the spinning frames to the sides of the tank. Honey drips down and collects at the bottom. A gate valve or simple faucet is attached to the side of the tank (Fig. 8-7). When the level of honey rises to a point above the gate valve, the valve is opened and honey flows out through a strainer into a container.

Most extractors in the beginner's price range have frames that must be lifted out and turned around by hand to extract the other side. Some hold two frames; others hold four frames. Larger, more expensive machines have a reversible mechanism that allows the frames to be flipped over with a lever without opening the lid of the extractor.

For the beginner it is best to rent an extractor from a local supplier or beekeeper. Many beekeepers whose operations have increased have purchased larger more efficient equipment. They keep their smaller extractors and rent them out. The cost ranges from $4 per day to $20 per weekend. Often an uncapping knife is included or available for an additional $2 or $3.

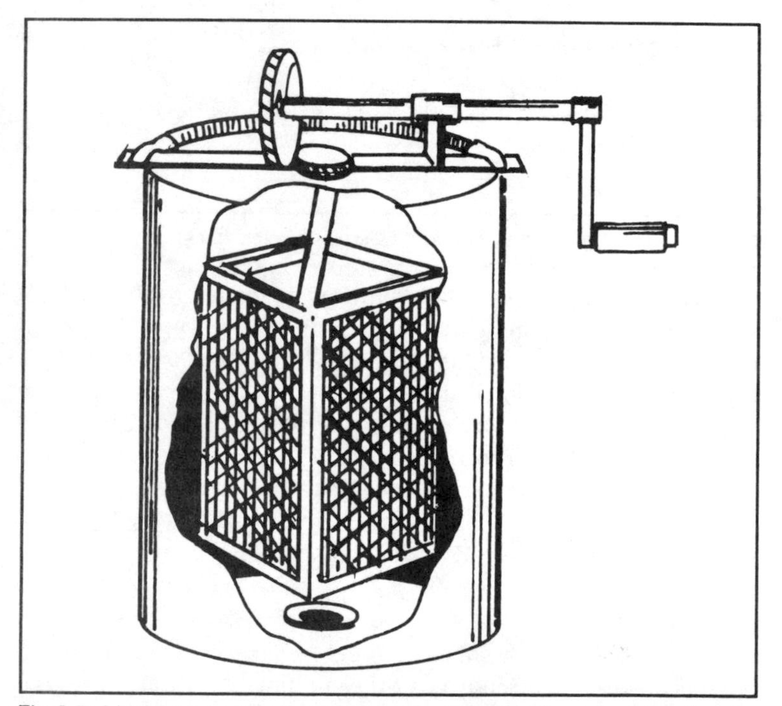

Fig. 8-7. A hand-powered extractor. Uncapped frames are put down into the wire baskets and spun by turning the handle. Then the frames are reversed to spin out the other side. Honey pours out into straining tanks through the gate valve at the bottom.

Smaller extractors do not come with legs or a stand and must be bolted to a work surface or held in place with your knee and foot to prevent rocking and sliding as you turn the handle. A bench, stool, or small sturdy table can be used. A heavy duty utility cart is very convenient. Supplies such as knife and jars can be kept on the shelves below, the extractor bolted to the top, and the whole thing wheeled out of the way between honey harvests.

If and when you decide to buy your own extractor, consider buying the hand-operated type for economy and motorizing it later with an industrial-quality, variable speed drill. The smallest power extractor costs $150 to $170—more than double that of a junior, bench, two-frame-hand-operated model. A variable speed drill will cost $75 to $100.

Containers and Strainers

A good container for straining honey is a heavy-duty polyurethane plastic bucket, equipped with airtight lids. Restaurants and fast food places receive soft drink powders in them, and bakeries get them packed with frozen fruit for pie. They may be available free for the asking, but with recycling becoming increasingly popular, it is more likely you will be charged about $2 to $5 depending on the size of the bucket. They come in 2-, 4-, or 5-gallon sizes. For ease in handling, two 2-gallon buckets are best, but require twice the work and expense to modify them into a straining tank. A gallon of honey weighs 12 pounds. Therefore, a 5-gallon container only two-thirds full will weigh 40 pounds to hoist up to a stand or counter so that you can fill your jars.

The best material for straining honey is a closely woven fine mesh nylon or polyester cloth, the type often used for the linings in clothing. It is available at fabric stores. You may also use 1- or 5-gallon paint straining bags available at hardware or paint stores. They wear very well, are easy to clean, and can be used again and again. Wire mesh strainers are available from bee supply outlets but at a greater cost than the cloth. For directions and illustrations to convert a bucket to a straining tank, see Chapter 13.

It is possible to use deep pots and mixing bowls as containers and to strain honey through clean discarded panty hose (Fig. 8-8). The panty part should be free of holes and runs. Fit it over the top of the pot or bowl, or around the whole thing, depending on size. Secure the panty hose as tight as possible by winding the legs around the sides and tie it in place.

There are problems with using panty hose. The mesh of the

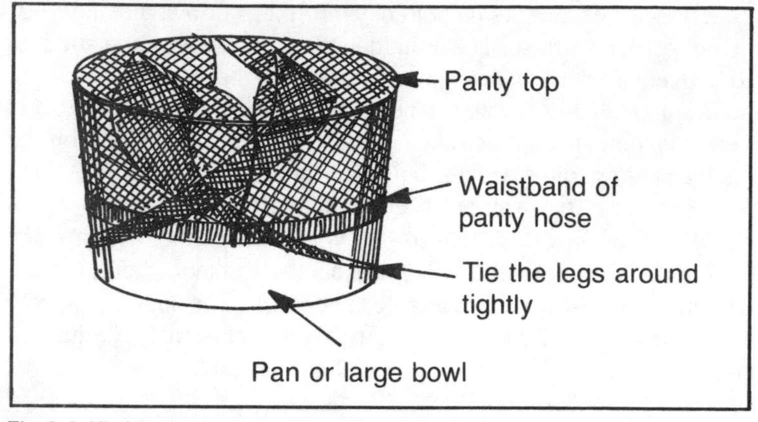

Fig. 8-8. Kitchen equipment can be used until better equipment is put together or purchased. A straining unit may be assembled from a deep bowl or pot with panty hose stretched over the top and tied on tightly.

hose is not as fine as the nylon-type strainer mentioned above, and you will not get as clear honey. Also, the panty hose tends to sag as the tied legs stretch. You have to be careful that the bottom of a hose strainer with the wax and residue on it does not sag into the surface of the strained honey. It is best to remove the hose carefully when the container is about two-thirds full. Then pour the honey through a funnel into jars.

If you are going to use most of the honey yourself or give it to family, friends, and neighbors, then use sparkling clean peanut butter, mayonnaise, and other similar jars and bottles. The wide mouths are easier to fill without a funnel. The narrow mouths are harder to fill but easier to manage when pouring honey into dripless spout servers or squeeze bottles.

It is not necessary to sterilize jars or plastic containers as you must with home preserving and canning. Honey is antibacterial and is not a medium for the growth of microorganisms. Jars that have been cleaned in the dishwasher or washed by hand rinsed in hot water, and air dried are perfectly safe for storing honey as long as they have tight-fitting lids.

If you are going to sell honey, you must have standard size new containers, available from honey suppliers. See Chapter 10 for more marketing information.

Cleanup will be easier if you put something on the floor, particularly if you are using your kitchen. Industrial weight (3 mil) plastic sheeting works well. It is available in a continuous roll and can be cut to fit your area. Afterward you can discard it. You can also use an old shower curtain cut to fit your space. Rather than have to scrub cabinets or table work surfaces—the honey isn't so bad but the little bits of wax and propolis have to be scraped off—lay down old beach towels under your supers or containers of frames. Just throw the towels in the washer when you're finished.

Newspapers are unsuitable. Honey spilled on newspapers will stick to objects placed on the paper. When you lift up the super, up comes the paper. The same goes for walking around on newspapers. Step in a sticky spot and the paper comes up when you move your foot.

Another good idea to save your carpets or floors in the rest of the house is to wear slip-on sandals or house shoes for easy removal when you want to leave the honey extracting room.

PROCESSING HONEY

From the time honey is removed from the hive throughout the extracting process and while in storage, it must be treated with care. Honey is hydroscopic; it absorbs moisture from the air. Containers of honey waiting to be strained or bottled should be covered.

The best-quality honey has no more than 17 percent moisture. Honey having a moisture content of over 17 percent may ferment; honey with over 19 percent moisture *will* ferment. The moisture content of honey produced in your area is related to the humidity. Summer honeys in Louisiana, where it is hot and humid, often ferment in the comb and cannot be harvested for human use.

The only positive way to measure moisture content is with a refractometer, an expensive piece of equipment not readily available. You can contact your closest agency of the United States Department of Agriculture for the address of the Agricultural Marketing Service Inspection Service nearest you. Then take or send a sample of your honey for grading. This includes a test for percent of moisture.

You can check with your apiarian inspector or agricultural extension agent, who will probably have a good idea of the average moisture content of honeys during major nectar flows in your area. If moisture content is too high, you may have to circulate warm air over your frames before extracting. One idea is to place supers on a floor heating outlet. Another possibility is to use a home dehumidifier with the supers or frames stacked in a small closed room.

With a few frames you can rig up a hair dryer on low setting so that air blows across the frames.

The beekeeper is sitting on the horns of a dilemma as far as heating honey is concerned. To prevent fermentation and deter crystallization, some experts unequivocally recommend heating honey to 140° to 145°F for 22 to 30 minutes. Heating at that temperature weakens or destroys the enzymes. These may be very meaningful to customers who buy from a beekeeper and not in the market to obtain as natural and nutritious a product as possible (Fig. 8-9).

Some heating is necessary to facilitate straining, but do not use a high temperature and do not heat the honey for very long. Honey will liquefy easily in about five minutes at 86 to 100°F. The buckets or other containers should never be placed over direct heat. Set them in tubs or pots of warm water or in a very low temperature oven. With a gas oven, the pilot light often provides enough heat to liquefy honey. An electric oven may not have a low enough setting so you may have to turn on the oven for a few minutes; then turn it off! (You will probably have to remove a shelf or two for the containers to fit.)

A microwave oven can be used on high for 30 seconds. Use only glass containers.

A warming unit can also be constructed from an old refrigerator if the gaskets on the doors are still in reasonably good condition. See Chapter 13 for details.

If you have a lot of honey to warm for extracting, you can heat whole supers of frames under a light bulb or with an industrial light clamped to the side of the super.

The proper storage of honey is very important to preserve its freshness, taste, and color and to prevent fermentation. If you

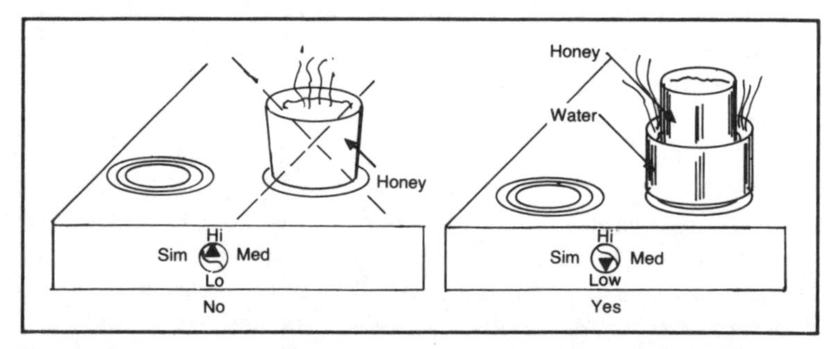

Fig. 8-9. If honey has granulated or is too thick to be strained, it can be heated in a pan of hot water. Never heat it over direct heat, and always use a low setting.

choose not to pasteurize the honey as do most hobbyists, the best temperature for storage is 50°F. In many areas, honey can be stored over winter in an unheated shed, garage, or section of the basement. Once the temperatures warm up, the honey is immediately subject to fermentation and a new storage area must be found. As storage temperatures rise above 50°F, the honey will tend to granulate. This will detract from its appearance and salability. You can always feed it back to the bees assuming it was taken from a healthy colony.

A beekeeper can test storage effects of honey by putting a sample in the freezer over the period of time that the bulk of honey is stored elsewhere. At the end of three or six months of storage, take out the sample. After warming it to room temperature, compare the color and taste against that of the regularly stored honey. If you have enough space in your freezer, this is the ideal way to store all the excess honey you can't use or sell soon after extracting. Freezing does not alter flavor, color, or consistency after thawing.

Strangely, refrigerator temperatures, of 40°F will cause honey to granulate. Serving pitchers or pots should be kept in a cool dark place to keep the honey tasty and retain its best color, but they should not be refrigerated. In most families, honey pots and honey bears have to be refilled long before there is any problem with color or flavor change because of storage.

REMOVING THE HONEY FROM THE HIVE

Your extracting place is organized and your equipment purchased, borrowed, built, rented, or reserved. Now you must go to the bee yard, remove the honey, and get it home with as few bees (or ideally no bees), as possible.

Honey should not be pulled off until it is ripe. This means most or at least three quarters of each side of the frame is capped. Unripe honey can sour and ferment and often contains too much moisture to qualify as salable honey. Honey with more than 17 percent moisture ferments easily even after packing into jars and storing.

You can test the ripeness of your honey by turning the frame over horizontally. If the nectar drips out, it is not ready; if it stays put, it is ready to take. Unripe honey is more likely to be found while the nectar flow is still on, in very humid areas, or during periods of humid weather when the bees have a harder time drawing out the excess moisture from the nectar.

There are four ways to get the bees out of the way to harvest the honey:

- Shake and brush
- Bee escape
- Chemicals
- A blower

The shake and brush technique is rather slow and takes patience, as do many procedures with bees, but it requires no extra expenditure for equipment and can be done in one visit (Fig. 8-10). It is most helpful to have two people working as partners for this method. After smoking the supers well, one person pulls the frames and dislodges the majority of the bees with two or three vigorous shakes at the entrance. He then hands the frame to the partner, who brushes off the remaining bees. The partner then carries the frame some distance away where an empty super has been placed. When brushing, check the corners and any depressions or holes in the comb; bees are notorious for hiding in those spots. Pop the beeless frame into the super, cover it with an extra hive lid, inner cover, a sheet of plywood, or heavy duty plastic sheet, and return for the next frame.

A bee escape is a gadget that permits bees to leave the super but not return because of a special spring mechanism. A bee escape is designed to fit the oblong opening in an inner cover. If you are not using an inner cover or have a flat or migratory top, you will have to make or buy one along with the bee escape.

A bee escape is put on late in the day. It is most effective when the evenings are cool enough for the bees to move down into the brood chamber at night to warm the brood. Under ideal conditions, bees will move down from the honey super in 24 hours. But it *can* take several days.

A couple of precautions to know about using a bee escape. Be sure that the super being vacated by the bees is sealed tight with no possible entry for robber bees. You can use masking tape to cover any chinks or holes in the wood. Do not leave the escape on during hot weather because without the bees to ventilate them the combs can melt. A ventilated bee escape is available for use in hot weather with two escapes and a screen arrangement to allow the bees to cool the frames without reentering the super. The board with the bee escape is placed beneath the super to be removed, with the center hole of the escape up.

Two chemicals have been approved for use in driving bees from honey supers: butyric anhydride, sold under the trade name Bee-Go, and benzaldehyde. Butyric anhydride has a putrifying odor

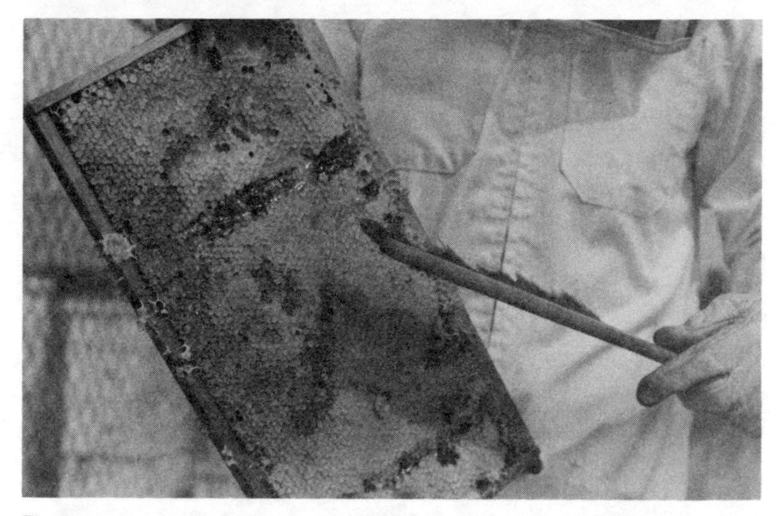

Fig. 8-10. A simple but slow way to remove honey from the hive: shake the bees from the frames and brush off any remaining bees.

and is repungnant to humans as well as bees. Benzaldehyde smells like bitter almonds. The chemicals are applied on a *fume board*, a heavy framed lid of thick wood or wood lined with metal to slow evaporation of the chemical by the sun. A pad of flannel or similar absorbent material fits inside.

To use a chemical repellent, smoke the bees down well. Sprinkle the substance on the pad and put the lid on. Bees will vacate the super in a few minutes. As with any strong substance, use the amount specified and carefully follow the directions for mixing and applying!

Although heavy duty special bee blowers are available from suppliers, the expense (around $300) pretty well precludes their purchase by a hobbyist. Blowing bees out is a fast safe method and may be accomplished in any weather suitable for working bees. Beekeepers can use a tank-type vacuum cleaner with the hose switched to the opposite end or an air compressor with a crevice tool attachment, hooked up to a gasoline engine or a power source.

To use a blower, put yourself and the equipment on the side of, but close to the front of the hive, out of the way of returning field bees. Set up a stand of bricks, cement blocks, or a couple saw horses where there will be an opening below the super. Set the super up on this stand and blow the bees out toward the entrance of the hive. Usually very few bees are harmed, and they are back in the hive working normally in a short while.

With any system of removing bees from honey supers, the supers should be covered quickly and tightly as soon as they are off the hive to prevent robbing. They can be placed on an extra bottom board or any clean surface up on a wheelbarrow, garden utility cart, or wooden pallet on a hand truck to facilitate moving. If you can park close to your hives, you can set them on a truck bed or in the trunk immediately upon removing.

Chapter 9

Honey

The United States Department of Agriculture defines honey as, "An aromatic sweet viscous substance produced by honeybees from the nectar of blossoms or from secretions of or on living plants which they collect, modify, and store in honey combs." Most of the honey we get from bees is collected from the nectaries of flowers. Bees can produce honey from other plant secretions, and this type is known as *honeydew honey*. It is usually dark and has a molasseslike flavor, but it is wholesome and edible unless contaminated with mold or fungus.

FLAVORS AND COLORS

The flavors and colors of honey cover a wide spectrum and reflect the magnificent variety of nectar sources on which honeybees forage. The appearance and flavor range from the water white, very mild taste of clover and sage, to the golden brown tones and deep rich flavor of buckwheat and avocado (Fig. 9-1). Honey from some plants, such as dandelion and almond, is too strong and off-taste for human palates and is almost always left for the bees. The most common honeys in the United States are clover, sage, orange, and mixed wildflower.

When a commercial packer labels a honey, he merely has to have a product that tastes predominantly of the named source. The word SAGE on a label does not mean that the honey is from only sage plants. A packer deals with many beekeepers who bring a

Fig. 9-1 A frame of beautiful, capped water white sage honey, known for its delicate flavor and tendency not to granulate.

variety of honeys to him. Therefore, his bottled honey may often be a blend of nectar sources, with the prevalent flavor being characteristic of the variety shown on the label.

Honeys from rarer plant sources are called exotic honeys. Many beekeepers try to specialize in such honeys and receive a premium price for them. If you should notice a different color of honey filling up some frames, keep it separate, taste it, and try to determine the source. Be sure to extract it independently of the other honey. Bottle and label it carefully. It may be years before the special favorable condition of weather brings on a good flow of that particular nectar again. Or, you may be able to put your bees in an area with a great number of those plants and manage your hives so that you harvest some each year (Fig. 9-2).

One beekeeper in California noticed that honey being stored in his hive had a greenish tint. He discovered its source was a hillside of anise plants. He was careful to pull it and keep it separate. He has enjoyed giving this unusual honey, with its delicate licorice flavor, to special friends and trading a jar for a jar of another exotic honey at conferences.

Floral sources not only give honey its distinct color, taste, and aroma but also its rate of granulation. For example, sage honey does not granulate, but some kinds of eucalyptus will granulate within the first month (see Table 9-1).

COMPONENTS OF HONEY

The composition of honey naturally varies depending on the nectar source(s). In general honey is largely composed of levulose or fructose (average 38 percent), dextrose (average 31 percent),

Fig. 9-2. The tulip poplar is found in the Eastern and North Central United States. It has a beautiful flower and is copius in nectar, up to one-half teaspoon per blossom. Tulip tree honey is dark brown with a mild quincelike flavor.

Table 9-1. Common U.S. Nectar Sources.

Plant	Characteristics
Alfalfa	light, mild
Avocado	dark, hearty
Basswood	light, somewhat greenish
Bramble berries (black, boysen etc.)	light, mild
Borage	whitish with yellow-grey tint
Buckwheat	dark golden brown, strong flavor, aroma
Concurbits (melons, cucumbers)	light amber
Dandelion	intense golden yellow, sharp flavor
Goldenrod	deep yellow, strong flavor
Sage	white, mild, does not granulate
Sourwood	very light, delicate flavor
Soya bean	light, thin, peculiar unpleasant flavor
Stone fruit (apple, plum, cherry)	light, delicate flavor
Sunflower	egg-yolk yellow, strongly aromatic
Tulip poplar	dark brown, heavy, mild quince like flavor
Tupelo	white, mild, does not granulate
Willow	light amber, mild fine aroma

and sucrose (1.3 percent) with moisture comprising about 17 percent. Acids make up about ½ percent. The major acid is gluconic with traces of acetic, butyric, citric, formic glycolic, lactic, maleic, oxalic, succinic, pyroglutamic, a-ketoglutamic, or 3-phosphoglyceric, a- or b-glycerophosphate, and glucose 6-phosphate. The presence of acids contributes to the flavor of honey and is partly the reason microorganisms cannot live in honey.

Analysis of various honeys shows traces of proteins and amino acids identified with .04 percent of nitrogen. Minerals found in honey in order of degree are: potassium, chlorine, sulfur, calcium, sodium, phosphorus, magnesium, silica, iron, manganese, and copper. Darker honeys contain more minerals than lighter honeys. A dark honey measured in a lab at the University of Wisconsin, had 1,676 parts per million (ppm) of potassium as compared to only 20 ppm in a light honey. There were 76 ppm of sodium in a dark honey and only 18 ppm in light honey.

Honey has minute traces of vitamins as free amino acids, considered by most scientists too slight to be of significant nutritional value. However, the presence of enzymes in honey help make it the unique sweetening agent that it is. Enzymes are complex protein materials that bring about chemical changes. Many of these are essential to sustaining plant, animal, and human life. The principal enzymes in honey are invertase, diastase, and glucose oxidase. Invertase splits the sucrose in honey to its simpler sugars, dextrose and levulose. Diastase (amylase) digests starch to simpler compounds. Glucose oxidase converts the dextrose into gluconic acid and forms hydrogen peroxide during its action on dextrose. This is the main reason why honey is antibacterial.

HONEY AND NUTRITION

Honey is a high-energy carbohydrate, quickly and easily digested. It is relatively high in calories: 1 tablespoon has about 60 calories, and a cup has about 1000 calories. Since honey is more concentrated than sugar or corn syrup, much less (from three-quarters to one-half as much) can be used to achieve the same sweetness.

Honey must be counted just like sugar in the diet of a diabetic. Like sugar, it will cause dental decay without proper cleansing of the teeth and gums after eating.

Initial research on rats by scientists at the Federal Agricultural Research Service indicates that the single moleculed sugars in honey called monosaccharides are easier to metabolize with less stress to the body than the double moleculed or disaccharides of table sugar. Rats fed on disaccharide diets had larger livers, more fat in the blood, higher levels of insulin, and more body fat—all risk factors toward diabetes and heart disease—than rats on the monosaccharide diet.

HONEY IN COMMERCIAL PRODUCTS

Commercial uses of honey include baked goods and desserts like muffins, breakfast rolls, breads, cakes, cookies, candy, and ice cream. Honey spreads such as honey-butter, honey-fruit combinations, maple-honey, and creamed honey (also called spun or whipped), are available.

Honey is often used in dry cereals. It is more often used in a combination with sugar to counteract the hydroscopic quality of honey that works against the crisp texture desired. Granolas and trail mixes are often enhanced with honey. Meat packers use honey as an agent in processing. Ham particularly is often marketed with a honey glaze or smoked or baked with honey.

Honey is used in processing tobacco and helps keep it moist to prevent it from burning too hotly.

Honey is an ingredient often found in cough syrups, lozenges and other medicines to improve the taste or mask an unpleasant chemical flavor.

HONEY IN ALCOHOL PRODUCTS

The use of honey in alcoholic beverages is recorded in the writings of the Greeks and Romans. Many historians believe that *mead* was indeed the first alcoholic drink of early man. Honey was available long before grains and grapes were widely cultivated and utilized in distilling wines, beers, and other spirits.

The word *honeymoon* is derived from the early Vikings, who celebrated weddings with a month long festival of feasting and mead drinking.

Mead was a popular drink in central and northern Europe as early as 334 BC and was the national drink in England from medieval times up to the 1700s. Notes on early recipes indicate that a great many spices and herbs were added, probably to cover off-tasting batches resulting from inadequate knowledge of fermentation.

Compared to other wines, mead did not retain its popularity into the twentieth century because of the length of time necessary for fermentation when compared to those with a base of grain or fruit. Research in the latter half of this century has been devoted to speeding up the fermentation with wine yeasts, thus improving the flavor.

A study in Japan of the fermentation of several types of honey resulted in a recipe for delicious mead using buckwheat honey with 11.5 percent alcohol. It ferments in only one month. Further research and more sophisticated chemical analysis has brought about complex formulas for honey wines involving the addition of salts and other additives such as citric acid, ammonium sulphate, potassium phosphate aim to increase fermentation and control the pH. The result is a dry light mead with an alcoholic content of 14 to 15 percent. Mead is aged in barrels for six months, then decanted, filtered, adjusted for acidity, pasteurized, and bottled while hot.

Generally clover honey is the most popular type for mead making, yielding a mild, sauternelike wine.

Brewing beer with honey is a centuries old tradition of many central and eastern African tribes. As most beekeeping is carried out with logs or barrels or simply by raiding natural bee nests, the honey put into the beer brew is in natural form with pollen, comb, and bees mixed in. Sometimes sugar is added. A native fruit like muratina is almost always added for body, flavor, and possibly as an aid to fermentation. Usually this honey beer is consumed a day or two after fermentation begins and is often used for bartering, payment of village fines, celebrating feasts, or as an award for outstanding feats.

Several cordials and liqueurs are distilled with honey. Probably the best known is Drambuie, an elegant liqueur exclusive to

Scotland and prepared from a secret family recipe dating back to 1745. It uses Scotch, heather honey, and several herbs. Others of world wide reputation are Irish Mist, from Irish whiskey, honey, and herbs; Krupnik, from Poland; and Forbidden Fruit, an American cordial of citrus fruits and honey.

HONEY IN COSMETICS

Because honey is an excellent *humectant*—retainer of moisture—it has been used since ancient times as an emollient for skin and hair. The Greeks and Romans used it. It is recorded that Poppea, Nero's wife, mixed honey with donkey's milk for a face lotion. Madame du Barry, the mistress of Louis XV (1710-1774) of France, and England's Queene Anne (1665-1714), were advocates of honey for beauty uses.

In modern times honey is included in a wide variety of beauty products, not only because of its hydroscopicity but also because it never spoils or sours and it makes cosmetics feel rich and thick. Lotions, handcreams, facial masks, bath salts, hair conditioners, and shampoos are some of the cosmetic products that contain honey. Honey is used as a clarifier in manufacturing soap to give it transparency.

Here are two formulas to try at home. They are reprinted by permission from *The Complete Book of Natural Cosmetics* by Beatrice Traven with cosmetic formulations by Robert L. Goldemberg.

Milk-and-Honey Mask

¼ cup strong fennel tea
¼ cup milk
¼ cup honey
½ ounce pectin

Mix the tea, milk, and honey together to form a homogenous mixture. Then sprinkle in the pectin as you slowly beat the mixture with your electric mixer. When the pectin is accepted completely and the mixture is smooth, stop beating. Put the resulting gel into a jar and let it stand overnight to "swell."

The mild, elastic milk-and-honey mask will spread lusciously on your face. It treats you to the proteins of milk, the smoothing of pectin, the humectants of honey—and may be the first aid for wrinkles attributed to fennel by the old, optimistic herbalists.

Golden Scarecrow Beauty Drops

1 egg
2 tablespoons sesame oil
2 tablespoons honey

Separate the egg. Drop the yolk into a small jar. To the jar add the sesame oil and the honey. Stir the ingredients by hand until they are thick, rich, and smooth. To the mixture add the egg white. Close the jar and shake it hard. The mixture will thin out somewhat and become even smoother. Dab it on dry skin or wrinkle areas—throat, elbows, upper lip, and especially those nasty crow's feet around your eyes.

HONEY AND HEALING

Not only is honey excellent in maintaining healthy skin but from early times it has also been used as a healing agent. Reverend Charles Butler in *The Feminine Monarchie* (1609), claimed that honey was good for "improving the appetite, as a laxative and diuretic, to prolong life, for the blood, healing ulcers, curing poisoning from bites, and lung ailments." Although not all of these claims have been tested, in holistic medical practice, honey is today being put to use as a dressing for wounds in some hospitals.

In the Department of Gynecologic Oncology at the University of South Florida, College of Medicine, honey was used in the treatment of 12 post-operative patients. Honey was poured into the surgical wound of each patient twice daily and covered with gauze. According to the director, Dr. Denis Cavanagh, "Bacteria in the wounds disappeared completely within three to six days. Complete healing occurred in all 12 cases within eight weeks, one in only three weeks.

According to Dr. Cavanagh, honey is more effective than the topical antibiotics the department had previously used. In any type of abdominal surgery such as appendectomies, hysterectomies, and gallbladder, honey doubles the healing rate of the tissue at the site of the incision.

In England, honey has proven a successful dressing for burns, providing a more comfortable covering than most other dressings since it is nonadhesive.

In Switzerland, honey has been found helpful for patients with radiation sickness, due to the easy assimilation of fructose. Honey is helpful for sobering up from excessive use of alcohol for the same reason.

Table 9-2. Honey Production 1979-81.

State	Colonies				Yield per Colony			Honey Production			
	1979	1980	1981	1981 as of 1980	1979	1980	1981	1979	1980	1981	1981 as of 1980
	(thousands)			(percent)	(pounds)			(1,000 pounds)			(percent)
Ala.	45	44	42	95	20	36	43	900	1584	1806	114
Ariz.	65	67	64	96	58	67	53	3770	3819	3392	89
Ark.	30	32	31	97	45	49	44	1350	1568	1364	87
Calif.	504	504	500	99	34	46	18	17136	23184	9000	39
Colo.	39	45	41	91	67	52	62	2613	2340	2542	109
Conn.	8	8	8	100	36	24	24	288	192	192	100
Del.	4	4	4	100	27	25	23	108	100	92	92
Fla.	350	350	360	103	78	58	67	27300	20300	24120	119
Ga.	156	161	145	90	39	26	37	6084	4186	5365	128
Haw.	7	7	7	100	130	123	125	910	861	875	102
Idaho	101	109	108	99	54	36	37	5454	3924	3996	102
Ill.	36	38	41	108	59	49	26	2124	1862	1066	57
Ind.	75	76	76	100	36	38	22	2700	2888	1672	58
Iowa	83	85	88	104	80	74	39	6640	6290	3432	55
Kans.	40	43	40	93	50	50	49	2000	2150	1960	91
Ky.	52	52	56	108	33	27	21	1716	1404	1176	84
La.	31	31	30	97	40	55	65	1240	1705	1950	114
Maine	5	7	8	114	36	19	28	180	133	224	93
Md.	14	14	15	107	35	30	26	490	420	390	93
Mass.	12	12	11	92	33	24	23	396	288	253	88
Mich.	106	102	98	96	61	43	50	6466	4386	4900	112
Minn.	160	180	190	106	99	76	43	15840	13680	8170	60
Miss.	49	45	41	91	38	35	45	1862	1575	1845	117
Mo.	124	124	128	103	64	53	36	7936	6572	4608	70
Mont.	103	103	108	105	128	104	100	13184	10712	10800	101
Nebr	140	120	122	102	40	64	40	5600	7680	4880	64
Nev.	12	11	12	109	35	60	35	420	000	420	64
N.H.	4	4	4	100	28	17	23	112	68	92	135
N.J.	34	43	38	88	40	33	35	1360	1419	1330	94
N. Mex.	14	17	18	106	45	32	39	630	544	702	129
N.Y.	113	117	116	99	62	43	34	7006	5031	3944	78
N.C.	180	170	187	110	30	30	29	5400	5100	5423	106
N. Dak.	190	220	265	120	120	65	87	22800	14300	23055	161
Ohio	83	82	85	104	31	30	22	2573	2460	1870	76
Okla.	55	44	48	109	50	45	36	2750	1980	1728	87
Oreg.	57	58	59	102	37	34	33	2109	1972	1947	99
Pa.	74	80	85	106	41	41	30	3034	3280	2550	78
R.I.	1	1	1	100	34	26	24	34	26	24	92
S.C.	59	55	52	95	20	24	22	1180	1320	1144	87
S. Dak.	204	184	180	98	85	44	51	17340	8096	9180	113
Tenn.	135	140	150	107	23	35	34	3105	4900	5100	104
Tex.	190	198	190	96	60	35	60	11400	6930	11400	165
Utah	46	46	46	100	48	33	37	2208	1518	1702	112
Vt.	9	9	9	100	50	28	45	450	252	405	161
Va.	78	77	73	95	32	19	31	2496	1463	2263	155
Wash.	87	90	87	97	38	42	35	3306	3780	3045	81
W. Va.	104	67	62	93	25	29	20	2600	1943	1240	64
Wis.	135	125	125	100	65	48	33	8775	6000	4125	69
Wyo.	39	41	44	107	85	71	72	3315	2911	3168	109
U.S. total	4163	4141	4213	102	57.3	48.2	44.1	238690	199756	185927	93

Sum of state totals exceeds the U.S. total because of duplication of colonies between states.

Courtesy Crop Reporting Service, United States Department of Agriculture.

In 1962, Dr. J.W. White and colleagues in the United States discovered that the antibacterial effect of honey results from the accumulation of hydrogen peroxide created by the natural glucose oxidase system. The healing quality of honey is also related to its high sugar content and acidity. The antibacterial factors are thought to be introduced by the bees in converting nectar to honey. Bees themselves and most of the materials in the colony contain antibiotic elements.

HONEY PRODUCTION IN THE UNITED STATES

In the United States, nearly 186 million pounds or 84.3 thousand metric tons of honey was produced in 1981, according to the report issued in January of 1982 by the Statistical Reporting Service of the Crop Reporting Board, USDA. The break down by states is shown in Table 9-2. Florida was number one with North Dakota a close second and Texas third.

The average price per pound was $0.632. This is the price commercial beekeepers receive from packers for unfiltered honey in 60-pound cans or 55-gallon drums. The price a hobbyist beekeeper can get for bottled, clear strained honey runs about a dollar per pound. The price depends on the local market, container size, and the availability or scarcity of a given type of honey. (See Chapter 10.)

Chapter 10

Marketing Your Honey

If you expand the number of hives you maintain or your yields are so high that your honey production exceeds the needs of your family, friends, and neighbors, you will want to consider selling your honey. Usually there is a good demand for local honey and it is fairly easy to sell. With two to five hives and an annual yield of 300 to 400 pounds (assuming you keep 60 to 75 pound for yourself and for gifts), you can certainly start earning back some of your equipment and supply expense.

DETERMINING A PRICE

A fair way to price your honey is to set an amount between health food store prices and the price of an equivalent weight of supermarket honey. You will notice if you take a survey of a few stores, the smaller containers cost the consumer more per unit (ounce or pound) than the larger sizes. You should do the same. Charge higher prices per unit for the smaller sizes, less per unit with larger containers.

Once you set your price, it is wisest to stick with it and not haggle. If a person should exclaim that your price is more than at so-and-so market, be pleasant but tell them that you feel your honey is fairly priced for the quality and that they are free to buy their honey any place. Often "bargain" honey sold in 3 to 5 pound cans is darker and stronger and will not compare in color or flavor to yours.

CREATING AN INTEREST

For the first season or two that you have excess honey, but not enough to mount a sales program, you may want to create an interest in your honey for the time when you *will* begin selling. One beekeeping couple donated some honey for their church's pancake breakfast. They were able to claim a tax deduction for the donation and found to their delight that when they did begin selling, they had a contingent of people who had enjoyed their honey and were eager to buy it.

Many community organizations, clubs, schools, and athletic teams, as well as churches, have breakfasts, chili suppers, dime-a-dip dinners, and food booths at fairs where honey would be a welcome condiment. Honey can be donated for door prizes or to auction or sell at charity bazaars and boutiques.

Another place to generate interest is your place of work, that of your partner, or other members of the family. Sometimes this begins with a barter arrangement. Someone has a plant or seedling, an abundance of fruit in season, or a handmade craft product you are interested in. Offer a jar of honey in trade. Set the honey on a desk or in your work area where others see it. You are bound to get questions, then customers. From time to time a person at work does a favor for you and you want to express your thanks. A sample gift of honey is almost always well received. For samples, four ounce baby food jars are excellent.

SELECTING CONTAINERS

Honey jars come in glass and plastic from 1 to 4 pound sizes. Some purists prefer glass because of the hydrocarbons in plastic, but many beekeeping suppliers no longer carry glass containers because of the extensive breakage during shipping and handling. Neither will most suppliers ship glass unless the order is large enough (25 to 30 cases) to warrant shipment by private freight truck. You may also use pint and quart canning jars, which are available in cases of 12 at supermarkets and discount stores.

Which sizes to buy? At first you may want to offer three or more sizes until you see what your customers prefer. The smaller sizes will give you slightly more profit but will also take more time to fill—opening and closing the gate valve, wiping more rims and sides, screwing on more lids. You will spend less time bottling the larger sizes with the same amount of extracted honey and spend less on containers (Fig. 10-1).

The price of a 1 pound jar is about 30 cents. The 2 pound jar

Fig. 10-1. Containers come in many sizes and shapes; you will soon learn which sizes and types sell best for you. (Courtesy, Smith Container Corporation, Atlanta, Georgia.)

averages about 45 cents. If you sell two 1 pound jars, you have a container cost of 60 cents but if you sell one 2-pound jar, the container costs is only 45 cents.

You must assess your own market. You can see what goes best. Usually you will build up a lot of repeat business from people who are honey lovers (especially of yours) and who will naturally realize the economy of buying the bigger size. You may find some customers who want to buy in large quantities. Offer them the 5-pound size. On the other hand, you may narrow the choice to honey bears and 3-pounders if that's what the majority buy. Honey bears are nice to offer around the holidays for gift giving.

LABELS

When selling honey, you are required to label it with your name, address, and the weight of honey. If you want, you can have your honey checked and put a grade like Grade A, B, etc., on the label too. Attractive peel-off labels on rolls to fit different size jars are sold at suppliers.

They have the words "Pure Honey" at the top, "net wt." at the bottom, and the directions. "To liquefy, put in warm water." You must fill in personal data. You may want to have a rubber stamp made to speed up this phase.

One enterprising beekeeper asked an artistic friend to draw a logo and had a printer make sheets of labels on special gummed paper (Fig. 10-2). Not only did it personalize her product but saved her time in writing, typing, or stamping in the personal data required to complete the commercial labels. She lines up a stack of label sheets, cuts them with a paper cutter, jots in the weight, presses them on a sponge, and sticks them on her jars (Fig. 10-2).

WHERE TO SELL

If you live on a farm or on the outskirts of town, you may want to try a roadside stand, especially if you might have some produce to sell from time to time. You can keep it simple with a sturdy table under a tree, a sign, and an attractive display of jars and containers of honey. Or you can rig up a stand with a roof and a counter. You will want to man the stand when there is the most traffic on your road, probably late afternoon and weekends. This is a good way for an older child to earn part of his or her allowance.

If you don't have the manpower to keep someone posted at the stand, you can nail up a large bell for customers to ring when they want service. Some beekeepers use the honor system. If you try that be sure to post sizes and prices and a note that customers can come to the door for more help if needed. This lets people know that the beekeeper is around and someone is checking on the cash box from time to time.

You can also sell from your door if you prefer to take care of business that way. In any case, it is very important to post a weatherproof sign about one-half to three-quarters of a mile in both directions from your home or stand. Make it large enough so that it can be read by someone driving by at the prevailing speed. You don't need detail, just "HONEY FOR SALE" in large bold letters. You can display hours, prices, and type(s) of honey on another sign by the stand or in front of your house.

Many communities now have direct produce markets that enable farmers and others who have home grown products to cut out the middle man and sell directly to the public. Usually a large area like a parking lot, fairground, or athletic field is used. The market is open for five or six hours on a specific day each week during the season.

Selling at the farmer's market is fairly simple. Most folks just load up some boxes of honey in the trunk of their car. Take along a

U.S.
ROVING IRIS BRAND
CHOICE
raw, wild,
unheated,
and unfiltered
locally produced
PURE
HONEY

PACKED BY WILLA JANE BOWMAN
8686 tern avenue
fountain valley, california
phone (714) 968-8024

all honey will granulate in time - to liquefy,
place container in warm water.

NET WT. ___________

Fig. 10-2. You can design your own label like this one done by a beekeeper's artistic friend.

card table or portable camp table, a folding chair, a sign, tasting set up, and a box for cash. Some like to take a notebook for recording sales as they go along. Line up your car with the other stands, open your trunk, set up your table, put out your honey, and you are in business (Fig. 10-3).

Another possibility is a swap meet. There is a cost for booth space but you have the advantage of selling where there are large crowds and a great deal of impulse buying. Many community colleges have parking lot swap meets on weekends during fair weather. The cost to participate there is more reasonable than at a commercially operated swap meet.

If you haven't the time or inclination to set up a stand or sell from your home, and you're willing to earn less profit, you can get others to do the selling for you. Use either people in business or community groups. Potential commercial enterprises should include health food stores, produce marts, either permanent or seasonal, drive in dairies (which often sell as many non-dairy products as they do milk and butter), and small mom-and-pop stores that are not tied into quantity buying from set suppliers.

It is smart business for both you and the proprietor to work out a written agreement about the price, and percent profit you each will earn, and other details.

Community clubs, sports teams, and youth groups often need a good product like honey to sell and often have a built in clientele of supporters. You can earn a profit for yourself and help them at the same time. You will want to appraise them of any selling aids, like tasting supplies, and signs, that they will need or provide them (Fig.

Fig. 10-3. One place to sell your honey is at a community farmer's market, often sponsored by chambers of commerce, growers' coops, churches, and other organizations.

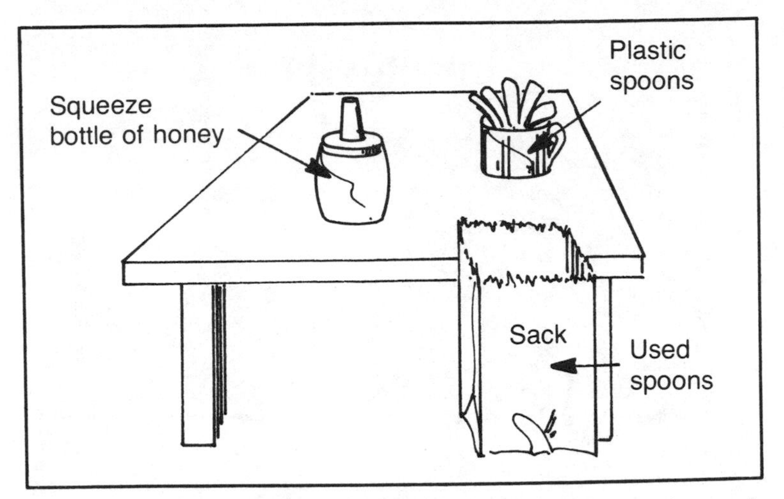

Fig. 10-4. To stimulate interest, offer tastes. Put your honey or honeys in squeeze bottles and put a small amount on small plastic spoons or coffee stirrers for each person. Provide a paper sack for used spoons.

10-4). When you give them the cartons of honey, hand them a list of the quantities of honey you have provided, e.g., three cases, six each of 2-pound and twenty honey bears; the price for each size, the total amount in cash they will have if all sold, the amount they keep, and what they owe you.

Chapter 11

Cooking with Honey

Honey is a popular ingredient in baking because cookies, cakes, and breads made with it stay fresh longer. In fact, the moisture content of a honey cake is greater on the third day than on the first day. Honey can be nicely substituted for sugar in all other culinary endeavors. It can be used in salad dressings, main dishes, nutritious snacks, and even in food preserving, both freezing and canning.

The advantage is that it takes much less honey to give the same amount of sweetness to a food than sugar. As a beekeeper you will no doubt have honey on hand most of the time. You will want to enjoy it in as many ways as you can.

BAKING WITH HONEY

Certain rules have been formulated for using honey in baking. Recipes must be changed to accommodate honey's superior sweetness and the fact that you will be substituting a liquid for sugar (Fig. 11-1).

Honey varies in density but the standard accepted weights are given in Table 11-1. The traditional rule of thumb has been that ⅞ cup of honey is equal to 1 cup of sugar. Modern nutritionists, in striving toward healthier diets, often suggest ¾ to ½ cup of honey to replace 1 cup of sugar. If your family and friends have sweet-tooths, you might start by substituting with the larger amount, decreasing it a little each time you make a given recipe.

In recipes using oil or shortening, place it in the measuring cup

Fig. 11-1. Banana Nut Bread and other fruit breads are excellent when made with honey. Bake bread in 1-pound coffee cans or 1- to 1½-pound loaf pans.

first, pour it into the batter, then put the honey in the same cup. It will slip out easily and none will be wasted.

Honey should be added gradually to cake, cookie, bar, and bread recipes in a thin stream.

Baking Temperatures

Lower oven temperature by 25°F. If you are using a glass dish instead of a metal pan, lower the recipes another 25°F.

Adjusting for Liquid and Acidity

Cut down on the other liquid in the recipe by ¼ cup. In cookie recipes that include eggs and no other liquid, or in recipes where a

Table 11-1. Standard Weights of Honey.

Honey	Equals
12 pounds	1 gallon
3 pounds	1 quart
1½ pounds	1 pint
¾ pound	1 cup
12 ounces	1 cup

(Sugar weighs 7 ounces to a cup)

thick dough is desired, increase flour content by 2 to 3 tablespoons for every cup of honey to give the required consistency.

In baking with honey, unless sour milk or buttermilk is called for, add ⅛ to ¼ teaspoon of baking soda to compensate for the acidity of honey.

Types of Honey to Use

Generally the milder flavors like sage or clover are preferred for cooking since the honey is not likely to mask the other flavors. Stronger flavored honeys are fine in cakes, cookies, dressings, and sauces where spices and/or herbs are included as flavorings. Here is a sample recipe adapted to substituting honey:

Banana Nut Bread with white sugar

4 or 5 ripe bananas, medium
1¾ cups sugar
¾ cups oil
3 eggs
⅓ cup buttermilk
3½ cups flour
(2 cups white flour and 1½ cups whole wheat is good)
2 teaspoons baking soda
1 teaspoon baking powder
1 cup chopped nuts (optional)
½ cup chopped dates (optional)

Preheat the oven to 350°F. Peel and chop bananas into chunks; then mash the chunks with the beaters of a mixer. Add sugar and oil, beat to mix. Add eggs, one at a time, beating on medium. Sift the flour with the baking powder and soda. Add the dry ingredients to the batter alternately with buttermilk.

Banana Nut Bread with Honey

4 or 5 ripe bananas, medium
⅞ cup honey
½ cup oil
3 eggs
⅓ cup buttermilk
3¾ cups flour
(2 cups white flour and 1¾ cups whole wheat is good)
2 teaspoons baking soda
1 teaspoon baking powder
1 cup chopped nuts (optional)
½ cup chopped dates (optional)

Preheat the oven to 325°F. Peel and chop bananas into chunks; then mash the chunks with the beaters of a mixer. Blend in oil and eggs, one at a time, beating on medium. Add the honey gradually in a fine stream. Sift the flour with the baking powder and soda. Add the dry ingredients to the batter alternately with buttermilk.

Coat pieces of dates in ¼ cup of flour called for before adding to batter.

Mix in nuts and dates (if used). The batter should be thick!

Grease the inside surfaces of two 1-pound coffee cans with a pastry brush dipped in oil. With a rubber spatula, scrape the dough into prepared cans up to the two thirds mark. Place the pans in center rack of the oven.

Bake for 45 to 50 minutes. Test the bread with a clean broom straw or barbecue skewer. Bread is done when it begins to pull away from the sides of the can and when the tester comes out clean. If the top browns too fast, cover the cans lightly with a square of aluminum foil.

Place the pans on a cake rack to cool. While still warm, use a table knife to loosen the sides from the can and ease the bread out carefully. When the bread is cool, slice it with a bread knife. It's excellent plain or buttered and may be toasted on a light setting of toaster.

RECIPES

The following recipes have been taken from various sources which are noted. Recipes not credited are from my own recipe file. These recipes were chosen as a sampling of the variety of dishes in which honey may be used and particularly because honey is the only sweetener. The cookbook and pamphlets mentioned may be ordered (Fig. 11-2).

Fig. 11-2. Honey can be substituted for sugar in your favorite salad dressings.

Luau Bites

From *Favorite Honey Recipes*, reprinted courtesy Honey Queen Committee, California

10 water chestnuts, canned
5 chicken livers
5 strips bacon
¼ cup soy sauce
1½ tablespoons honey

Cut 10 water chestnuts in half; quarter 5 chicken livers. Wrap a piece of water chestnut and liver in one-half slice of bacon; fasten with a toothpick.

Mix soy sauce and honey.

Marinate the appetizers in the marinade for about four hours in the refrigerator. Occasionally spoon the marinade over the appetizers. Drain. Place the appetizers on a broiler rack. Broil about 3 inches from heat until the bacon is crisp, turning each over once. Yield 20 appetizers.

Cranberry Relish

Courtesy, Honey Queen Committee, California

1 package of cranberries
2 or 3 oranges, peeled
2 or 3 apples, peeled
1 can crushed pineapple (1 lb.)
1 to 2 cups of honey

Grind the cranberries, oranges, and apples. Add the pineapple. Then add honey. Mix thoroughly. Chill for at least 2 or 3 hours. (Can be made a day ahead.)

Honey Salad Dressing

Courtesy of Louisiana State University Extension

1 teaspoon paprika
½ teaspoon dry mustard
½ teaspoon salt
½ teaspoon celery salt
½ cup liquid honey
3 tablespoons lemon juice
¼ cup vinegar
1 cup salad oil

Mix the dry ingredients together. Add the honey, lemon juice, and vinegar. Slowly add the salad oil, beating until well blended. Makes 2 cups of salad dressing.

Dressing for Cabbage Slaw

1 cup mayonnaise
¼ cup oil
¼ cup vinegar
¼ cup honey
3 or 4 drops hot pepper sauce
½ teaspoon salt or salt substitute

1 teaspoon dill, caraway, or celery seed

½ teaspoon garlic powder (optional)

Beat all ingredients together thoroughly. Makes enough dressing for one small, chopped head of cabbage plus ½ cup of chopped bell pepper or green onion.

Meats, Marinades, and Vegetables

Polynesian Marinade

Courtesy of California Honey Advisory Board

¼ cup honey
¼ cup fresh orange juice
2 tablespoons fresh lemon juice
¼ cup soy sauce
6 kumquats, finely chopped
2 tablespoons grated orange peel
½ teaspoon ground ginger
¼ teaspoon pepper

Blend all ingredients well and pour over chicken. Marinate 4 to 5 hours in the refrigerator, turning occasionally. Makes 1½ cups. Chicken may then be barbecued on spit, in pieces over charcoal or gas, or baked in the oven. Use marinade as a basting sauce (Fig. 11-3).

Barbecued Lean White Fish

This is good to use with any boneless, firm-fleshed white fish such as halibut, rockfish, lingcod, or sea bass. Cut the fillets into 1-inch thick serving size pieces. The recipe makes enough for four pounds of fish.

½ cup soy sauce
2 cloves garlic, crushed
½ cup salad oil
1 cup dry white wine
2 tablespoons honey
1 teaspoon powdered ginger
2 tablespoons rosemary
2 tablespoons lemon juice
6 tablespoons fresh chopped parsley

Mix all ingredients and pour the mixture over fish. Marinate for four hours. Pour off and reserve the marinade. Barbecue the fish in a hinged wire boiler over low coals. Baste with the marinade. Cook until the fish flakes when tested, about 10 to 15 minutes.

Super-Duper Scrumptious Barbecue Sauce

May be used for chicken, pork ribs or chops, and beef ribs.

2 cans of tomato soup
1½ cans of water
3 tablespoons worchestershire sauce
5 or 6 drops hot pepper sauce
1 teaspoon ground allspice
1 tablespoon prepared mustard
¼ cup lemon juice

Fig. 11-3. Honey is great in marinades and barbecue sauces for meats, fish, and poultry.

¼ cup honey
2 cloves garlic, mashed
¼ cup ground onion
flour (for chicken only)
cornmeal (for chicken only)

For chicken: Coat the chicken with flour and corn meal. Sear the chicken in a small amount of oil until brown on both sides. Pour off excess oil. Place in casserole or baking dish in one layer. Spoon on barbecue sauce. Bake in oven at 350°F for 45 minutes.

For pork or beef ribs, pork chops: Brown the meat in a pan over a burner or in the oven using medium high heat (about 425°F). Pour off excess fat. Spoon on barbecue sauce. Bake at 350°F until tender, about 45 minutes.

Herb Baked Squash

Courtesy of Honey Queen Committee of California

6 4" by 4" pieces of banana squash
3 small acorn squash, halved
1½ teaspoons crushed rosemary
3 tablespoon butter
⅓ cup mild honey

Remove any seeds from squash. Place the squash in a single layer in a greased baking dish. Sprinkle ¼ teaspoon rosemary over each piece and dot with butter. Bake 40 minutes at 350°F or until almost done. Drizzle pieces with honey and continue baking until tender. Serves 6.

Honeyed Onions

Mary's Family Recipe

4 medium, sweet, onions
½ cup tomato juice
2 tablespoons butter or margarine
1 teaspoon crushed basil
3 or 4 drops hot pepper sauce

Place butter, tomato juice, and honey in a small pan and heat over low heat until butter is melted. Peel and cut each onion in half-cross-wise. Place the onion in a single layer in a shallow casserole dish or baking pan. Pour the tomato juice mixture over the onions and sprinkle the tops with basil. Bake at 325°F for glass dishes and 350°F for metal pans for 35 to 45 minutes for crunchy onions, or up to 60 minutes if you want them very tender. Remove the onions carefully with spatula to keep them intact. Pour a little pan juice over each. Honeyed onions go very well with beef or pork roast or ground meat main dishes. Serves 8.

Breads

Dutch Double Dill

from *Honey . . . Any Time,* Courtesy California Honey Advisory Board.

1 package (1 ounce) active dry yeast
2 cups water, 105 to 110°F
3 tablespoons honey
1 cup plain yogurt or sour cream
2 teaspoons salt
1 tablespoon dill seed
1 tablespoon dried dill weed
1 tablespoon caraway seed
5 cups whole wheat flour
3 cups rye flour

In a small bowl or measuring cup, combine the yeast and ½ cup warm water. Set aside for 5 to 10 minutes to allow yeast to activate (swell and bubble). Meanwhile, combine the remaining water with salad oil, honey, yogurt, salt, dill, and caraway. Add the yeast mixture. Then add whole wheat flour, one cup at a time, stirring well after each addition.

Add rye flour, cup by cup, until mixture becomes too difficult to stir. Begin kneading the dough, adding additional flour to keep the dough from becoming too sticky. Knead for at least 10 minutes. Shape the dough into a ball. Lightly grease a clean mixing bowl. Place the dough in the bowl, turning the dough over so the greased side is up. Cover. Place the bowl in a warm, draft-free place until the dough is double in size (about 1½ hours).

Punch the dough to remove all air bubbles. Turn the dough out onto a lightly floured board. Knead for 1 minute. Shape the dough into round loaves or place the dough in greased 9-by-5-by-3-inch loaf pans. Cover the pans and place in warm, draft-free place until the loaves are double in size (about 30 minutes).

Bake at 425°F for 15 minutes. Reduce heat to 350°F. Bake 25 minutes. Remove the pans from the oven. Turn the bread out of the pans and tap the bottom of the loaves. Loaves will sound hollow if done. If not, return them to the pans and bake for an additional 5 to 10 minutes. Makes 3 medium or 2 large loaves.

Healthy Whole Wheat

1 cup hot water
5 tablespoons dry yeast
2 teaspoons sugar
5¾ cups warm water
1 cup honey
1 cup oil
2½ tablespoons salt
1 cup nonfat dry milk
6 cups white, unbleached flour
14 cups whole wheat flour

(Note: 10 cups each of whole wheat and rye or 12 cups whole wheat and 2 cups of bran and/or wheat germ may be substituted.)

Put 1 cup of hot water in a small bowl. Place a candy thermometer in the bowl. When the water temperature is 110°F, sprinkle the dry yeast over the top of the water; then sprinkle sugar over that, taking care to distribute the sugar over the entire surface. Set aside and allow to "proof" (swell and bubble).

Meanwhile, in a large bowl, measure 5¾ cups warm water. Add to that 3 cups of white flour and 3 cups of whole wheat. Beat. Add 1 cup oil, 1 cup honey, and salt. Beat. Add 6 more cups of flour, including bran and wheat germ if used, and beat until thoroughly mixed. Add proofed yeast mixture and beat 2 minutes. (This recipe is not only healthy to eat but provides healthy exercise while making it.)

Mix the dry milk in 1 cup of measured flour and add to the yeast mixture. Beat. Add last 7 cups of flour, one or two at a time. Beat the flour in until the dough is too difficult to beat. Start kneading.

The dough will be quite sticky but will become easier to handle as you knead. Set a timer and knead for 10 minutes. (Don't cheat, kneading is the key to light, lovely loaves.) Divide the dough into two large balls. Place each ball in larger greased bowls. Flip the balls over so that greased sides are up. Cover and set in warm place until dough has doubled in size (½ hour to 45 minutes).

Punch the dough vigorously. Place each ball on a lightly floured board. Cut each ball into 4 chunks, shape each into a loaf, and put each into a loaf pan. Allow the bread to rise in a warm place until doubled in size, about 30 to 40 minutes.

Bake at 350°F for 40 to 45 minutes.

Remove one loaf from the pan and test by thumping the bottom. If the loaf does not sound hollow, return it to the oven for 5 to 10 more minutes. Makes 7 or 8 one-pound loaves or 6 loaves and 1½ dozen dinner rolls. May also be used for pizza dough.

Sunday Morning Cinnamon Rolls

Honey Queen Committee of California.

2 cups biscuit mix
2 tablespoons honey
2 tablespoons shortening
1 cube of butter
½ cup honey
1 tablespoon cinnamon
½ cup chopped nuts

Mix the biscuit mix, honey, and shortening together. Add enough milk to make a kneading consistency. Roll out the dough on a floured board. Spread very soft butter over the dough. Drizzle honey on the dough, then sprinkle cinnamon on and add chopped nuts. Roll into long roll and cut into about 12 rolls. Place the roll cut side up on a greased baking pan. Bake at 375°F for 20 minutes. Serve warm.

Easy Brown Bread

½ cup white flour
1 cup whole wheat flour
1 cup corn meal
½ cup honey
2 cups buttermilk
2 teaspoons soda
1 teaspoon salt
1 cup raisins

Coat raisins in part of the flour. Then mix all ingredients

together. Pour the batter into two well-greased 1-pound coffee cans up to two-thirds full. Allow the batter to rise for ½ hour.

Bake in 350°F oven about 45 to 50 minutes. When the top is brown, cover it with a square of aluminum foil to prevent burning.

Allow the bread to cool on a rack. Gently slide a table knife around the sides to loosen and turn out the bread. Its good served with butter or cream cheese mixed with honey.

Desserts and Snacks

Apple-Spice Honey Cookies

Virginia Truesdell, Orange County Beekeepers Association.

½ cup margarine or butter
1 cup honey
2 eggs
1½ cup all purpose flour
½ teaspoon baking soda
½ teaspoon baking powder
½ teaspoon salt
½ teaspoon cinnamon
½ teaspoon nutmeg
1½ cup apples, finely chopped
1 cup chopped dates,
raisins, or mixture
½ cup chopped nuts
2½ cups rolled oats

Cream the margarine; then add the honey in a fine stream. Beat in the eggs. Combine flour, soda, baking powder, salt and spices and stir the mixture into the wet ingredients. Add apples, dates, nuts, and oats. Drop by teaspoonfuls onto a lightly greased baking sheet. Bake at 350°F for 10 minutes. Makes 3 to 4 dozen.

Honey Walnut Tea Cookies

Courtesy Honey Queen Committee of California.

1 cup butter (or ½ cup butter
½ cup vegetable shortening)
½ teaspoon salt
1 teaspoon vanilla
½ cup mild flavored honey
2⅓ cups sifted flour
1 cup finely chopped nuts

Cream butter, salt, and vanilla. Continue creaming while adding honey in a fine stream. Mix in flour and nuts. Chill one hour. Shape the dough into logs and wrap each log in waxed paper. Chill, another hour and slice. Bake at 350°F for 12 to 14 minutes. Makes about 3 dozen.

Jogger Bars

Courtesy California Honey Advisory Board.

2 tablespoons butter or
margarine
2 teaspoons cinnamon
1 teaspoon vanilla

¼ cup peanut butter, smooth or chunky
½ cup honey
1½ cup chopped nuts
⅛ teaspoon salt
½ cup raisins or chopped dates
2 cups whole bran cereal

Combine butter, peanut butter, and honey in 3-quart pan. Cook over low heat, stirring constantly, just until mixture begins to boil. Remove from heat. Add chopped nuts, cinnamon, vanilla, and salt. Mix until blended. Stir in raisins and bran. Mix until well-coated. Turn mixture into greased 8-inch square pan. Firmly press the dough into the pan. Let cool. Cut into 16 bars.

Ragged Robins

Courtesy Honey Queen Committee of California.

2 egg whites
pinch cream of tartar
½ cup honey, warmed
2 cups corn flakes
1 cup chopped dates
1 cup chopped nuts
1 teaspoon vanilla

Beat eggs until foamy. Add cream of tartar and beat until stiff. Continue beating while adding honey in a fine stream. Combine corn flakes, dates, and nuts in a large bowl. Mix gently. Fold in egg white mixture. Add vanilla. Drop by teaspoonfuls onto greased cookie sheet. Bake at 350°F for 15 minutes. Cool before removing from cookie sheet.

Super Carrot Cake

4 eggs
¾ cup honey
2 cups whole wheat flour
2 teaspoons cinnamon
1 teaspoon salt
1½ cups oil
2 teaspoons baking soda
4 cups grated carrots

Beat eggs. Add honey in fine stream. Add oil and beat again. Add dry ingredients. Beat again. Fold in carrots. Turn into greased unfloured 9-by-13-inch pan. Bake at 325°F for about 40 minutes or until cake springs back when lightly touched. Turn off the oven but leave the cake in until the oven is nearly cool. Remove the pan from the oven and place it on a wire rack. Frost the cake with cream frosting below (Fig. 11-4).

Cream Frosting

7 tablespoons softened butter
8 ounces softened cream cheese
1 or 2 tablespoons honey
1 cup chopped walnuts

Fig. 11-4. Used in cakes, honey helps to preserve moisture, as in this Super Carrot Cake from *Favorite Honey Recipes* compiled by the Honey Queen Committee of California.

Blend butter and cream cheese. Slowly drizzle honey over mixture, stirring until it is a creamy consistency. Add chopped nuts and spread over cooled cake.

Honey Chocolate Cake

Louisiana State University Agricultural Extension.

2 cups sifted cake flour
1½ teaspoons baking soda
1 teaspoon salt
½ cup shortening
1¼ cups honey
⅔ cups water
1 teaspoon vanilla
2 eggs, unbeaten
2½ squares unsweetened chocolate, melted

Mix shortening just to soften. Sift in dry ingredients. In

another bowl mix honey, water, and vanilla. Add one-half of the honey mixture and the eggs to the batter. Mix until the flour is dampened, then beat one minute at low speed. Add remaining liquid and melted chocolate (cooled to room temperature) and beat two minutes longer. Batter will be thin. Grease 9-inch layer pans or 10-by-10-by-2-inch pan and cover the bottoms with waxed paper. Turn the batter into the pans. Bake in 350°F oven about 30 minutes for a layer cake or 40 minutes for square cake. Frost with favorite white icing or fudge frosting.

Honey Pumpkin Pie

Louisiana State University Agricultural Extension.

1½ cups canned or steamed pumpkin
¾ cup honey
1 teaspoon cinnamon
½ teaspoon ginger
½ teaspoon salt
3 eggs
1 cup milk
½ cup cream or evaporated milk

Mix ingredients in order given and bake in a one-crust pie shell. Serve with honey drizzled whipped cream.

PRESERVING AND FREEZING WITH HONEY

Fruit Leather

California Honey Advisory Board.

4 cups fruit puree (apples, peaches, pears, apricots, plums, cherries or berries or combination) plus ¼ cup mild honey.

Puree fruit in a blender and blend with honey. Pour into a saucepan and heat to almost boiling (required for peaches, pears, apples, apricots, cherries, or nectarines to retain color and prevent darkening). Not cooking is required for fresh plums, raspberries, blackberries, cranberries, strawberries or boysenberries.

Line trays or baking sheets with plastic wrap and pour in the puree. Each layer of fruit puree should be no more than ¼-inch thick.

Place the trays in a dehydrator at 140°F or in the oven at 150°F for 4 to 6 hours, or outside in the sun for 1 to 2 days. The leather is done when it is leatherlike but still pliable.

Remove the leather from the trays while it is still warm and roll it up. Wrap in plastic. Makes four to five 8-by-10 inch sheets.

Strawberry Jam

4 cups crushed strawberries

2 boxes (1¾ oz.) powdered pectin
1¾ cups mild flavored honey
2 tablespoons fresh lemon juice

In 5 quart saucepan, combine strawberries and pectin. Bring to a boil. Cook at a rapid boil for 1 minute, stirring constantly. Add honey and lemon juice. Bring to a full rolling boil and boil for 5 minutes, stirring constantly. Skim off foam. Ladle into hot sterilized jars and seal. Makes six ½ pint jars.

Microwave Method Strawberry Jam

2 cups crushed strawberries
1 box (1¾ oz.) powdered pectin
¾ cup mild honey
1 tablespoon fresh lemon juice

In a 3 quart casserole, combine strawberries and pectin. Cook on HIGH for 4 minutes, stirring once. Stir in the honey and lemon juice. Cook on HIGH for 6 minutes, stirring twice. Skim off foam. Ladle into hot sterilized jars and seal. Makes three ½ pint jars.

Freezing with Honey

Many fruits can be successfully frozen in a mild-flavored honey syrup. For success the freezer must be equipped with a zero or below temperature control. A freezer without a separate temperature control in the refrigerator is *not a below-zero freezer*.

Use only firm, fully ripened fruit. Freezing does not improve flavor or quality.

Honey should be light in color and mild in flavor. It will then enhance the fruit's flavor and color. Thin to medium syrup is recommended for best results.

Thin Syrup

Add a cup mild honey to 3 cups very hot water. Makes 4 cups syrup. Blend and chill before using.

Medium Syrup

Add 2 cups mild honey to 2 cups very hot water. Makes 4 cups. Blend and chill before using. Use 1 cup of syrup for a one-quart container.

Freezing Peaches

Two pounds of fresh peaches is usually sufficient for one-quart yield. Work with small quantities. Wash peaches. Immerse them in boiling water for 1 minute. Cool the peaches in cold water. Slip the skin off one peach at a time. Pit the peach and slice it directly into a carton containing chilled syrup. Place a crumbled piece of foil on top to keep the fruit under syrup and prevent darkening. Seal at once, date, and freeze.

Freezing Strawberries

Wash firm ripe strawberries gently in ice water. Hull and slice in half. Carefully blend ½ cup chilled honey syrup into 4 cups prepared berries. Pack gently into freezer containers. Seal, date, and freeze.

Chapter 12

Other Honeybee Products

Honey is not the only product of the honeybee that is widely used. Wax has hundreds of uses and is an important product in other industries besides beekeeping. Pollen, propolis, and royal jelly have a more limited market. They have enjoyed increased demand with the heightened interest in nutrition, natural foods, and food supplements, and the renewed enthusiasm for holistic living.

Bee venom and propolis are being successfully integrated in some medical clinics and hospitals in other countries as healing agents. Research using bee venom on animals suffering from arthritis is taking place in the United States. Renewed interest in apiotherapy had led to the establishment of the North American Apiotherapy Society, which serves as a forum for information. Funding for formal research on bee venom therapy for humans is being promoted by a leading arthritis foundation.

RENDERING WAX

When you have collected and stored a quantity of wax and especially if you need to purchase more foundation, it is time to process or render your wax into clean, salable or usable form. Most suppliers will give credit toward new foundation for properly recycled wax. They will pay you so much per pound or give credit toward the purchase of other supplies and equipment. If you decide to try candlemaking with your wax, keep the wax from the drained cappings separate because it makes the best clean burning candles.

You will also have wax from the burr comb and propolis from in between and off the tops of frames, sides, bottom boards, and from old combs where the cells have been reduced in size from the buildup of wax and are too small for good brood rearing.

One of the best devices for rendering wax is the solar wax melter. Generally a solar unit has these components:

- Box or large container
- Lid of framed glass
- Large pan to hold the wax
- Smaller pan to catch the melted wax
- Screen or filtering cloth to keep out extraneous particles

Until you can make a unit, you can melt wax in small batches on the stove. NEVER PUT A CONTAINER OF WAX DIRECTLY ON A BURNER OR IN THE OVEN. WAX IS VERY FLAMMABLE AND A WAX FIRE IS HARD TO EXTINGUISH.

Place the wax in an old pot or a 3-pound coffee or shortening can. To prevent spill over, put in only enough wax to fill the container to about the ¾ mark. Set the can of wax in a pan of water or use a double boiler. Turn heat to medium-low or to a setting of approximately 145°F, the melting temperature of wax. Keep an eye on it. After it is melted, remove it from the heat and allow it to cool. This will minimize cracking when you put it into molds.

While still in liquid form, pour the wax into bread pans of stainless steel or aluminum. (Other metals are not recommended because they can discolor or impart an odor to wax.) Teflon-coated metal is easiest to use, but if you haven't any, you can coat the inside of the pan with honey to make removal of the hardened wax easier. Disposable aluminum bread pans or clean, used aluminum frozen food pans work well too. Do not use oil.

When you take the wax molds from the pans, there will be a dark residue at the bottom called *slumgum,* which you scrape off.

Another method of rendering wax is to put it in a clean burlap bag and immerse it in hot water. There should be at least 4 inches of water above the bag. If you have hard water, add some vinegar to prevent soapiness. Weight the bag down with rocks so that it does not float to the top. As wax melts and rises from the bag, you can ladle it off. Or you can turn off the heat when it appears that all wax has melted. Once the whole mass has cooled, you can lift it off the water. To speed up the process, jab the wax in the bag with a cooking fork from time to time to break it up. When you dispose of the residue in the bag, be sure bees cannot get to it.

If the wax still is not clean enough, you can remelt it and filter it through a fine nylon mesh like the one described for straining honey.

Wax is subject to mold if not well dried and ventilated. It should not be stored in plastic, foil, or anything airtight. It can be put in clean gunny sacks or wrapped in loosely woven cloth. Small blocks can be put in old socks or hose.

Not many beekeepers have access to a wax rendering plant as only a few states authorize them—California, Florida, Nebraska, Pennsylvania, Utah, and Washington. If you have one in your vicinity, it bears looking into. Commercial wax plant operators use steam and pressure and are able to salvage much more of the wax than individuals using home equipment (Fig. 12-1).

Fig. 12-1. Some states permit wax rendering plants, which use steam and pressure to render the wax. This is the Yates Wax Plant in Mentone, California, with the proprietor, Zekai Nazikoglu.

Local suppliers usually want only clean wax for credit but larger companies such as Dadant & Sons, Inc. will accept unrendered wax brought or shipped to them. It does not pay to send less than 100 pounds. Combs or cappings must be broken up, well drained, and washed in warm water prior to shipping. As a beginner it will take you some time to collect that much wax. You might go in with another hobbyist or barter your wax for used tools, hive parts, a queen, or some combs of brood from an established beekeeper.

To give you an idea of the quantity of wax you can get from various sources, two guidelines are offered by Dadant & Sons, Inc. in their catalog:

- Four deep frames of old comb usually amounts to 1 pound.
- Cappings from 1000 pounds of honey produces 7 to 10 pounds.

USES OF WAX

According to a California wax rendering plant manager, the market for wax is stronger than the market for honey. Wax has a thousand uses. About 35 percent is used for foundation, 33 percent for candlemaking, 10 to 20 percent for cosmetics and the rest for art, painting, and electronics (Table 12-1).

In ancient times, wax was used in a number of unusual ways. It was used as a seal for urns and jars for food storage and as an embalming agent for the dead. The Romans had a wax-coated writing tablet that they wrote on with a stylus. Imprinted wax emblems are still used to seal legal documents.

In the artistic world, wax becomes a substance to color and mold into lifelike flowers and fruit, human faces, and figures. Wax museums have long been a popular tourist attraction. Wax is used in the batik drying process to prevent the dye from covering specific segments and shapes. This allows a design to be created from the contrast of undyed or light and dark colors.

Beeswax candles are the finest because they are smokeless and dripless. Many churches still follow the tradition of allowing only beeswax candles for special rites and ceremonies.

Today wax is found in such diverse products as color crayons, chewing gum, carbon paper, dental supplies, furniture polish, cold cream, and lipstick. In cosmetics, wax is superior to manmade products because it is hypo-allergenic. A big consumer of wax is the beekeeping industry itself, for manufacturing foundation.

Not only can you sell the wax you render or get credit for new

Table 12-1. Honey and Beeswax: Production and Value of Production and Honey Stocks, 1972-81.

Year	Honey						Beeswax		
	Colonies	Yield Per Colony	Production	Price Per Pound	Total Value	Stocks on Hand	Production	Price Per Pound	Total Value
	Thousands	Pounds	1,000 Lbs	Dollars	1,000 Dollars	1,000 Lbs		Dollars	1,000 Dollars
1972	4,085	52.8	215,607	.302	65,049	30,114	3,997	.621	2,482
1973	4,124	58.0	239.089	.444	106,108	37,417	4,251	.744	3,161
1974	4,210	44.6	187.855	.510	95,766	34,427	3.450	1.14	3,937
1975	4,206	47.4	199.179	.505	100,575	33,155	3,405	1.03	3,495
1976	4,269	46.4	198.000	.499	98.827	34,310	3,346	1.12	3,764
1977	4,323	41.2	178.091	.529	94,274	30,043	3,091	1.58	4,869
1978	4,090	56.6	231.457	.546	126,471	32,238	3,965	1.74	6,890
1979	4,163	57.3	238,690	.593	141,498	37,997	3,788	1.75	6,643
1980	4,141	48.2	199,756	.615	122,811	40,518	3,905	1.83	7,163
1981	4,213	44.1	185,927	.632	117,559	48,623	3,712	1.91	7.103

Beeswax production totaled 3.71 million pounds (1680 metric tons) in 1981, 5 percent less than the 1980 wax production of 3.91 million pounds (1770 metric tons). The average price of beeswax at $1.91 per pound was 8.0 cents above the 1980 price and 16.0 cents above 1979. (Figures as reported by the Crop Reporting Board, USDA.)

foundation from a supplier, but you can also do a lot with it right in your home. It is handy for stuck zippers, windows, and drawers. You can rub it on thread and fishing line for ease in handling. It helps nails and screws penetrate more easily. You can use it for a wood filler and make a polish that is an excellent wood preserver.

Tools can be treated with wax to retard rusting. Screws that must withstand weathering in items like lawn furniture or patio covers and porch fixtures can be coated with wax for longer wear. Melted wax can be poured on top of homemade preserves and jellies—the original paraffin—to prevent mold. Surfers apply wax to their fiberglass boards to get a firmer hold with their feet. The list is practically endless. You will no doubt figure out some special uses yourself for this versatile bee product!

FORMULAS

Here are some formulas using wax you may like to try:

Cosmetics

From *The Complete Book of Natural Cosmetics* by Beatrice Traven (published by Simon and Schuster) with cosmetic formulations by Robert L. Goldemberg. Reproduced courtesy of Simon and Schuster.

Beeswax Base

¼ cup beeswax
¼ cup olive oil

Measure the olive oil into a Pyrex measuring cup; then add enough chipped beeswax (beeswax is hard) to bring the level up to ½ cup. You've now added ¼ cup beeswax. Set the measuring cup in very hot water in an electric fry pan and carefully stir until the wax and the oil are thoroughly melted together and all the wax has dissolved. Pour into a wide-mouthed jar and allow to cool.

You now have a soft "mother" base that is much easier to measure than beeswax itself. It will keep indefinitely, and can be used wherever equal parts of beeswax and oil are called for. Naturally the base can be made with other oils too, by the same method, and the results will be the same.

Easy Lip Gloss

2 teaspoons beeswax base (see recipe above)
6 tablespoons mink oil

Melt the ingredients together over boiling water until they're thoroughly "married." Then pour it into your prettiest small jar and let cool.

This is a lip pomade of truly awesome glossiness and emolliency. It can make you look more kissable, or it can do harder work and soothe and smooth chapped, dry, or sunburned lips.

Floor and Furniture Care

Brick Floor Sealer

Formulated by the Louisiana State University Cooperative Extension Service and reprinted by permission.

1¼ pound beeswax
1 gallon turpentine
½ pint Japanese dryer (obtainable at paint stores)

Mix ingredients in a large can that is sitting in a larger container with boiling water—a double boiler effect. (Note: do not let water boil over into sealer mix.) When all the wax is melted and the ingredients are very well mixed and hot to the point of smoking, it is ready to apply over bricks. This will seal bricks as it penetrates and gives them a wet look.

If you want a deeper color, add raw umber color tint (from paint stores) in amounts desired. Test on a spare brick. Before applying, make sure your bricks are as dry as possible. While very hot, sop or mop the sealer on thickly. After a few minutes, lightly rub off the excess. Apply a second coat. Let the bricks dry for some days; then wax with Indian Sand Treewax (Pasto) Buff. Maintain the brick floor with simple damp mopping.

Bee's Wax Polish

Formulated by the Louisiana State University Cooperative Extension Service and reprinted by permission.

1 quart clean beeswax
1 quart paint thinner (any kind)
3 quarts polyurethane semigloss varnish
¼ pint (2 oz.) Japan Dry (paint drying agent)

In a large can sitting in hot water, melt beeswax slowly. The wax should be hot to the touch but should not boil. Add paint thinner, semigloss varnish, and Japan Dry one at a time, mixing thoroughly before adding next ingredient. Stir mixture constantly with a long wooden spoon handle or paddle.

IMPORTANT NOTE: Work in a well-ventilated area or outside as the fumes are combustible.

Once all the ingredients are mixed, the polish is ready. Apply it with a brush while it is warm. After it has been applied and allowed to cool, wipe down or polish with a soft cloth.

During storage, the polish will separate in the container. To use, simply warm it in a water bath and stir until the mixture becomes a solution.

BEE VENOM

You may think that calling venom a "product" is a misnomer, but insect venom is indeed a product. It is becoming a more important one as more and more research is carried out to determine its positive effects. Bee venom is needed by allergists to desensitize individuals against insect stings. It has been found to give relief to persons suffering from arthritis and rheumatism.

To collect venom from honeybees, an electric ramp is installed in front of the hive. As the bees walk over it to get into the hive, they are shocked slightly. The shock causes the bees to automatically sting the silicone cloth underlying the grid. The collected venom is dried, packaged, and sent to drug laboratories. It requires stings from 10,000 bees to collect one gram of venom.

When an adult bee emerges from its cell, its stinger is not yet mature. It develops within the first 24 hours. By its second day, the new bee's sting has hardened and venom starts into the sac. By 15 days, the worker has a full dose of venom or about .1 mg.

Bee venom is composed of 60 percent water, 7 percent proteins, 24 percent protein subunits such as peptides and polypetides, and small biogenic compounds. The major components are enzymes. These are the allergens that cause reactions in most people. They are hyaluronidase, phospholipase, and mellatin.

Hyaluronidase dissolves intercell connections allowing the venom to get deeper into the tissue. Phospholipase reduces blood pressure and can bring on asphyxiation. Mellatin creates the pain of the sting, also causes asphyxiation and increases plasma cortisol. This last effect also gives the relief in treatment of arthritis.

The stinger of the bee consists of two lancets with sharp fishhook type barbs pointing downward like a miniature harpoon. When a bee inserts its stinger into an animal or person and tries to pull the stinger out, it invariably pulls out part of its abdominal parts with it and dies. The muscular mechanism continues to work, however and pushes the venom into your skin. It has been observed pumping for as long as 20 minutes after entry.

The first thing to do after a bee makes contact is to remove the stinger. DO NOT SQUEEZE OR PULL IT OUT. That increases the reaction and shoots more venom into the tissue. ALWAYS SCRAPE A STINGER FROM SIDE TO SIDE TO REMOVE IT.

Most people have a local reaction. First a sharp pain, then swelling and itching that can be relieved with ice packs and various astringent type solutions. It usually heals in a few days. If a reaction includes other parts of the victim's body, such as hives or severe swelling at the site of the sting, then the victim is allergic.

If the reaction includes difficulty in breathing, choking, and lowering of blood pressure, the condition is called *anaphylactic shock*. That person is highly sensitive to bee venom and immediate medical aid or emergency measures must be taken. Happily only 1 to 4 percent of the population is severely allergic to bee stings.

As with other allergies, doctors can desensitize individuals against insect venom, including bee venom. Some use an extract made from the body of the offending insect. More recently allergists are having better success with pure venom. People respond in various ways to the desensitization process. Some will need only a series of treatments. Others must continue for a long period with a booster injection once a month.

Most beekeepers develop a resistance and find stings progressively less of a problem. Two percent of the population becomes increasingly hypersensitive. Each sting brings on a worse reaction. Such people have to give up beekeeping.

Sometimes members of a beekeeper's family who do not work around the bees nor get stung develop a hypersensitivity. It has been discovered that exposure to dried venom can increase a sensitive person's reaction in nearly the same way as getting stung. Experts are advising that clothing, gloves, or any item that may have been injected by bees be left outside until laundered and not placed where children or other family members, especially those who are allergy prone, can come into contact with them.

Suggestions for avoiding stings have been mentioned throughout the book but here's a quick summary:

- Work bees in the mildest, sunniest weather possible during the hours when the majority of field workers are out.
- Avoid working bees in wind, rain, or before a thunderstorm.
- Smoke under the cover, across the frames, and wait two minutes.

- Move slowly and cautiously. Bees are sensitive to jarring and vibrations.
- To get bees to move and avoid hurting or crushing them, touch them lightly, on their backs with a hive tool or your finger.
- If a bee stings your glove or any other part of your clothing, wet the area with water to remove the scent, which attracts other bees.

Even though you may have ascertained that none of your neighbors or the folks near the area where you have installed your hives are allergic to bees, it is still prudent to be prepared for the possible guest or passerby who may be supersensitive. Get a prescription from your doctor for an insect sting emergency kit. Read the instructions carefully and check through the contents right away before a problem occurs. Then put the emergency kit in the gear box you take to your apiary.

The kits are marketed under the names "Anakit" from Hollister-Stier Laboratories or Anaphylactic Shock Drug Kit put out by Hoyt. The contents include a syringe with two single doses of Epinephrine, which helps restore normal breathing; anahistamine tablets, which relieves the itching; sterilizing swabs to cleanse the area to be injected; and a tourniquet to apply in conjunction with the injection.

The syringe has two doses of Epinephrine to be given in two separate injections and is marked so that a smaller dose can be given to a child.

The American Medical Society has approved a model bill and has mounted a campaign to get states to authorize lay persons to give Epinephrine to persons exhibiting anaphylactic shock, but some states have not yet passed the bill. In that case you would not be able to get a kit. You should carry the name/number of the closest ambulance service and emergency medical facility and know where the nearest phone is to your beehives.

BEE LOOK-ALIKES

Persons often blame honeybees for stings when it is in actuality another insect in the *hymenoptera* family such as a yellowjacket, wasp, or a hornet (Fig. 12-2). They are all colored in brown or black and yellow with gauzy veined wings and the general body appearance of a honeybee—at least to the untrained eye. Their stings create the same reaction; sharp pain followed by some swelling.

Fig. 12-2. Some of the bee look-alikes are (from left to right) the hornet, the wasp, and the bumblebee.

Certain hornets and wasps are not killed when they sting and can sting repeatedly (Fig. 12-3).

A list of insects that are confused with honeybees is given in Table 12-2.

PROPOLIS

Another product of the hive that has come into the limelight for its curative properties is propolis. Bees collect resinous substances like sap from buds. They add pollen and beeswax to make up their own special glue-propolis. It not only acts as a seal against rain, wind, and cold but also seems to prevent bacteria growth.

Fig. 12-3. The paper wasp builds a nest of hexagonal cells (as does the honeybee) and suspends it from eaves. (Photo by W. P. Nye, Apiculturalist Retired, Bee Biology and Systemics Laboratory, Logan, UT.)

Table 12-2. Honeybee Look-Alikes.

Name	Characteristics	Where Found
Bumble Bee	Three or four times larger than honeybee; black and yellow color; hairy	Small colonies in ground near clover alfalfa, lawns, and flowers.
Yellow jackets	Yellow and black striped abdomen	Brownish colored nests of partially decayed wood, usually underground.
Hornet	Black and white	Silvery gray football-shaped nest, often suspended from tree or buildings.
Paper wasp	Black and yellow; they fold wings behind them when they are not in flight.	Nests of hexagonal cells from thin slivers of wood like paper on eaves.

Beekeepers have noticed that bees will propolize any dead mouse or large insect they cannot move out of their hive. The body of the propolized creature stays intact with no decomposition, therefore no bacteria formation.

A Danish naturalist has developed an edible form of propolis that is being used by doctors in Europe. As an antibiotic, it surpasses synthetic drugs because it creates no after effects and because bacteria does not become resistant to it. An Austrian doctor has tried bee propolis on patients with duodenal and gastric ulcers. The group given regular treatment had a 10 percent record of relief while the group given propolis had a 70 percent relief record.

In West Germany propolis is used as one ingredient in making an antibiotic that has shown good results in preventing infection and as a dressing for wounds and burns. In Bucharest, Rumania, an entire clinical staff of doctors and a dentist is supplementing standard medical practice with bee products, among them propolis. Based on their observations and experiences they consider the use of propolis valid. One doctor treated 300 cases of pimples with propolis and got 80 percent success. Propolis is being used with good results for other skin problems such as herpes, infections in the mouth, and for burns.

Some scientists are not sure that the bees really add any special secretion to the substances they collect and develop into propolis. They suspect that plant propolis alone without any processing by the bees may have the same antibacterial effects. However, no laboratory in the United States has to date taken up research with propolis to prove or disprove the claims.

POLLEN

Interest in pollen for its nutritional effects has heightened a great deal in the last decade. Since 1978, many established beekeepers in the United States have turned to pollen collecting to supplement their honey and wax income.

The value of pollen is as frought with controversy as the worth of daily vitamins. Some scoff and say pollen is a fad because results have not been scientifically tested. Others claim increasing good health and are quite willing to pay a handsome price for their daily intake of pollen.

According to one report, importers deal in millions of pounds of pollen from Spain, Australia, Britain, and Canada. The largest importer of pollen is the United States. Before foreign pollen is permitted into our country, it must be heated and fumigated with ethyl dioxide to prevent any disease organism from being brought in. American beekeepers do not use any chemicals on their pollen and should, proponents say, be able to compete most favorably with the imported product on the home market.

Pollen is collected in traps set below a wire screen. When the bee passes over the screen some of the pollen is scraped from her legs. It is harvested every two to three days with an average yield of ¼ to 1 pound per day per trap. It is then stored in a freezer or dried, then bottled or packaged for sale.

Pollen collecting and marketing is not free of problems. It can be detrimental to colony health. One researcher in Georgia found that heavy pollen collecting reduced brood rearing up to 25 percent. Another problem is the liability of selling pollen as a food supplement. Many people are allergic to it and could have severe reactions to ingesting it.

APIOTHERAPY

Apiotherapy is the study and application of bee products to achieve medical and nutritional benefits. Although the use of propolis, pollen, royal jelly, and bee venom for treatment is being actively researched and is supported by governments of several European nations, the Soviet Union, and some South American countries, the American medical establishment has been slow to realize the potential value of these products.

To date research with bee venom has been carried out clinically only on horses, rats, and dogs. A scientist in Texas and veterinarians in Louisiana and Virginia have achieved a high rate of success in applying bee venom therapy to arthritic dogs.

Exactly how the bee venom works in the body is still under investigation. Most experts believe that the mellatin increases the body's natural formation of cortisone and that other components apparently stimulate the immune system and increase the blood supply where the venom is injected.

The status of clinical testing with human beings, which entails careful diagnosis and detailed record keeping, depends on the availability of funds for research. Initial steps have been taken to gain the approval of thc Federal Food and Drug Administration. The Warren Memorial Arthritis Foundation, a private non-profit organization, is actively seeking resources to begin formal clinical research with bee venom as a treatment.

Initial interest in apiotherapy was stimulated by Dr. Bodog F. Beck's book, *Bee Venom Therapy* published in 1935 by Appelton-Century. Dr. Beck did not use extracted venom but actually treated his patients with direct bee stings. Since that time other physicians, despairing at the lack of success with conventional treatments for gout, rheumatism, and arthritis have tried bee venom therapy. Many were beekeepers and had had personal experience with the benefits of bee stings. Because of the increasing incidence of malpractice suits, few of those pioneers of the '30s through the '60s have continued with apiotherapy.

One doctor interviewed after retirement put it this way: "I was in it for 40 years. I treated a hell of a lot of arthritic patients. I estimate that I used pretty close to a million bees. Maybe that's an exaggeration, but I don't know. I would see 20 to 30 patients a day, putting on from 2 to 150 bees apiece. It doesn't take long to get into the hundreds and thousands before you know it.

"I've never been able to carry insurance. It's not accepted treatment."

"They wouldn't insure you?"

"No. They wouldn't accept the treatment. They told me, 'You're crazy to treat people that way.' So I had all the responsibility on my own shoulders. I'd say to the patient, 'Now look, I may be able to help you when nothing else has. You've tried everything else. Now try this if you wish.' But that doesn't mean I couldn't have been sued, and I wouldn't have had a Chinaman's chance if something had actually happened.

"Well, my experience is such that I feel very pleased and proud if I wanted to brag about it. What I've done in my lifetime with bees

I've been justified in doing. As I look back on it, I am very happy with what I was able to do. I've seen people who just couldn't walk, who are now walking."*

Since there is no law against lay people using bees to inject venom the natural way, some present day beekeepers have become unofficial therapists. Stimulated by success with their own treatment or that of family members, they have helped friends and others when they were not getting better with conventional methods. Several university level entomologists have also attested to the value of bee venom in relieving the pain and crippling effects of arthritis, and other similar diseases. Some of the success stories are truly amazing and are chronicled in the book, *Bees Don't Get Arthritis* by Fred Malone, published by E.P. Dutton, Inc.

A principal leader in the movement to give apiotherapy more recognition and to interest the medical profession in its worth is Charles Mraz, of Middlebury, Vermont. Mraz has collected venom for nearly 50 years and is the primary commercial source of the product for research (on animals) and for allergy desensitization. He is a regular feature writer for "Gleanings in Bee Culture," and appeared on the Today television program in 1978, in an interview with Frank Bourgholtzer.

Mraz is also one of the founders of the North American Apiotherapy Society, which grew from an annual symposium of interested persons in the early '70s to a full-fledged organization in 1978.

The mission of the NAAS is to collect and disseminate information on apiotherapy and provide a forum for researchers in apiotherapy to present their studies. Dues for membership are $10 per year. Applications and more information may be obtained by writing to: Ann W. Harmon, 15621 Aitcheson Lane, Laurel, MD 20707.

*From *Bees Don't Get Arthritis* by Fred Malone. Copyright © 1979 by Fred Malone. Reprinted by permission of the publisher, E.P. Dutton, Inc.

Chapter 13

Do-It-Yourself Equipment

Beekeeping equipment can be expensive, especially for the beginner. The easiest way to save money is to make most of the necessary tools of the trade yourself. If you're at all handy around the workshop, the following items should be simple and inexpensive to make at home.

UNCAPPING TANKS

An uncapping tank built with supers was conceived and developed by Ron Neese, Apiary Director Orange County Farm Bureau, Irvine, California. It is made from two medium or full depth supers. On the bottom of one super, nail or staple window screening. Inside the same super, at the top, nail in a cross board or two to support the frame you are uncapping. A screw may be inserted upside down with its point up above the bar to provide a nonslip contact for the frame (Fig. 13-1).

Bend and solder sheet metal into a pan. This pan will be placed at the bottom of the bottom super. Punch a hole in one side and poke in a short piece of pipe for the honey to drain through. Apply a sealant for a tight fit if necessary.

The wax should be allowed to drain until it is as dry as possible. Then render it by heating it in a can placed in a pan of hot water or in a solar wax melter. Or you can store it until you collect a quantity for rendering all at once.

Another uncapping tank design, conceived by Bill Montgom-

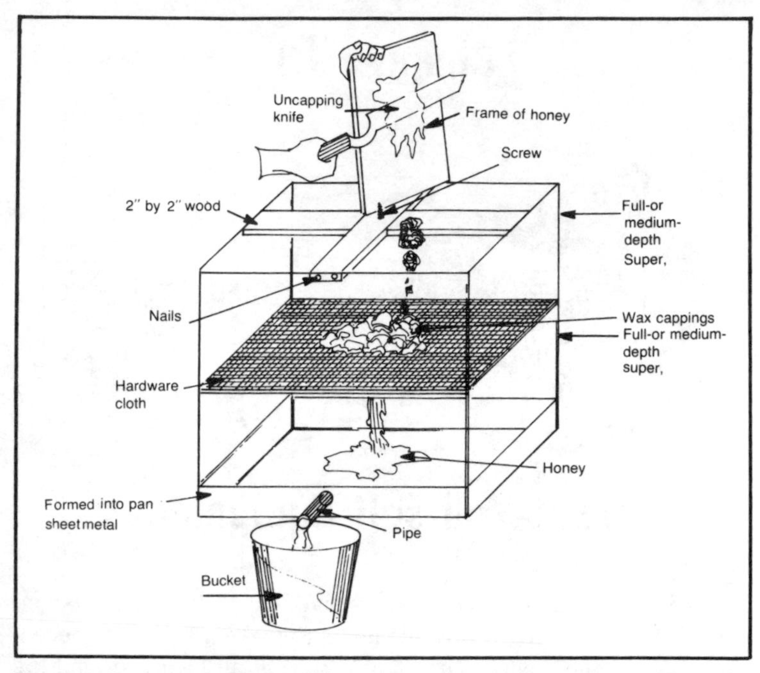

Fig. 13-1. An uncapping tank built from two supers with a fine screen or hardware cloth nailed to the bottom of the top one and a pan fashioned from sheetmetal fitted in the bottom of the bottom super. Pipe is inserted for the honey flow.

ery, Manhattan Beach, California, can be made from a large wash tub. Punch or bore a hole in the bottom for draining. Construct a platform of ¾-by-1½ inch scrap wood to place on the bottom to support the screen or hardware cloth. Attach a sheet of screen the same size as the bottom of the tub with nails, brads, or staples to the platform. Wedge a bar of wood inside the tub at the top to support the frame and secure with bolts (Fig. 13-2).

Place the tub on a support, either a block of wood or bricks and place a large pan underneath it to catch the honey.

If the area where uncapping is done is cool or honey is thick or granulated, an industrial light or heat lamp may be clamped to the side and directed down to warm the honey and speed up the uncapping and draining process (Fig. 13-3).

STRAINING AND BOTTLING TANKS

An inexpensive straining tank, conceived and designed by Ron Neese, may be put together using a heavy-duty plastic bucket with a tight-fitting lid, fine mesh nylon cloth, and a gate valve with an

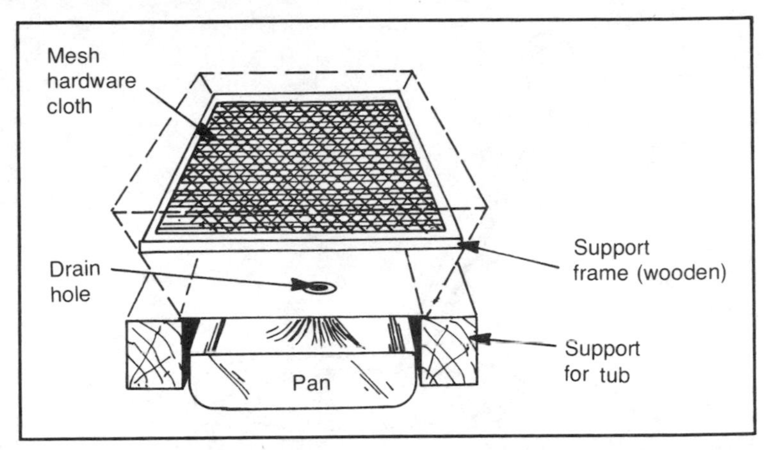

Fig. 13-2. An uncapping tank constructed from a large tub. Detail of bottom showing the wooden frame with mesh hardware cloth, drain hole, and catch pan.

O-ring. Plastic buckets are available from fast food places (they get the soft drink concentrates in them) or from bakeries that have their frozen fruit delivered in them, health food stores, or beekeeping suppliers (Fig. 13-4).

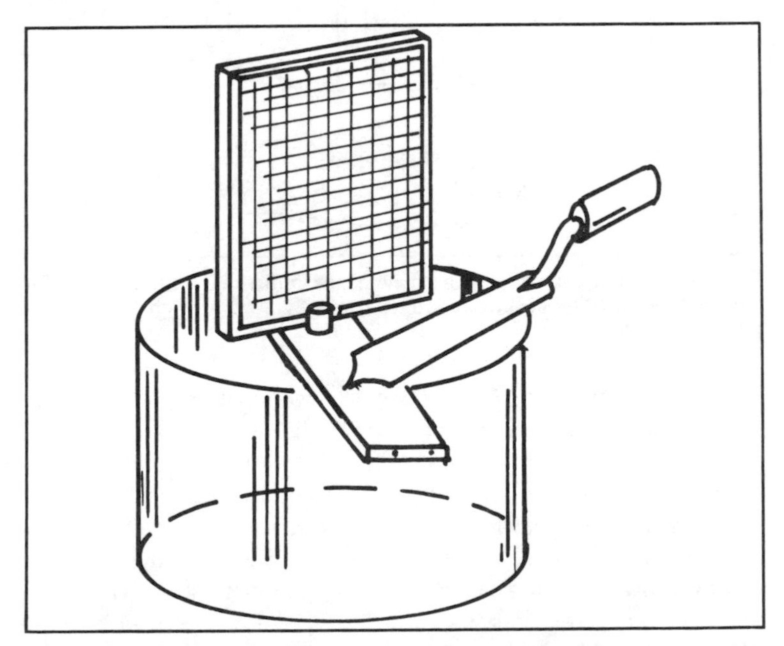
Fig. 13-3. Top detail showing the 2×2 wooden support bolted into the top of the tub. The frame is set on this for slicing with the uncapping knife.

Fig. 13-4. The first step in making a straining tank from a food storage bucket. Cut the inner section of the lid out leaving the rim intact. Have fine nylon mesh cloth or paint strainer ready.

You can buy 2- to 5-gallon sizes. Two smaller ones are more practical in that they are not so heavy to lift, but they are twice the expense and time to adapt for straining. However a 5-gallon one will weigh 60 pounds when filled with honey, or 45 pounds when three-quarters full—quite a bit to hoist around.

You will also need to procure a yard of fine mesh nylon bolting or cloth, available at fabric stores. Or you can use a nylon paint straining bag from the hardware or paint store. Beekeeping suppliers have the cloth and fine mesh metal adjustable strainers also.

The gate valve and O-ring is available at hardware, building supply, or plumbing stores.

Here are the steps:

1. Cut the inside of the lid out to the rim but leave the rim intact.

2. Cut a hole (start small and keep checking) slightly smaller than the interior circumference of the opening of the gate valve in the side of the plastic bucket, about 2 inches from the bottom (Fig. 13-5).

3. Push the gate valve through the hole with the handle on the outside.

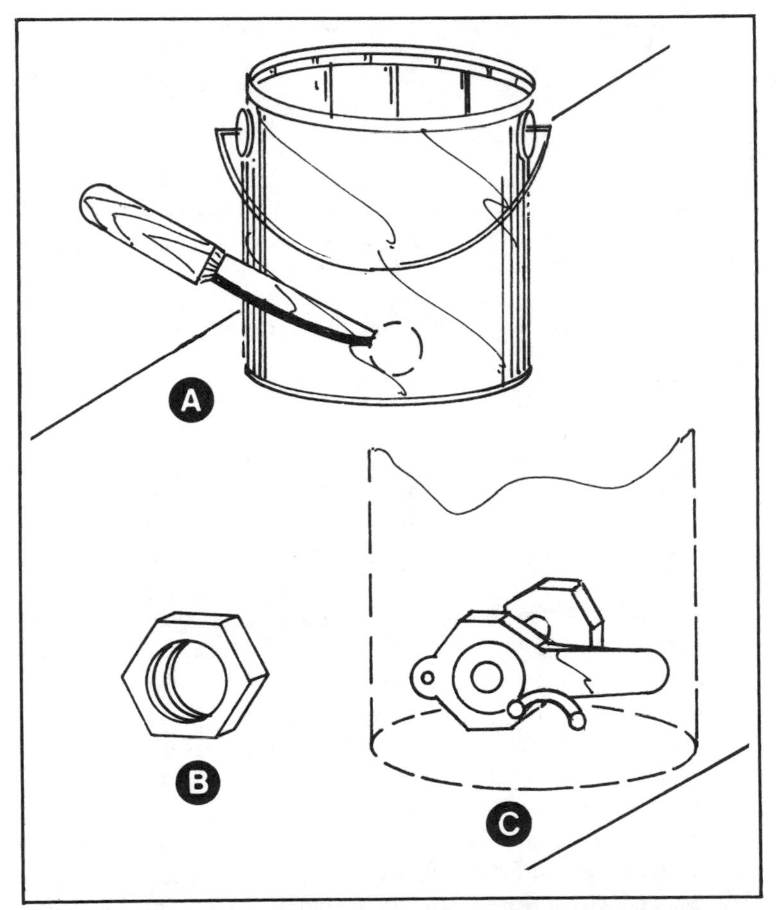

Fig. 13-5. (A) Cut a hole in the side about 2 inches from the bottom. (B) The O ring is placed over the hole inside. (C) The gate valve screws through the hole and is secured with the O ring inside.

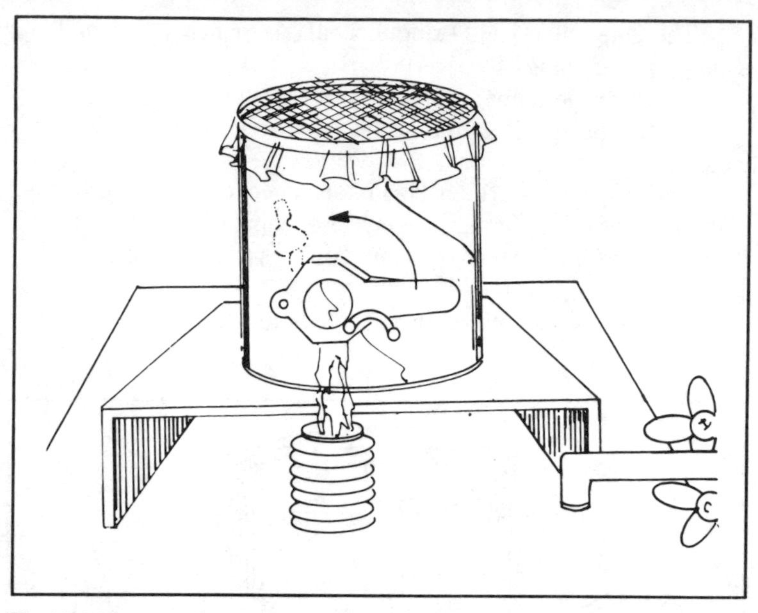

Fig. 13-6. The completed straining tank placed next to a sink. The gate valve can be adjusted to control the flow into the jars.

4. Secure the O-ring on the inside. If the fit is not tight, apply some plastic sealant and allow to cure.

5. Cut the nylon into a piece 3 inches larger than the circumference of the bucket, to allow for sag. Do not pull it taut as this will not allow enough space for the honey to sit while it is dripping through. Place the rim over the cloth and clamp it firmly in place.

A good place to set up the straining-bottling tank to fill your jars is on the edge of a sink. Place the jar in the sink to facilitate clean up (Fig. 13-6).

From P.F. (ROY) Thurber, long-time beekeeper in Kirkland, Washington, and columnist for "The Speedy Bee," comes this design idea for a honey warming unit from an old refrigerator. Follow the steps in Figs. 13-7, 13-8, and 13-9.

Choose an old refrigerator with a good door gasket. There should be no airspace between the door and the body of the refrigerator when the door is closed.

If the refrigerator is still in running order, no matter how poorly, disconnect it from any power source and remove the cord. You won't be plugging it in to warm the honey and it's possible to get a bad shock if you should hit a live wire.

With the proper drill bit or attachment, cut a hole in the bottom of the storage section. It need only be large enough to accommodate an electrical cord. Purchase a porcelain light socket. Place this over the hole and screw it firmly in place. Run the electrical cord from the socket out through the hole and under the refrigerator. Screw in one 100 watt light bulb.

Now take an empty 1-gallon paint can and punch holes randomly all over it. Place this over the 100 watt bulb to diffuse the heat from the lit bulb.

Put a reliable thermometer inside the refrigerator. Replace the shelves. Supers or containers of thick or crystallized honey can now be placed inside to warm. Be careful that the inside temperature does not exceed 120°F.

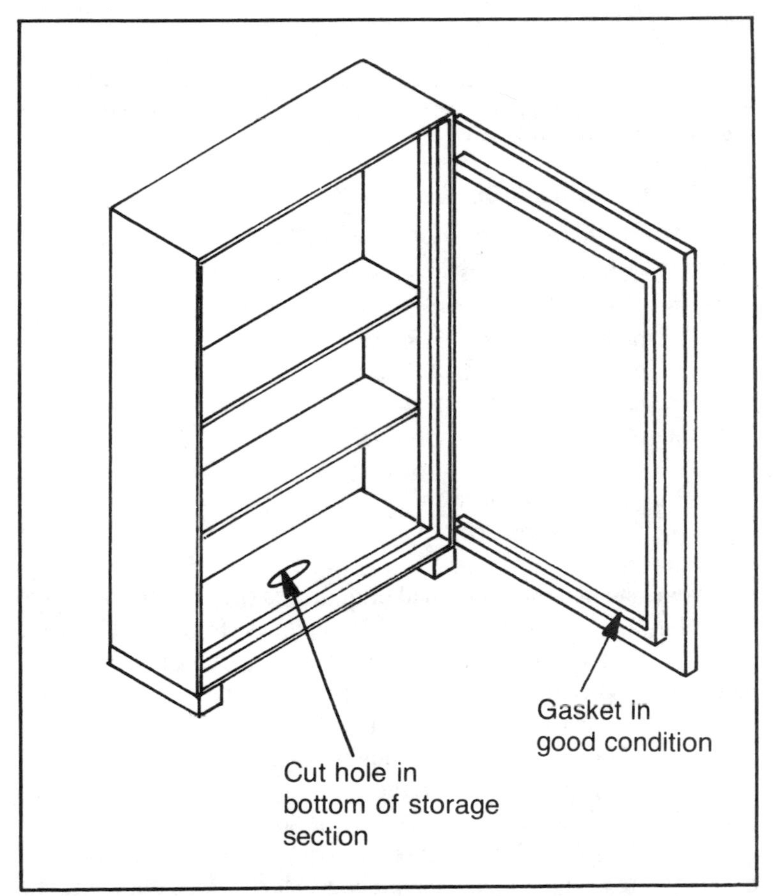

Fig. 13-7. You can make a honey warming unit from an old refrigerator. The gaskets on the door should be in good condition. Cut a hole in the bottom shelf of the storage section.

Fig. 13-8. Assemble a paint can with holes punched in it, one 100-watt light bulb, and a porcelain light socket with an electric cord.

A TEN-FRAME NAILING DEVICE

To make your own 10-frame nailing device like the one shown in Fig. 13-10, you will need the following materials:

2 pine pieces, 17 13/16 × 7⅛ × ¾ inch
2 pine pieces, 14⅛ × 6¾ × ¾ inch
2 pine pieces, 15¾ × 3 × ¾ inch
2 pine pieces, 15⅝ × 3 × ¾ inch
4 pine pieces, 1 3/16 × ¾ × ¼ inch
4 pine pieces, 7 × 1¾ × ¼ inch
2 16-inch screen door springs
4 ¼ × 1-inch wood screws

Glue and nail the four small pine pieces (Fig. 13-10F) into the lower left and right corners of the two pieces (Fig. 13-10A). Glue and nail the four small pine pieces (Fig. 13-10E) against those pieces (F) and running vertically to the top of the pieces (A). See Fig. 13-10 for clarification of locations.

Assemble main box by attaching D pieces to completed A pieces in the manner shown in the illustration. Use glue and large nails as this joint will take considerable load.

Attach the two pieces marked C together by screwing one end of the spring to the end of each piece as shown. Use both springs, one on each end. Place completed assembly C over the box to the position shown in the illustration.

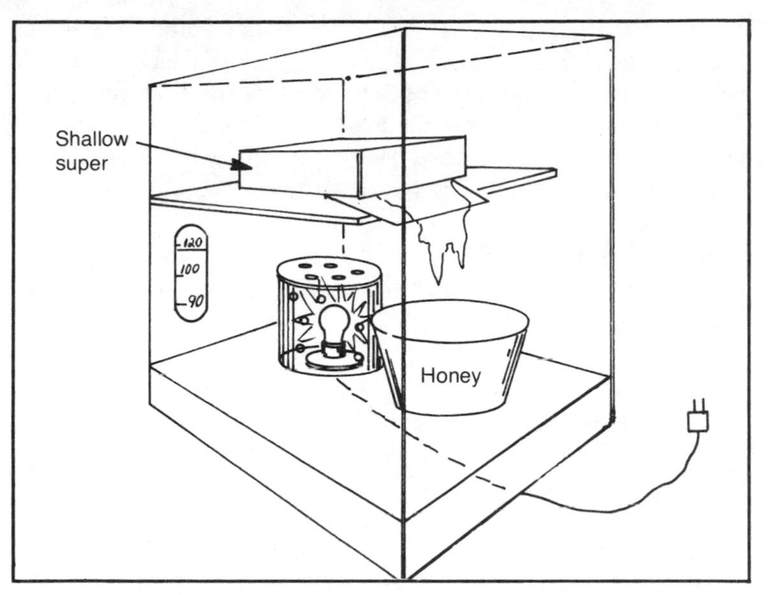

Fig. 13-9. Place the socket over the hole and run the cord to an outlet. Screw in the bulb and place the paint can over it to diffuse the heat. Set supers or containers of honey inside. A photographic thermometer can be placed inside. Temperature should not exceed 120°F.

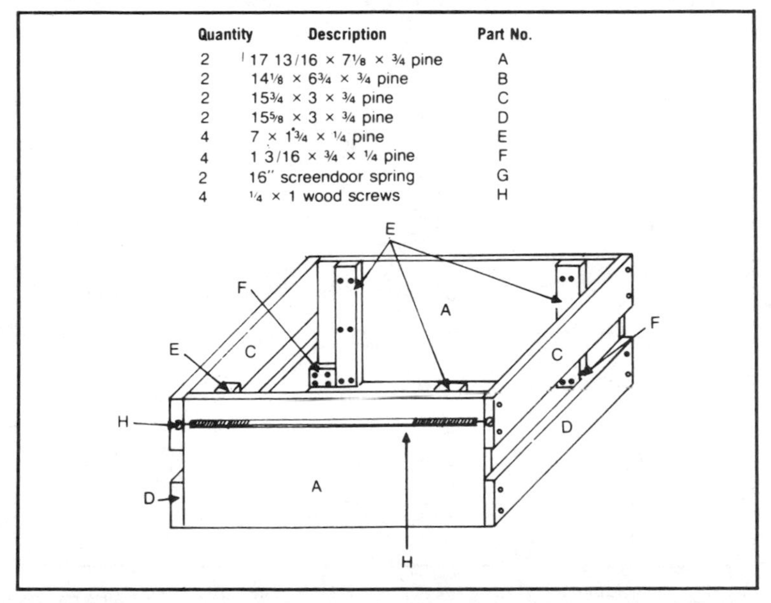

Quantity	Description	Part No.
2	17 13/16 × 7 1/8 × 3/4 pine	A
2	14 1/8 × 6 3/4 × 3/4 pine	B
2	15 3/4 × 3 × 3/4 pine	C
2	15 5/8 × 3 × 3/4 pine	D
4	7 × 1 3/4 × 1/4 pine	E
4	1 3/16 × 3/4 × 1/4 pine	F
2	16" screendoor spring	G
4	1/4 × 1 wood screws	H

Fig. 13-10. Ten frame nailing device bill of materials. (Design and directions by Ron Neese, Apiary Director, Orange County Farm Bureau, Irvine, California.)

Place the pieces marked B into the slots created by E and C. The B pieces will not be attached in any way and must move freely in and out of the box but must be supported by the F pieces.

It is beneficial to cover the inside face of C pieces with some sort of flexible material such as weatherstripping or indoor-outdoor carpeting.

A FRAME WIRING BOARD

To assemble the frame wiring board shown in Fig. 13-11, you will need the following materials:

1 piece of 36-by-12 inch plywood, ⅜ inch or thicker
3 1½-inch broom handle dowels
5 1 × ¾ × ¾ inch wooden blocks
1 screw eye
3 strips of wood, 1½ × ¾ × 12 inch
¼-inch bolts, nuts, and washers for spools
Miscellaneous wood scraps for spool holder

Decide whether you want the board to be for a right-handed person or a left-handed person. If for a right-handed person, spool holder will be on the left. If for a left-handed person, the spool holder will be on the right (Fig. 13-11).

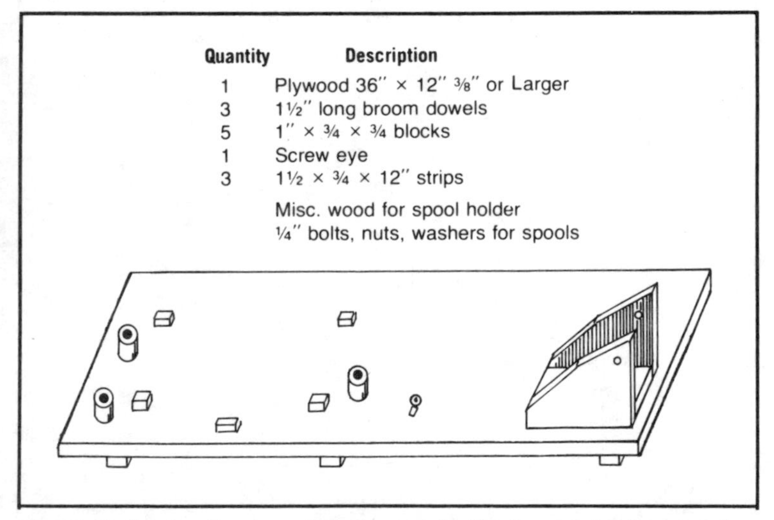

Quantity	Description
1	Plywood 36″ × 12″ ⅜″ or Larger
3	1½″ long broom dowels
5	1″ × ¾ × ¾ blocks
1	Screw eye
3	1½ × ¾ × 12″ strips
	Misc. wood for spool holder
	¼″ bolts, nuts, washers for spools

Fig. 13-11. Frame wiring board bill of materials. (Design and directions courtesy of Ron Neese, Apiary Director, Orange County Farm Bureau, Irvine, California.)

Using an assembled but unwired frame of standard size, place it on the end opposite that of where the spool will go so that it is about 4 inches from the end and about 2 inches from the long side closest to you.

Using a pencil, draw a line around the complete inside perimeter of the frame with the frame square to the plywood corner and in the above position. Also put lines where the eyelet holes occur in both endbars of the frame.

Remove the frame. Using the five blocks, place and nail four of them in the four corners of the box that you have just drawn. Be careful to locate them just inside of the lines so that the frame will fit easily over them. Locate the fifth block centered in the bottom line and hanging down over it by ⅜ to ½ inch.

Build the spool holder. It is easiest to build if you have a spool similar to the ones you will be using, and build the holder to fit. You want a close fit so that by tightening the spool bolt you can increase the tension on the spool.

Using the two small lines you made for the bottom eyelet holes, extend that line clear across the plywood. Attach the spool holder at the end of the plywood opposite the frame and so the center line of the spool holder is even with the line you just made.

Install the screw eye at least 4 inches from the frame along the same line you just made.

Now locate the three spools on the plywood so that they are 2 inches from the frame and centered between the appropriate eyelet hole lines.

The last step is to install the 12-inch-long wood strips. These should be located under the plywood between where the blocks and the spools are attached with one also under the spool holder.

AN EMBEDDING BOARD

To make this embedding board, you will need the following materials:

1 piece of 2 × 2 foot plywood, ⅜ inch or thicker
2 pieces of pine, 16¾ × 7½ × ¾ inch
3 pieces of 2 × 4 pine, 24 inches long
1 microswitch
1 110 volt electrical cord
1 12 volt doorbell transformer
Wire, sheetmetal, masking tape

Attach the two pieces of pine together, one on top of the other. Then locate them on the plywood in what will be the lower right hand corner with 2 inches of space on the borders of the pine (Fig. 13-12).

Cut 2 pieces of sheetmetal approximately 7½ inches long by 1 inch wide. These will be attached to the edges of the pine, which are 7½ inches long. Attach them so that they cover the side and extend up above the surface of the pine by about ½ the thickness of a sheet of foundation.

Drill a small hole through the plywood near the end of the sheet-metal pieces that you just attached. This hole only needs to be large enough for one wire to pass through. Cover the pine boards' surface with tape.

Lay an assembled and wired frame on the pine board so that the top bar of the frame is towards the bottom of the board and the frame

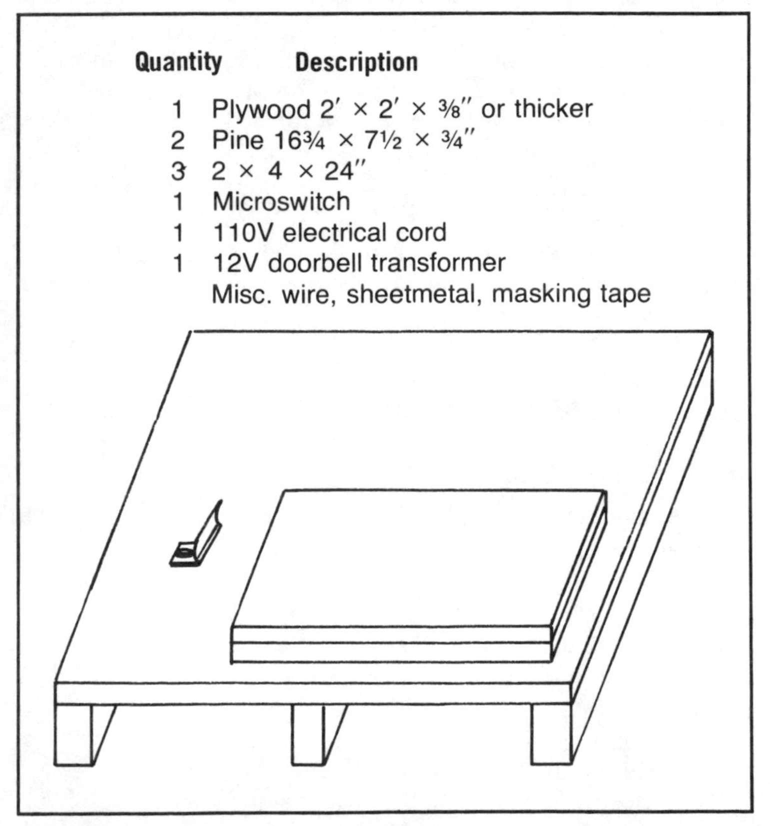

Quantity	Description
1	Plywood 2′ × 2′ × ⅜″ or thicker
2	Pine 16¾ × 7½ × ¾″
3	2 × 4 × 24″
1	Microswitch
1	110V electrical cord
1	12V doorbell transformer
	Misc. wire, sheetmetal, masking tape

Fig. 13-12. Embedding board bill of materials.

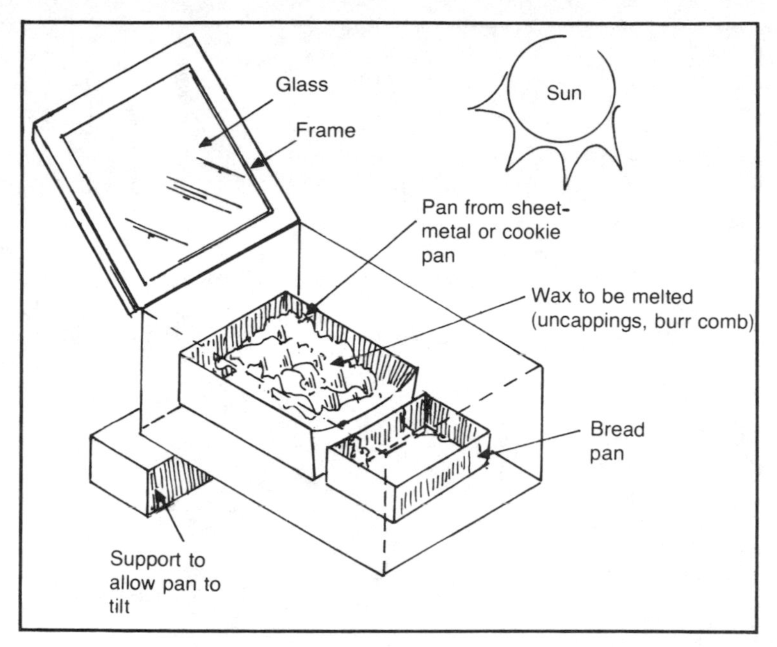

Fig. 13-13. Solar wax melter constructed from a full or medium depth super. (Concept by Ron Neese.)

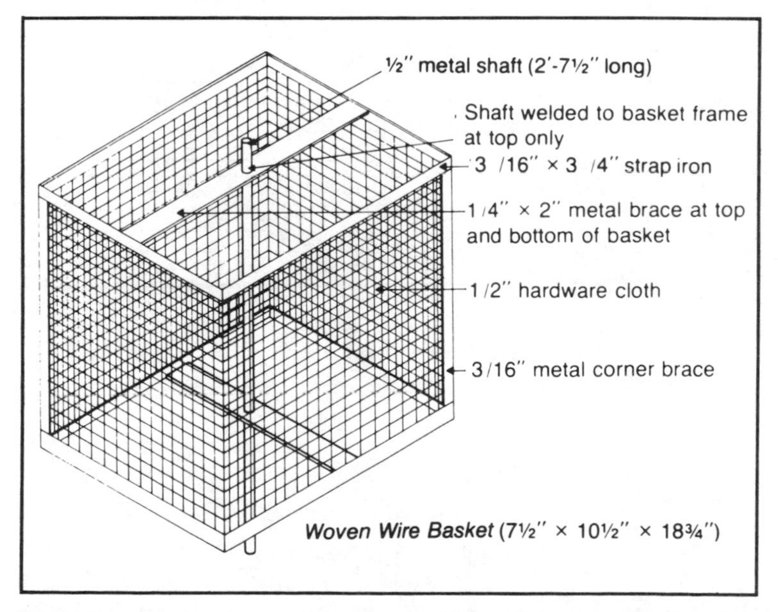

Fig. 13-14. Honey extractor. (Courtesy, Louisiana State University & A. & M. College.)

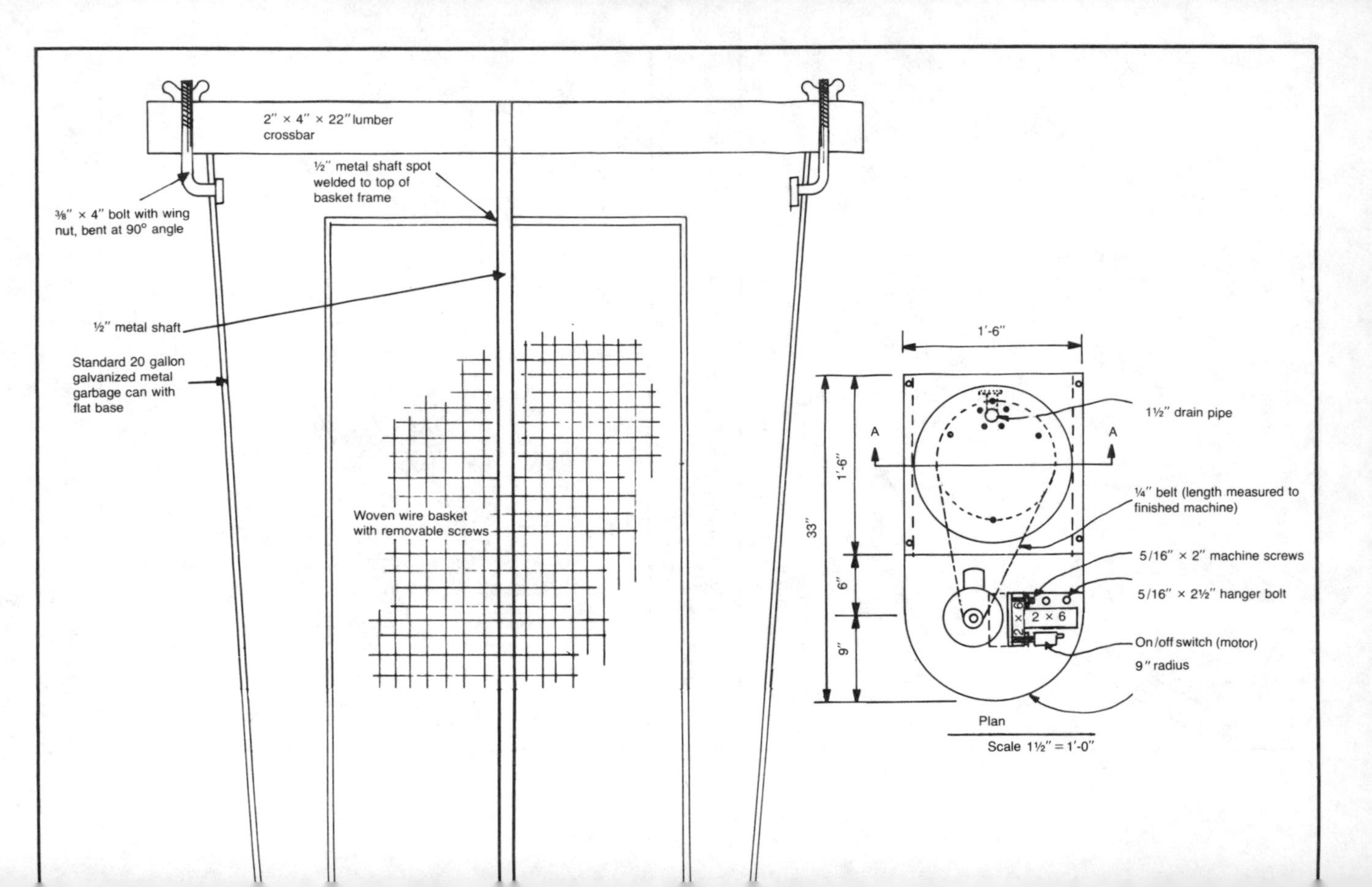

2" × 4" × 22" lumber crossbar
½" metal shaft spot welded to top of basket frame
⅜" × 4" bolt with wing nut, bent at 90° angle
½" metal shaft
Standard 20 gallon galvanized metal garbage can with flat base
Woven wire basket with removable screws
1'-6"
1½" drain pipe
A
A
1'-6"
33"
6"
9"
¼" belt (length measured to finished machine)
5/16" × 2" machine screws
5/16" × 2½" hanger bolt
2 × 6
9 × 2
On/off switch (motor)
9" radius
Plan
Scale 1½" = 1'-0"

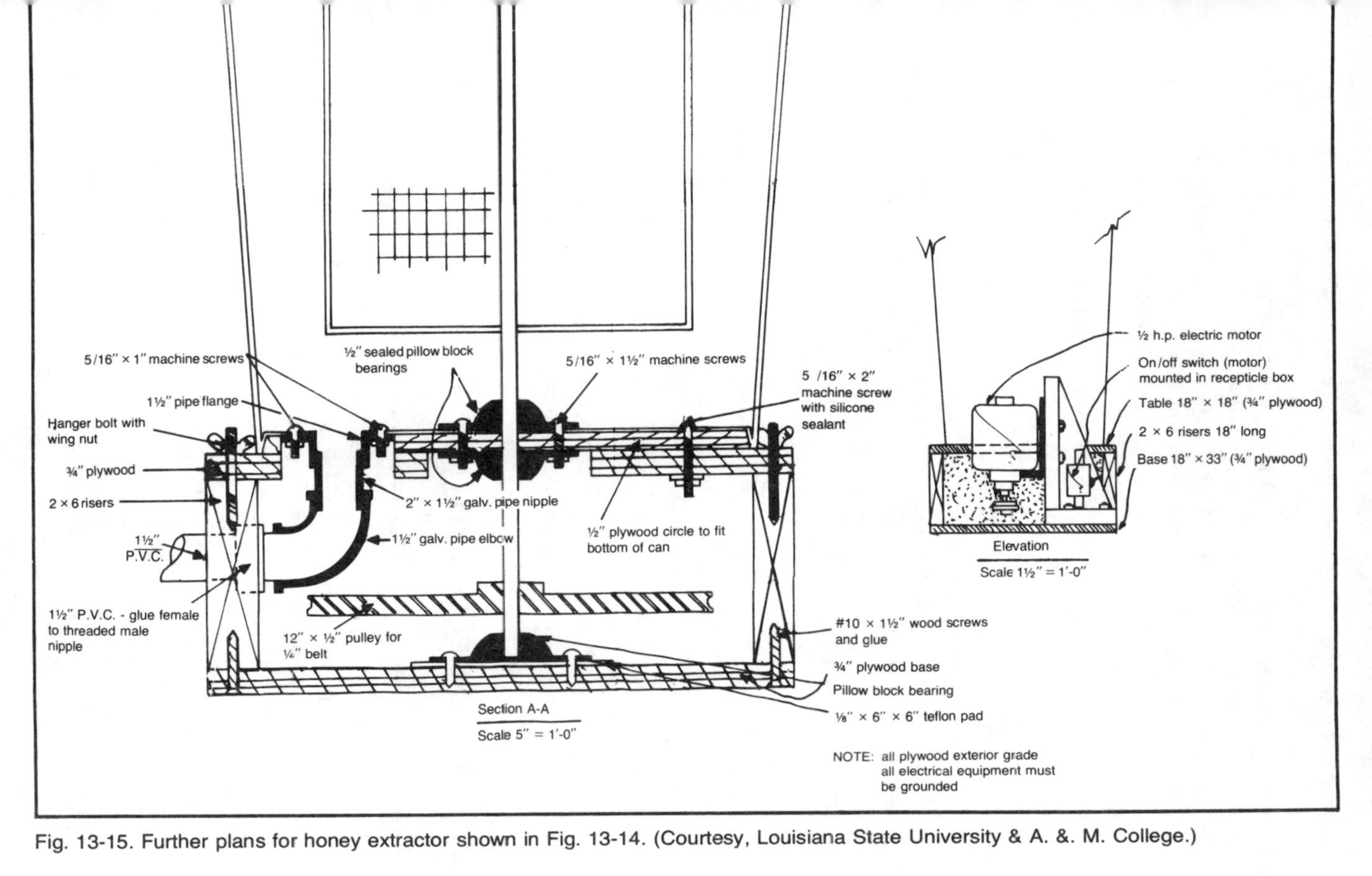

Fig. 13-15. Further plans for honey extractor shown in Fig. 13-14. (Courtesy, Louisiana State University & A. &. M. College.)

is positioned so that it surrounds the board and the wires hold it up. Now locate the microswitch so that it is in a comfortable position.

Using another piece of sheetmetal, fabricate a bracket for the switch, and locate it in the chosen position.

Mount the three 2 × 4s under the plywood in such a way that they are evenly spaced and run from top to bottom.

Mount the doorbell transformer in a convenient location on one of the 2 × 4s.

Run a piece of wire through the wire hole for the right contact. Solder this wire to one corner of the sheetmetal contact. Attach the other end of the wire to one of the 12V contacts on the doorbell transformer. You may have to drill a hole through one of the 2 × 4s for this wire depending on where you located the transformer.

Run a piece of wire through the wire hole for the left contact. Solder this wire to one corner of the sheetmetal contact. Attach the other end of this wire to the contact on the switch marked "normally open (NO)." You will have to drill a hole near the switch large enough for two wires.

Run another piece of wire through the hole by the switch and attach it to the other contact on the switch marked "normally open (NO)." The other end of this wire should be attached to the other contact on the transformer marked for 12V. You may have to drill a hole through one of 2 × 4s for this wire depending on where you located the transformer.

Attach the electrical cord to the doorbell transformer wires or contacts marked 120Vac. This may be done by soldering and taping or by using crimp connectors.

SOLAR WAX MELTER AND EXTRACTOR

The plans shown in Fig. 13-13 are for a do-it-yourself solar wax melter that was conceived and designed by Ron Neese. Using the slow, steady heat from the sun to melt your accumulated wax will both save you money on your utility bills and insure that the wax does not ignite from too high a heat.

Figures 13-14 and 13-15 are blueprints for a honey extractor that was designed by the Louisiana State University & A. & M. College and appear here with their permission.

Appendix A
State Universities, Extension Services and Inspectors

State universities often offer beekeeping courses or disseminate newsletters and pamphlets through the Apiculture or Entomology departments or Agriculture Extension Service. Another source of information is your state inspector.

State	**Professor in Charge of Beekeeping Course.** (Write Department of Apiculture c/o State University)	**Extension Personnel** (Write Beekeeping Extension Specialist, State University)	**State Inspector** Department of Agriculture State Capitol
AL	Dr. George H. Blake, Auburn	Carl Dennis, Auburn	Frank W. Randle, Montgomery
AK	Wayne Vondre, Anchorage		None
AZ	Dr. Norbert Kauffeld, Tucson		R.W. Hancock, Phoenix
AR			Donald E. Bailey, Little Rock
CA	Dr. Norman Gary, Davis	Dr. Eric C. Mussen, Davis	Leo Vanderpool, Sacramento
CO	Dr. J.W. Brewer, Ft. Collins		James Thurman, Denver
CT	Prof. Alfonse Avitabile, Waterbury		Allen Poole, New Haven
DE	Dr. Charles E. Mason, Newark	Dr. Dewey Caron, Newark	Phillip M. Bowman, Jr., Dover
FL	Dr. Frank Robinson, Gainesville	Dr. M. Sanford, Gainesville	James P. Herndon, Gainesville
GA	Dr. Alfred Dietz, Athens	Rodney Coleman, Athens	James P. Harron, Atlanta
HI			None
ID			Dr. Robert C. Saunders, Boise
IL			E.E. Killion, Paris
IN	Bill Chaney, West Lafayette	D.L. Matthew, West Lafayette	Claude F. Wade, Indianapolis
IA	Richard Trump, Ames	G. Stanley, R. Wells, Ames	Glen L. Staney, Des Moines
KS			Gary R. Ross, Topeka
KY	J.W. Stocker, Richmond	Dr. R. Scheibner, Lexington	Wm. G. Eaton, Frankfort
LA	Dr. Thomas Rinderer, Baton Rouge	Dr. Dale Pollet, Baton Rouge	Barby Carroll, Baton Rouge
ME			Paul Szott, Turner, MD
MD			Barton Smith, Jr. Annapolis
MA	Richard Bonney, Amherst	Richard Bonney, Amherst	Thomas Leonard, Hopkinton
MI	Dr. Roger Hoopingarner, East Lansing		

MN	Dr. Basil Furgala, St. Paul	David Noetzel, St. Paul	Richard A. Hyser, St. Paul
MS		J.H. Jarratt, State College	Harry R. Fulton, State College
MO	Dr. Flernoy Jones, Columbia	Joseph Francka, Columbia	J. Francka, Jefferson City
MT			Willard A. Kissinger, Helena
NE	Cliff Walstrom, Lincoln	Dr. David Keith, Lincoln	Marion D. Ellis, Lincoln
NV	Dr. W. Harold Arnett, Reno		Floyd Hilbig, Reno
NH			Robert H. Keating, Durham
NJ	Dr. R.B. Roberts, New Brunswick		J. Matthenius, Jr., Phillipsburg
NM			Bob G. Cambell, Las Cruces
NY	Dr. Roger A. Morse, Ithaca	Dr. Roger A. Morse, Ithaca	Gerald Stevens, Albany
NC	Dr. John Ambrose, Raleigh	Dr. John Ambrose, Raleigh	James F. Greene, Raleigh
ND			Bill Branvik, Bismark
NS		Lorne Crozier, Truro	Lorne Crozier, Truro
OH	Dr. Walter Rothenbuhler, Columbus		Gordon Rudloff, Reynoldsburg
OK			M. Vandeventer, Oklahoma City
OR	Dr. D.M. Burgett, Corvallis	Dr. D.M. Burgett, Corvallis	David Turner, Salem
PA	Dr. Robert Berthold, Doylestown	Dr. C. Collison, State College	James Steinhauer, Harrisburg
RI			Raymond Farnum, Hopkinton
SC	Dr. Rudy Holloway, Clemson	J. Howard, Jr., Clemson	J. Howard, Jr., Clemson
SD	Dr. Robert Walstrom, Brookings		Stuart Adeian, Pierre
TN	Dr. Charles Pless, Knoxville	H. E. Williams, Knoxville	Thomas Hart, Nashville
UT	Prof. William P. Nye, Logan	Reed S. Roberts, Logan	Ed Bianco, Salt Lake City
VT			Richard Drutchas, Montpelier
VA	Dr. Richard Fell, Blacksburg		Homer Powers, Richmond
WA	Dr. Carl Johansen, Pullman	Dr. Carl Johansen, Pullman	James C. Bach, Yakima
WV			Earl Cochran, Charleston
WI	Dr. Eric Erickson, Madison	Dr. Walter Gojmerac, Madison	Samuel Ferguson, Madison
WY	Dr. W.T. Wilson, Laramie		Walter Patch, Cheyenne

(Reprinted by permission from *Gleanings in Bee Culture*, April, 1982, The A.I. Root Company, publishers.)

Appendix B
State Associations

If you are not able to find a beekeeper's organization in your area or you want help starting one, contact your state association:

State	Secretary, Address
Alabama	Mrs. R.V. Harrell, Hayneville, 36040.
Alaska	Cook Inlet Beekeepers Association, P.O. Box 8-173, Anchorage, 99508.
Arizona	Clarence L. Benson, Box 858, Oracle, 85623.
Arkansas	Joe M. Parkhill, Rt. 2, Box 190, Berryville, 72616.
California	Frank Johnson, 2114 Westminister Drive, Riverside, 92506.
Colorado	Mrs. Tom Jones, 605 North Columbus, Yuma, 80559.
Connecticut	Fred Hartman, 46 Climax Road, Simsbury, 06070.
Delaware	John Landon, 747 Union Street Ext, Milton, 19968.
Florida	James C. Mashburn, 2412 Tupelo Terrace, Tallahassee, 32303.
Georgia	Cecil T. Sheppard, 3204 West Mart Lane, Doraville, 30340.
Hawaii	Lee Ong Chun, 2115 North School Street, Honolulu, 96819.
Idaho	Debbie Millet, Rt. 1, Box 8 Bee, Marsing, 83639.

Illinois	Hoyt Taylor, Rt. 2. Pleasant Plains, 62677.
Indiana	Claude F. Wade, Room 613, State Office Building, Indianapolis, 46204.
Iowa	Glen L. Stanley, Agriculture Department, Wallace Building, Des Moines, 50319.
Kansas	Duane Levin, Box 5, Stuttgart, 67670-0005.
Kentucky	Allen Holt, Rt. 2, Box 314, Frankfort, 40601.
Louisiana	James Bernard, Beaux Bridge, 70517.
Maine	Phillip W. Teague, Box 1621, Rockland, 04841.
Maryland	John Romanik, 3200 Pine Orchard Lane, Ellicott City, 21043.
Massachusetts	Milo R. Bacon, 8 Gradner Road, Norwood, 02062.
Michigan	Sharon Kussmaul, 12447 Matthews Highway, Clinton, 49236.
Minnesota	Fred Holte, 2185 W. County Road, B, Roseville, 55113.
Mississippi	Harry R. Fulton, P.O. Box 5207, State College, 39762.
Missouri	Marilyn Kay Smith, 4301 Walnut Tree Street, Charles, 63301.
Montana	JoAnne Speelman, 210 Harmony Road, Kalispell, 59901.
Nebraska	Jim Ollingle, Loop City, 68853.
Nevada	Mrs. Alma Nygren, 1225 Lovelock Highway, Fallon, 89406.
New Hampshire	Francis W. Dodge, P.O. Box 91, Goffstown, 03045.
New Jersey	Mrs. Elizabeth Rodrigues, 157 5 Point Road, Colts Neck, 07722.
New Mexico	Mrs. Alice Stubben, 6621 Arno N.E., Albuquerque, 87107.
New York	Jon MacDonald, Paris Hill Road, Sauquoit, 13456.
N. Carolina	James H. Bryant, Jr., 1208 Briarcliff Road, Burlington, 27215.
N. Dakota	Dewey Robson, 338 Joal Drive, Carrington, 58421.
Ohio	Nancy Osborn, 1411 Winona Drive, Middletown, 45042.
Oklahoma	Marie Tucker, 5213 South 76th Avenue, Tulsa, 75145.
Oregon	George Hansen, 293 Bradley Street, Woodburn, 97071.
Pennsylvania	Mrs. Glen Crimbring, Rd. 1, Canton, 17724.

Rhode Island	Charles W. McKellum, 107 Chatsworth Road, North Kingstown, 02852.
S. Carolina	Tom Batchelor, Dogwood Avenue, Goose Creek, 29445.
S. Dakota	Gary Schmidt, Star Rt. 2, Box 6, Martin, 57551.
Tennessee	Howard Kerr, Rt. 11, Box 7, Big Springs Road, Maryville, 37801.
Texas	Melinda Fuess, 443 Hughs, Irving, 75061.
Utah	David S. Miller, Box 15807, Salt Lake City, 84115.
Vermont	Corlie Magoon, Colchester, 05446.
Virginia	Mrs. Grace Bowman, Rt. 2, Box 57, Victoria, 23974.
Washington	Dick Hunger, 1462 Peterson Road, Burlington, 98233.
W. Virginia	Mrs. Sara Hutchinson, Webster Springs, 26288.
Wisconsin	Charles Kopf, Rt. 2, Box 225, Loganville, 54943.
Wyoming	Mrs. Robert Bryant, 901 Obie Sue, Worland, 82401.

(Reprinted with permission from *Gleanings in Bee Culture*, April, 1982, The A.I. Root Company, publishers.)

Appendix C

Organizations and Service Groups

Name	President or Chairman to Write for Information
American Beekeeping Federation*	Binford Weaver, Rt. 1, Box 111, Navasota, TX 77868
California Honey Advisory Board	Marilyn Kiser, P.O. Box 32, Whittier, CA 90608
Eastern Apicultural Society*	J.C. Matthenius, Jr., 516 Victory Avenue, Philipsburg, NJ 08865
Honey Industry Council of America	David Sunberg, Route 3, Fergus Falls, MN 56537
Ladies Auxiliary of ABF	Mrs. Phillis Taylor, Box 327, Stratford, SD 57474
National Four-H Council	7100 Connecticut Avenue, Chevy Chase, MD 20815
North American Apiotherapy Society*	Ann W. Harman, 15621 Aitcheson Lane, Laurel, MD 20707
Professional Apiculturists Association	Dr. Robert Berthold, Del-Val College, Doylestown, PA 18901
Southern States Beekeepers Federation	Steve Forest, Rt. 1, Box 135, Moravian Falls, NC 28654
Western Apiculture Society*	William P. Nye, Utah State University UMC 53, Logan, UT 84322

*Publishes a journal or newsletter.

Appendix D

Government Agencies

The U.S. Department of Agriculture has a program of research on various aspects of bee management, crop pollination, diseases and pests, protection of the honeybee from pesticides, biology of bees and wild bees, honeybee breeding and genetics, and honey chemistry, quality, uses, and handling. Cooperative projects are also carried on with state apiculturists.

USDA Agricultural Research Service
National Program Staff
Crop Sciences,
Room 307, Building 005
BARC—W
Beltsville, MD 20705

Development Programs
Speciality Crops Branch
Agricultural Marketing Service
Fruit and Vegetable Division
Agricultural Marketing Service
USDA
Washington, D.C. 20250

Extension Service
Pesticide: Use & Impact Assessment
USDA
Washington, D.C. 20250

Research is carried on at seven laboratories:

Location	Focus of Research
Bee Biology & Systemics Laboratory UMC 53, Room 261 Utah State University Logan, UT 84322	Study selected species of wild bees attempt to manage those useful in crop pollination, test usefulness where pollination problems exist in specific crops.
Bee Breeding & Stock Center Lab RR 3, Box 82-B Ben Hur Road Baton Rouge, LA 70808	Develop a selection index of important characteristics of bees, test new insemination equipment, study components of aggressive behavior in bees, liason with Africanized bee projects in South America Control of wax moths with nonchemical means.
Bee Management Laboratory Room 436 Russell Laboratories University of Wisconsin Madison, WI 53706	Management of hives for most effective bee pollination of crops, and honey production, effect of environmental electricity on bees, wintering bees.
Bioenvironmental Bee Laboratory Building 476, Room 200 BARC-East Beltsville, MD 20705	Study bee nutrition and develop pollen substitutes. Test substances for controlling diseases, pests.
Carl Hayden Bee Research Center 2000 East Allen Road Tuscon, AZ 85719	Pollination of crops, bee nutrition and phsiology, identification, and role of micro-organisms of the honeybee.
Eastern Regional Research Center 600 East Mermaid Lane Philadelphia, PA 19118	No permanent assignment.
Honeybee Pesticides/Diseases Research Laboratory University Station, Box 3168 Laramie, WY 82071	Effects of pesticides on bees, research on serious losses caused by pesticides, methods of residual analysis, methods of control for chalkbrood.

Appendix E
Bee Literature Collections

A number of notable collections of bee literature are maintained and some are accessible to the public. If your local library does not have a specific book that you want and you do not wish to buy it, check with your reference librarian on inter-library loan procedure and fees, either with other libraries in your county or state or with the following*:
A.I. Root Co.

Established in 1870 by the founder of the company, the collection consists of 500 monographs, bound volumes of *Gleanings in Bee Culture* and the "American Bee Journal (from 1870)" with a number of rare and historical books. Also, collections of the work of L.L. Langstroth, Moses Quinby, and C.C. Miller. Primarily a reference source for the staff of A.I. Root Co.

Dadant & Sons, Inc.
Dadant & Sons, Hamilton, IL

Collection started by the founder of the company. Contains 1400 monographs, 542 bound volumes of periodicals and over 500 unbound issues, also newsletters from 25 states. Thousands of State, federal, and foreign bulletins and reports, as well as hundreds of beekeeping supply catalogs. Also a large collection of letters, postcards, clippings and photographs from L.L. Langstroth. Public access is restricted because of business and space limitations.

Everett Franklin Phillips Memorial Beekeeping Library
Cornell University, Ithaca, NY

---

* Excerpted from United States Department of Agriculture Handbook 335, 1980 revision.

Established in 1924. Based on the collection of E.F. Phillips former head of apiculture research, USDA, and professor of apiculture at Cornell. Contains 4500 monographs and periodicals. Many rare items printed before 1900. Includes manuscripts and books donated by Rev. L.L. Langstroth, Moses Quinby, Evard French, John Anderson, of Scotland, and C.C. Miller.

Michigan State University

Founded on the donation by Ray Stannard Baker, in 1946, of his library of historical apicultural works. This collection is notable for material on bees written in English. Most of which are historical and printed before 1850 and housed in the Special Collections Division. The university also has a working collection of books, reprints, and journals in the library of the Department of Entomology.

Shields Library, University of California
Davis, California

Contains 1600 monographs, 337 bound journals, calendared records, photographs and clippings with 90 rare volumes. Receives a large number of foreign and several American bee journals.

Technical Information Systems
Lending Division
Beltsville, MD 20705

Largest collection in the U.S. and a foremost among world collections. Over 7000 apicultural monographs, bound periodicals and theses. Receives about 100 periodicals, over half in foreign languages. May borrow on inter-library basis only. Specific articles may be copied upon request for a fee.

University of Minnesota

Built upon the collection of Friar Francis Jaeger, the first chief of the Division of Bee Culture, Department of Agriculture on the St. Paul campus. The library now houses 1050 monographs, 325 of which are considered rare, and an extensive group of books from Eastern Europe dating back to 1634.

University of Wisconsin

The Miller Memorial Beekeeping Library, founded in 1923 with the private collection of C.C. Miller by friends and associates who purchased it for the university. Augmented in 1929 by the extensive collection of Lt. Col. H.J. O. Walker, of England. Has over 2000 rare and historical books and 6000 monographs and bound volumes of journals and receives over 50 periodicals. Monographs are circulated; rare books may be used only in the library.

Table E-1.

STATE OFFICE	ADDRESS	TELEPHONE	PRESIDENT	ADMINISTRATOR SECRETARY
ARIZONA FBF	2618 S. 21st Street Phoenix, AZ 85034	602/257-8655	Cecil Miller, Jr.	Andy O. Kurtz Executive Secretary
ARKANSAS FBF	Farm Bureau Center P.O. Box 31 Little Rock, AR 72203	501/224-4400	Nicky H. Hargrove	Arnold A. Berner Executive Vice President
CALIFORNIA FBF	1601 Exposition Blvd. Sacramento, CA 95815	916/924-4000	Henry J. Voss	Robert P. Simpson Secretary & Treasurer
COLORADO FB	2211 W. 27th Avenue P.O. Box 5647 Denver, CO 80217	303/455-4553	Keith Propst P.O. Box 218 Merino, CO 80741 303/522-0090	Dean Kittel Administrative Officer
CONNECTICUT FB ASSN., INC.	101 Reserve Road Hartford, CT 06114	203/249-6208	Luther E. Stearns RD. #2 Willimantic, CT 06226	Stanley R. Knecht Administrator
DELAWARE FB, INC.	233 S. DuPont Highway Camden-Wyoming, DE 19934	302/697-3183	John F. Walton R.R. #1, Box 177 Magnolia, DE 19962 302/697-6960	Sherman Stevenson Executive Vice-President
FLORIDA FBF	P.O. Box 730 Gainesville, FL 32602 5700 S.W. 34th Street Gainesville, FL 32608	904/378-1321	Walter J. Kautz	Scottie J. Butler Executive Director
GEORGIA FBF	2960 Riverside Drive P.O. Box 7068 Macon, GA 31298	912/474-8411	Robert L. Nash 5416 Barnesville Hwy. The Rock, GA 30285	Mrs. Bette C. Winter Secretary
HAWAII FBF	215 Mokauea Street Honolulu, HI 96819	808/848-2074	Dickey H. Nitta	Carol Dougherty Information and Program Coordinator
IDAHO FBF	845 W. Center Box 4848 Pocatello, ID 83201	208/232-7914	Oscar Field Star Rt. B, Box 221 Grand View, ID 83624 208/834-2488	Lynn Parke Executive Vice President
ILLINOIS AG. ASSN.	1701 Towanda Avenue P.O. Box 2901 Bloomington, IL 61701	309/557-2111	Harold B. Steele	Kent M. Karraker Secretary
INDIANA FB, INC.	130 E. Washington Street Indianapolis, IN 46204	317/263-7851	Marion Stackhouse	C. W. Stall Secretary
IOWA FBF	5400 University Avenue West Des Mones, IA 50265	515/225-5400	Dean Kleckner	Dale W. Nelson Executive Director and Secretary-Treasurer

KANSAS FB	2321 Anderson Avenue Manhattan, KS 66502	913/537-2261	John J. Armstrong	Don Wilson Secretary-Manager
KENTUCKY FBF	120 South Hubbard Lane Louisville, KY 40207	502/897-9481	Ray Mackey Route 7, Box 123 Elizabethtown, KY 42701 502/369-8476	Paul D. Everman Executive Vice President
LOUISIANA FBF, INC.	P.O. Box 15361 Broadview Station Baton Rouge, LA 70895	504/926-1944	James Graugnard	Delano Clark Assistant to the President
MAINE FB ASSN.	478 Western Avenue P.O. Box 430 Augusta, ME 04330	207/622-4111	Peter W. Curra RFD #2 Thorndike, ME 04986 207/382-6161	Jon Olson Executive Secretary and Administrator
MARYLAND FB, INC.	8930 Liberty Road Randallstown, MD 21133	301/922-3426	Leon B. Enfield 649-B Jefferson Pike Knoxville, MD 21758 301/834-7488	Jerry Y. Placek Secretary-Treasurer
MASSACHUSETTS FBF, INC.	85 Central Street Waltham, MA 02154	617/893-2600	Charles Dowse 100 N. Main St. Sherborn, MA 01770	James F. Slattery Administrator
MICHIGAN FB	7373 W. Saginaw Highway Box 30960 Lansing, MI 48909	517/323-7000	Elton R. Smith	Robert E. Braden Administrative Director
MINNESOTA FBF	1976 Wooddale Drive P.O. Box 43370 St. Paul, MN 55164	612/739-7200	Merlyn Lokensgard	Gerald W. Hagaman Chief Administrator and Secretary
MISSISSIPPI FBF	429 Mississippi Street Box 1972 Jackson, MS 39205	601/948-7401	Hugh M. Arant	Mrs. Lucy H. Hill Secretary-Treasurer
MISSOURI FBF	701 S. Country Club Drive P.O. Box 658 Jefferson City, MO 65102	314/893-1400	C. R. Johnston	Lowell Mohler Secretary
MONTANA FBF	502 South 19th Bozeman, MT 59715	406/587-3153	T. M. Mack Quinn P.O. Box 353 Big Sandy, MT 59520 406/378-2337	William W. (Bill) Brown Executive Vice President
NEBRASKA FBF	P.O. Box 80299 Lincoln, NE 68501	402/423-2822	Bryce Neidig Rt. 2 Madison, NE 68718	Douglas A. Gibson Secretary-Treasurer

Table E-1. (Continued from page 222.)

STATE OFFICE	ADDRESS	TELEPHONE	PRESIDENT	ADMINISTRATOR OR SECRETARY
NEVADA FBF	1300 Marietta Way Sparks, NV 89431	702/358-7737	Dave Fulstone 12 S. Main Yerington, NV 89447 702/463-2829	Charles White Executive Vice President
NEW HAMPSHIRE FBF	99 North State Street Concord, NH 03301 (temporary)	603/224-1934	Errol S. Peters RFD Lisbon, NH 03585 603/838-5532	Maurice Chapin Executive Secretary
NEW JERSEY FB	The Farmhouse 168 W. State Street Trenton, NJ 08608	609/393-7163	Lauren De Cou President	Walter Ellis, Jr. Executive Vice President
NEW MEXICO FARM & LIVESTOCK BUREAU	421 N. Water Street Las Cruces, NM 88001	505/526-5521	L. E. (Pete) Davis Rt. 2, Box 138 Clovis, NM 88101 505/985-2317	B. J. Porter Executive Vice President
NEW YORK FB, INC.	Route 9W, Box 100 Glenmont, NY 12077	518/436-8496	Richard McGuire Cambridge, NY 12816 518/854-3143	John S. Gold Administrator
NORTH CAROLINA FBF	5301 Glenwood Avenue Box 27766 Raleigh, NC 27611	919/782-1705	John Sledge	Elmer Burt Secretary-Treasurer
NORTH DAKOTA FB	1101 First Ave., N. P.O. Box 2064 Fargo, ND 58107	701/237-9717	Robert Kadrmas Route #3 Box 113 Dickinson, ND 58601 701/225-2061	Robert Shepard Executive Vice President
OHIO FBF, INC.	35 E. Chestnut P.O. Box 479 Columbus, OH 43216	614/225-8711	David O. Miller 325 King Road Newark, OH 43055 614/366-5419	C. Wm. Swank Executive Vice President
OKLAHOMA FB	2501 North Stiles Oklahoma City, OK 73152	405/523-2300	James L. Lockett	Ken McFall Executive Secretary
OREGON FBF	1730 Commercial St., SE P.O. Box 2209 Salem, OR 97308	503/581-1486	Frank Setniker Route #2, Box 206 McMinnville, OR 97128	Clare L. McGhan Executive Vice President
PENNSYLVANIA FARMERS ASSN.	510 S. 31st Street P.O. Box 736 Camp Hill, PA 17011	717/761-2740	Keith W. Eckel	Richard Newpher Administrative Secretary
PUERTO RICO FB	Condominio San Martin 1605 Ponce de Leon Ave. Santurce, PR 00909	809/724-5970	Luis Becerra	Luis F. Martinez Executive Director

RHODE ISLAND FBF, INC.	2550 Post Road Warwick, RI 02886	401/737-5212	William Stamp 219 Comstock Parkway Cranston, RI 02920 401/942-7593	Secretary
SOUTH CAROLINA FB	P.O. Box 754 Columbia, SC 29202	803/796-6700	Harry S. Bell	Tom Warren Assistant to the President
SOUTH DAKOTA FBF	2225 Dakota S. Box 1426 Huron, SD 57350	605/352-6731	Richard Ekstrum Kimball, SD 57355 605/778-6443	Mike Held Administrative Director
TENNESSEE FBF, INC.	Box 313 Columbia, TN 38401	615/388-7872	James Putman	Dan Wheeler Assistant to the President
TEXAS FB	7420 Fish Pond Road P.O. Box 489 Waco, TX 76703-0489	817/772-3030	Carrol G. Chaloupka Route 1, Box 137 Dalhart, TX 79022	Warren Newberry Executive Director
UTAH FBF	5300 South 360 West P.O. Box 30045 Salt Lake City, UT 84130	801/261-2424	Frank O. Nishiguchi	C. Booth Wallentine Executive Vice President
VERMONT FB, INC.	141 Main Street Montpelier, VT 05602-2986	802/223-3636	Rupert C. Chamberlin RFD #1 Barton, VT 05822 802/525-6635	Deacy F. Leonard Executive Director
VIRGINIA FBF, INC.	200 W. Grace Street Box 27552 Richmond, VA 23261	804/788-1234	S. T. Moore, Jr.	Louis P. Chisholm Secretary
WASHINGTON SFB	111 W. 21st Street P.O. Box 2569 Olympia, WA 98507	206/357-9975	Herb Streuli 20101 S.E. 436th St. Enumclaw, WA 98022 206/825-4386	Donald H. Ahrenholtz Executive Vice President
WEST VIRGINIA FB	Route #3, Box 156-A Buckhannon, WV 26201	304/472-2080	Paul Nay Route #2 Jane Lew, WV 26378 304/884-7408	Richard Hannah Secretary-Treasurer
WISCONSIN FBF	7010 Mineral Point Road P.O. Box 5550 Madison, WI 53705	608/833-8070	Donald Haldeman	Marie Lane Corporate Secretary
WYOMING FBF	406 S. 21st Street P.O. Box 1348 Laramie, WY 82070	307/745-4835	Dave Flitner Shell Route Greybull, WY 82426 307/765-2961	Herbert F. Manig Executive Vice President

The American Farm Bureau Federation, the nation's largest farm organization, with its Goals and Affirmative Action Program is of interest to and supportive of the needs of beekeepers. Some county farm bureaus sponsor seminars on beekeeping and encourage direct produce selling, providing beekeepers with a market for their honey.

The AFBF maintains a Washington office from which staff members monitor the affairs of Congress as it applies to agriculture and lobby on those issues affecting the rights of farmers. A list of state Farm Bureau officers and addresses to which you may write for information on your local county situation is given in Table E-1.

Appendix F
First Aid for Bee Stings

WARNING: If any other reaction occurs over any other part of the body other than at the site of the sting, such as hives, coughing, or difficulty in breathing, the individual is hypersensitive to insect venom. He should be taken to a doctor or emergency medical facility immediately.

The most common reaction is a sharp pain followed by burning, swelling, and then itching. Here's what to do:

- *Scrape* off the stinger. Do not squeeze or pull it out. This increases the venom flow and spread (Fig. F-1).
- Apply ice packs to reduce feverish feeling and soreness.
- Any of the following topical solutions often gives relief: (Every beekeeper has a favorite)
  Baking soda
  Solution of one part household ammonia and three parts water
  Meat tenderizer dissolved in water
- If the victim has incurred several stings, an antihistamine tablet may be advised.

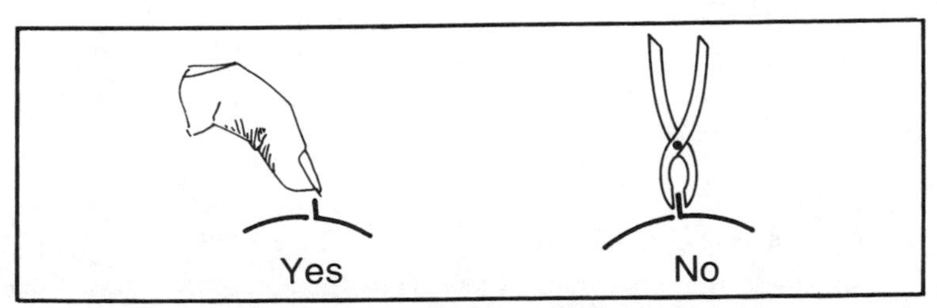

Fig. F-1. The right way and wrong way to remove a bee sting.

Suppliers

Your local supplier is often a primary source of information and help as well as equipment and tools. If you haven't a supplier near you, or you want to make some price comparisons or gain access to a wider selection, write for catalogs from a regional or national supplier. Here is a directory by beekeeping regions. (See References, Fig. R-4.)

WEST

Dadant & Sons, Inc.
P.O. Box 7996
Fresno, CA 93747
(209) 292-4666

Established in 1863. Large reliable firm, manufacturer and supplier of leading products with ten branch locations throughout U.S.

Pierce Manufacturer and Bee Supplier
2840 East White Star Avenue
Anaheim CA 92806
714-630-0890

Home of the Speed King Line of Uncapping knives.

Strauser Bee Supply, Inc.
P.O. Box 991
Walla Walla, WA
Toll free number: 1-800-541-8908

Good selection and variety including precision cut wooden ware from elite to budget quality. Write for catalog for branch locations.

MOUNTAINOUS

Superbee, Inc.
10727-6075 Road
Montrose, CO 81401
(303) 249-4666

Complete line, specializing in wooden ware, innovative equipment.

SOUTHWEST

Crockett/Stewart Honey Company
1880 East Buchanan
Phoenix, AZ 85034
(602) 254-2371

Home of the "Superior Lifetime Extractor," parts for extractors and full line of supplies.

PLAINS

Dadant & Sons, Inc
P.O. Box 146
Paris, IL 61944

Honey Valley Nursery
Sapulpa, OK 74066

NORTH CENTRAL

The A.I. Root Company
Headquarters
P.O. Box 706
623 West Liberty Street
Medina, OH 44258

Major manufacturer and supplier since 1869 with over 200 dealers nationwide. Send for catalog for directory or check yellow pages.

B & B Honey Farm
Rt. 2, Box 245
Houston, MN 55943

Independent dealer and wholesaler, NUCs and Queens, book in February.

Fields of Ambrosia
6810 Watts Road
Madison, WI 53719
Toll free number: 1-800-5333

Hubbard Bee Supply and Apiaries
P.O. Box 160
Onstead, MI 49265

Package bees and Queens available in Spring, must be preordered.

Leahy Manufacturing Company
406 West 22nd Street
P.O. Box 451
Higginsville, MO 64037
(816) 584-2641, 584-7878

Manufacturer of wooden ware, distributor for major equipment companies.

SOUTHEAST

American Bee Supply, Inc.
P.O. Box 555
Rt. 7 Sparta Pike
Lebanon, TN 37087
(615) 444-7903

Distributor of finest quality supplies and equipment plus large selection of books/manuals.

Bee Jay Farm
1524 Drowning Creek Road
Dacula, GA 30211
(404) 962-1067

Manufacturer of Tidewater Red Cypress woodware. Three frame NUCs, Apr-Ju, must preorder.

SPECIAL SUPPLIERS AND SERVICES

Smith Container Corporation
3500 Browns Mill Rd, S.E.
P.O. Box 82566
Atlanta, GA 30354
(404) 768-8725

Distributor for glass, plastic, tin, steel, and fiber containers

Beekeeping Education Service
P.O. Box 817
Cheshire, CT 06410
(203) 271-0155

Has films, cassettes, slides, large selection of books, manuals, posters, and other visual aids for use in club presentations, workshops, talks to schools, displays at fairs, other community events, or personal library.

References

A wealth of organizations, agencies, and reference material is available for you to explore to learn more about the practice of beekeeping, bees, honey, or any aspect of this complex and broad subject.

Probably the best resource is an established, experienced beekeeper who will allow you to accompany her on the rounds of her apiaries or, better still, work alongside her for a day to get hands-on training.

Local county, regional, or state beekeeping associations are invaluable. Membership is generally comprised of people in all phases of beekeeping, from the novice to the commercial operator who has been in beekeeping all his life. Associations provide opportunities to hear guest speakers who are specialists in various phases of beekeeping, from requeening to wax rendering. You can have questions answered, and to participate in demonstrations, workshops, and county or state fairs. This also supports an important medium to foster education and a positive public image of bees and beekeeping. Don't just sign up! Be active and you will be rewarded with a lot of help with your new hobby. You'll get to know other beekeepers to consult as you want to expand, become more efficient, and begin marketing your honey.

On a more formal basis, beekeeping courses or weekend seminars are often sponsored by community colleges, county Farm Bureaus, and through the Cooperative Extension Service of the State University's agricultural school or college. Usually these courses include demonstrations in the field with colonies of bees.

Parks, nature centers, and museums often have displays and/or observation hives—an active colony presented in a small glass-sided hive from which a pipe leads to the outside for the bees to carry on their regular foraging. Also, very often beekeeper associations will include an observation hive in their display booth at the county fair. Watching an observation hive is a good way to see bees in action without a direct encounter. It is a beneficial way to gain interest and support from your family, friends, and neighbors.

Your county or area inspector and/or county agricultural extension agent will answer questions and share his knowledge of beekeeping. He may also have printed materials for the asking. Look under Agriculture in your county listings in the white pages of the phone directory.

Pamphlets, books, and newsletters are available also from the Cooperative Extension Service of the State University, the U.S. Government Printing Office, state inspectors, state associations, beekeeping federations, and private industry such as honey cooperatives. Local regional, and national suppliers will send catalogs on request.

Local beekeeping suppliers are anxious to help new beekeepers. Many are experienced apiarians and are happy to share their knowledge on the local situation of locating hives, foraging plants available, zoning laws, and sound beekeeping practices. Most suppliers are quite conscious of a beginner's budget and take a practical approach in suggesting products.

U.S. GOVERNMENT PUBLICATIONS

These can be obtained from the U.S. Government Printing Office, Washington, DC 20402.

The Honey Bee. Smithsonian Institution Press, Leaflet 482, revised 1979, $2.25.

Brief history of beekeeping—worldwide and U.S.A. Summary of biology, colony organization including communication dances, capsule reports on honey, wax, and pollination. History of observation hives at the Smithsonian.

Beekeeping in the United States. Agricultural Handbook #334, Revised 1980, $7.50.

Detailed and comprehensive explanations of many phases of beekeeping with good illustrations. Good reference for background and theory, not a how-to-do-it book, however. Each chapter written by expert in specialty covered.

Beekeeping for Beginners. Home and Garden Bulletin 158, 12 pgs, $1.75.

Very brief outline of how to start with bees.

STATE EXTENSION SERVICES PUBLICATIONS

Beekeeping in the Midwest, by Elbert R. Jaycox. Circular 1124, 169 pages, 1976.

Practical, well-illustrated how-to-do-it manual for beekeepers in Illinois, Indiana, Wisconsin, Michigan, Ohio. Available through University of Illinois at Champaign-Urbana College of Agriculture—Cooperative Extension Service, Urbana, IL 61801.

Beginning With Bees in Nebraska. December, 1977, 22 pages.

Step-by-step summary of starting beekeeping in Nebraska. Text only, no illustrations. Available through Cooperative Extension Service, University of Nebraska, College of Agriculture, Apiary Division, Lincoln, NE 68508.

Beginning With Bees (Louisiana) by E. Oertel, E.A. Cancienne and D.K. Pollet.

Easy to follow how-to booklet, illustrated with photos. Available through Louisiana Cooperative Extension Service, Louisiana State University and A&M College, Knapp Hall, University Station, Baton Rouge, LA 70803.

Beekeeping: General Information (New York) by R.A. Morse and E.J. Dyce Cooperative Extension, 1977, 12 pages.

Covers main points of beekeeping in New York with detailed summary of seasonal management, some photo illustrations. Cooperative Extension, New York State College of Agriculture and Life Sciences. Send request to: Mailing Room Building 7, Research Park, Ithaca, NY 14853.

4H Beekeeping Manuals, (Indiana), Working with Honey Bees, 4-H 486; Understanding Honey Bees, 4-H 571; Advanced Beekeeping Methods; $1.00 each, by Robert Abrams, Purdue University.

A set of work manuals with text, test questions, and suggested activities for young people to be used with recommended resource books such as *Starting Right With Bees* from A.I. Root and Co. Available through: Agricultural Publications Mailing Room, AGAD Building, Purdue University, West Lafayette, IN 47907.

Hum of the Hive (Florida), Monthly newsletter by Malcom T. Sanford, Extension Apiculturist.

Well-written, practical and timely how-to's and when-to's slanted toward the Florida beekeeper but often has information and ideas of interest to all beekeepers. Extension Apiculturist, Florida Cooperative Extension Service University of Florida, Institute of Food & Agricultural Services, 3101 McCarty Hall, University of Florida, Gainesville, FL 32611.

PERIODICALS

Three excellent periodicals are published in the United States. They average less than a dollar a month. All three have similar content: reports on research, updates on beekeeping news, activities and conferences of the major beekeeping organizations, monthly honey production figures, ideas on how-to's for hobbyists and side-liners from hobbyists and side-liners, accounts of beekeeping in other countries, question and answer forum, features on individual beekeepers and commercial operators, and illustrated articles on do-it-yourself gadgets and equipment plus regular columns as listed below.

In addition, there are ads for equipment, supplies, speciality items and bees.

A good way to build a library quickly is to request part of your subscription in back issues. Publishers are willing to cooperate, subject to availability.

American Bee Journal, published by Dadant & Sons, Inc.

Regular features include: "ABJ-25, 50, 75 and 100 years ago" by the editors, "The Classroom," by the staff, "Burr Combs," by Joe Graham, "Notes from a Country Dairy," by Howard Veatch, and "The Family," by Robin Scheetz. Available from American Bee Journal, Hamilton, IL 62341. Telephone (217) 847-3324.

Gleanings in Bee Culture, published by A.I. Root.

Regular features include: "Gleanings Mail Box," "Questions and Answers," "Research Review," "Bee Talk," by Richard Taylor; "Old Timer," "Notes from the Straw Skep," by Bess Clarke; and "Strictly Backlot," by Carl Callenbach. Available from Gleanings in Bee Culture, P.O. Box 706, Medina, OH 44258-0706.

The Speedy Bee, published by Troy H. Fore.

Regular features include "The Foreward," by Troy Fore; "Coming Events," (listing of courses and special events of local, regional, state beekeeping associations); "Students of the Honey Bee," "Thurber's Tips," by Roy Thurber; "Shortcuts and Gadgets," by readers. Available from The Speedy Bee, P.O. Box 998, Jesup, GA 31545.

INTERNATIONAL PERIODICALS

Three journals are published by the International Bee Research Association: *Bee World, Apicultural Abstracts,* and *Journal of Apicultural Research.* For an application for membership, catalogs of publications, or information on subscriptions, write to International Bee Research Association, Hill House, Chalfont St. Peter, Gerrards Cross, Buckinghamshire, England SLO ONR.

APIMONDIA, the International Federation of Beekeepers' Associations, in Italy, publishes Apicata, quarterly, and Agrindex, monthly. For catalogs and information write to Apimondia, Corso Vittorio Emanuele 101, Rome, Italy.

COOKBOOKS

Favorite Honey Recipes compiled by the Honey Queen Committee of California, 76 pages. Over 200 recipes, plus kitchen and homemaking tips. To order, send $4.00 in check or money order to: Yvonne Koehnen, California Honey Queen Committee, R 1. Box 242, Glenn, CA 95943.

Honey . . Any Time, by California Honey Advisory Board.

Thirty-two pages of tested recipes in 10 categories. To order, send $1.00 in check or money order to: California Honey Advisory Board, P.O. Box 32, Whittier, CA 90608.

For free recipe pamphlets from the Honey Advisory Board, send self-addressed envelope *with one first class postage stamp* to same location.

BOOKS

Literally thousands of books have been written on the practical, scientific, theoretical, and historical aspects of beekeeping, apiculture, honey and other hive products, abstracts, journals, research reports, monographs and theses. Here is but a handful, relatively speaking, of references in bibliographic form.

Crane, Eva (ed.). *Honey.* New York, NY: Crane, Ressack and Co., Inc., 1975.

A scientific encyclopedia on honey written by several authors. Covers physical and chemical characteristics of honey, its role in human history, myths, and economics.

Dadant & Sons. *Beekeeping Questions and Answers.* Hamilton, IL: Dadant & Sons, 1976.

Down to earth answers and advice on bees, equipment, management, and honey production for a reasonable price. 250 pages.

Gojmerac, Walter L. *Bees, Beekeeping, Honey and Pollination.* Westport, CN: The Avi Publishing Co., Inc., 1980.

Written by a professor in entomology, the 208 pages of material is designed to aid operating beekeepers and farmers and to provide more technical input for those researching apiculture.

Malone, Fred. *Bees Don't Get Arthritis.* New York, NY: E.P. Dutton, 1979.

Anecdotal accounts of healing with bee venom and other products of the hive. Although research presented is not scientifically conducted, the material is interesting and provocative. 178 pages.

More, Daphne. *The Bee Book.* Universe Books, 1976.

Especially good on the natural history of the bee and the history of beekeeping in general. 143 pages.

Root, A.I., E.R., H.H., and J.A. *ABC & XYZ of Bee Culture,* 36th edition. Medina, OH: The A.I. Root Company, 1979.

A classic text of 726 pages, presented in encyclopedia format.

Snodgrass, R.E. *Anatomy of the Honey Bee.* Ithaca, NY: Comstock Publishing Associates, Cornell University Press, 1956.

Although nearly 30 years old, this book remains an important reference on the biology of the bee.

von Hirsch, Karl. *Bees: Their Vision, Chemical Senses, and Language.* Ithaca, NY: Cornell University Press, 1971.

Revised edition. Small, scientific paperback on how honeybees see, detect odors, and transmit information in the hive. 157 pages.

von Hirsch, Karl. *The Dance Language and Orientation of Bees.* Cambridge, MA: The Belknap Press of Harvard University Press, 1967.

A detailed scientific account of the research done by Professor von Hirsch and his students on bee behavior.

Glossary

American Foulbrood (AFB)—Infectious disease of immature honeybees caused by the Bacillus larvae.
apiary—Place where beehives are kept, bee yard.
apiculture—The study of using honeybees for man's benefit.
Apis—The genus to which honeybees belong.
Apis mellifera—Scientific name of the Western honeybee.
Apis mellifera adansonii—Scientific name of the African honeybee.
Apis mellifera scutellata—Another reference name for the African bee.
apitherapy (or apiotherapy)—The use of hive products, honey, propolis, royal jelly, pollen, and bee venom for medical or nutritional purposes.
artificial insemination—Fertilizing a queen by means of an instrument.

bee escape—A device with a special spring which allows bees to leave hive but not reenter, used to empty super for honey removal.
bee hive—The home prepared by the beekeeper for the colony, usually a wooden box of standard dimensions with movable frames, a lid, and a bottom.
bee space—The space required for a bee to move about but not large enough to allow for comb building, utilized by Langstroth in creating the movable frame hive.
beeswax—Wax produced by the bees and secreted from special glands on the underside of the abdomen, used to build comb.
bottom board—The floor of the hive.
brood—Eggs, larvae and pupae, in all stages of development, sealed and unsealed.
brood chamber—The area of the hive where the queen lays eggs and

where the brood develop and are cared for by worker bees, usually comprising one or two bottom supers.

burr comb—Small sections of comb built on top of, between or below frames or on the sides and bottom board and underneath the lid of the hive body.

cappings—The top slices of beeswax which have been cut from a sealed frame of honey before extracting.

castes—The three types of bees—workers, drones, and queens—which form the adult population of a colony.

cell—A single compartment of the honeycomb, constructed in the shape of a hexagon used for raising brood and storing pollen and honey.

cleansing flight—The flight bees take after being confined for a long period in order to dispose of feces.

clustering—Bees forming themselves in a tight group usually to warm brood in winter.

colony—The total family or unit of bees usually having only one queen.

comb—A unit of contiguous hexagonal cells created by the honeybees from wax, averaging five worker cells to the inch and four drone size cells per inch.

drawn comb—Comb with the cells built up (drawn out) to about ½ inch by the bees on a sheet of foundation.

drone comb—Comb with larger cells that are raised or dome topped, in which drone pupae are developing. Or larger celled comb from which drones have emerged.

drone layer—An old queen whose supply of sperm is exhausted. Capable of laying only unfertile eggs that always become drones. Or, an unmated queen, or a worker whose ovaries are stimulated by loss of queen and lays only unfertile eggs.

enzyme—An organic component produced in animal or plant cells that works on other substances through catalytic reaction.

Epinephrine—A drug used to counteract severe allergic reactions to bee stings or stings from other hymenoptera insects.

European Foulbrood (EFB)—An infectious brood disease caused by the bacterium, streptococcus pluton.

extracted honey—Honey in liquid form taken from the comb with an extractor.

extractor—A machine operated by hand or electric power that uses the principle of centrifugal force to spin the honey from the uncapped frames.

forager—A field bee that collects pollen, nectar, and/or water for the colony.

foundation—A sheet of beeswax, beeswax sprayed on plastic, or plastic imprinted with the hexagonal cell design, which is fastened into a frame and upon which the bees build cells to hold eggs, larvae or pupae, pollen, or honey.

frame—A wooden or plastic rectangle that forms the perimeter and support for the wax foundation and is suspended inside the hive body.

fume board—A general name for any shallow wooden cover used to hold chemicals for getting bees to move out of supers.

glucose—A principal sugar of honey.

granulated honey—Honey in which crystals of sugar have formed.

hive body—A single wooden box fitted with frames used by the bees for rearing brood (brood chamber) or for storing honey (a super).

hive cover—The lid or roof of the hive.

hive tool—A metal bar, like a crow bar, used to pry apart the lid from the supers, and hive bodies from each other, and to separate frames inside the hive body.

honey—A sweet, viscous liquid produced by honeybees from the nectar of flowers.

inner cover—A thin lid used under the standard telescoping cover.

Langstroth hive—A hive with movable frames developed by L.L. Langstroth using the principal of "bee space" or ¼ to ⅜ inch.

larva (pl. larvae)—The immature form of a bee or any insect resembling a grub; the stage in between the egg and the pupa (pupae).

levulose—One of the sugars contained in honey.

mandibles—The jaws of an insect.

mating flight—The flight(s) of the virgin queen in which she mates with the drones, usually about half mile up in the air and with 6 to 10 drones at two separate meetings.

mead—A wine made with honey.

migratory beekeeping—A system of beekeeping in which colonies are moved from location to location to take advantage of different nectar flows and/or to provide pollination services.

nectar—A sweet secretion of flowers that honeybees collect to make honey for food.

Nosema disease—Disease of bees caused by protozoan spore-forming parasite, Nosema apis.
nucleus (NUC)—A small colony of bees with a laying queen, which may be formed from splitting a large colony or purchased to start a new colony or an additional one.

package bees—Two to four pounds of bees, usually with a queen placed in a wooden and screened box. May be purchased to begin beekeeping or boost existing colonies.
Paradichlobenzene (PDB)—A white crystalline substance used to fumigate combs to kill or repel wax moths.
pheromones—Chemicals secreted by animals, including insects, to convey information or to affect behavior of other members of the same species.
pistil—The female part of the flower, which includes the stigma, style, and ovary.
pollen—Male reproductive cells of a flower. Collected and used by bees as the protein food for developing young bees.
pollen basket—An area on the hind legs of a bee, formed by the concave segment of the leg and the stiff hairs around it, in which she packs and carries pollen from flowers to the colony.
pollination—The transfer of pollen from the anthers of the flower to the stigma of that or another flower.
proboscis—The mouth parts of a bee that come together like a straw for sucking up nectar, water, or honey.
propolis—Plant resins collected by bees and used by them as "glue" to seal cracks and spaces between parts of a hive.
pupa (pl. pupae)—Stage in life of developing bee between larva and emerging adult.

queen—Sexually developed female, the mother of all the bees in the colony.
queen cell—A cell in which a queen is developed by feeding a very young larva (one to three days) royal jelly. Extends beyond the plane of the other comb, looks like a small peanut. Often, but not always located on the lower row of cells.
queen excluder—Sheet of wood, wire, or both designed to allow workers to pass through but with spaces too small for a laying queen (but often large enough for a virgin or newly mated queen to get through).
queenright colony—A colony with a healthy, productive queen.

refractometer—An instrument for measuring the percent of soluble solids in a solution to determine the percent of moisture in honey.

rendering wax—Melting old combs, cappings, and burr comb and removing extraneous materials to refine the beeswax for sale or trade for foundation or home use.
requeening—Removal of an old, ineffective queen and replacement with a new queen.
ripening—Process by which bees reduce moisture from nectar and convert its sucrose to dextrose, glucose, levulose, or fructose, thus producing honey.
robber bee—A field bee from one colony that takes or attempts to take honey from another colony.
royal jelly—Glandular secretions of worker bees fed to developing queens.

sacbrood—A common virus disease of larvae, usually not fatal to the colony.
scout bees—Field bees that locate new sources of food, water, propolis, or a new home for a swarm.
sealed brood—Immature bees in their late larval and pupal stages residing within capped cells.
skep—An old-fashioned domeshaped beehive of wicker or straw, lacking movable frames (necessitating killing bees to remove honey), illegal to use in most states.
slumgum—A dark residue of brood cocoons and pollen left after wax is rendered.
smoker—A metal container with an attached bellows in which materials are burned to create smoke to calm honeybees when working around them.
solar wax melter—A glass covered box in which wax is placed to be melted by the sun and recovered in a solid block form.
stamen—Male part of the flower on which pollen producing anthers are located.
stigma—The surface of the female organ of a flower which receives the pollen.
sting—The organ of defense of the honeybee.
sucrose—The sugar in nectar before inversion into simpler sugars.
super—Any hive body placed above the brood chamber for the storing of honey.
surplus honey—An excess of honey that the colony stores and the beekeeper removes.
swarm—A mass of bees that have split off from another colony and is gathered together in the process of locating a new home.

thorax—The middle part of the bee.

uncapping—Cutting away a thin layer of wax that covers the cells of honey in a frame of comb.
uncapping knife—A tool, heated with water, steam, or electricity used to cut away the wax sealing the honeycomb.
uniting—Combining one colony with another.
unsealed brood—Eggs and larvae in open cells.

virgin queen—An unmated queen, can only lay unfertile eggs that become drones.

wax moth—Insect, the larvae of which feeds on and destroys wax combs.
wired foundation—Comb foundation with wires embedded in it for added strength.
worker bees—Sexually undeveloped female bees that comprise the bulk of a colony and carry on all functions necessary for colony survival, except egg laying and queen mating.

Index